## Date Due

# EXPERIMENTAL METHODS
# IN MAGNETISM

1

SERIES OF MONOGRAPHS ON SELECTED TOPICS
IN SOLID STATE PHYSICS
*Editor:* E. P. WOHLFARTH

# Experimental Methods
# in Magnetism

## 1. GENERATION AND COMPUTATION OF MAGNETIC FIELDS

*BY*

## H. ZIJLSTRA

*Philips Research Laboratories*
*N.V. Philips' Gloeilampenfabrieken*
*Eindhoven, Netherlands*

1967

NORTH-HOLLAND PUBLISHING COMPANY–AMSTERDAM

PUBLISHERS:

## NORTH-HOLLAND PUBLISHING CO. – AMSTERDAM

SOLE DISTRIBUTORS FOR U.S.A. AND CANADA:

INTERSCIENCE PUBLISHERS, a division of

## JOHN WILEY & SONS, INC. – NEW YORK

PRINTED IN THE NETHERLANDS

Fixed charges
Physics

# PREFACE

Only too often in the literature on magnetic phenomena little or no information is given on the measuring methods used. In particular it is not always clear to what extent the result is influenced by the methods of preparation and measurement of the sample. Literature on measuring apparatus is scattered in a great number of scientific periodicals and fluctuates considerably as regards what is considered as known and what is explained.

This book presents a treatment of the principles of a number of widely-used methods for measuring magnetic quantities. It is hoped that the book will be useful to those engaged in magnetic experiments, whether in scientific research or in routine measurements. The reader is presumed to be familiar with the basic concepts of magnetism and with elementary vector analysis. The latter, however, is not necessary if the proofs are taken for granted and only the results are used.

To increase the practical value of this book much attention has been given to those details of a method where errors are liable to be introduced and how this can be prevented.

The book is certainly not meant to give a complete survey of the literature. The examples are mainly chosen from the immediate neighbourhood of the author; this does not of course imply that there may not be better or earlier ones. However, several chapters are provided with a bibliography of books and survey articles consulted by the author; these contain fairly complete lists of the literature.

For technical reasons the book is split into two parts. The first part contains two chapters on the theory of the magnetic potential needed for the understanding (though not for the application) of several subjects discussed in the subsequent chapters of the book. It further contains a chapter on the generation of magnetic fields by ironless solenoids. This chapter is rather detailed as it is considered that the experimenter is often faced with the design and construction of coils of all sorts when building his apparatus. On the other hand a chapter on iron-core magnets is kept very elementary as these magnets are commonly bought and thus only a limited understanding of their differences is required.

Part 2 of the book deals with the measurement of magnetic quantities. For the discussion of the various methods use is often made of the results obtained in Part 1. Therefore the two parts should be considered as one whole. Two important fields are not treated, namely neutron diffraction and domain techniques. This is because the experimental techniques used in the former field are covered in detail in a book by BACON [1955] and two books on the latter subject have appeared recently (CRAIK and TEBBLE [1965] and CAREY and ISAAC [1966]). The chapter on resonance methods (Ch. 6) is kept very elementary because here too several books are available, mentioned at the end of that chapter.

As to the remaining subjects it is hoped that the book presents a useful supplement to the already existing literature. If so, this is in no small measure due to the generous help I received from my colleagues K. Compaan, P. Cornelius, U. Enz, W.P.J. Fontein, N.J. Freedman, P.R. Locher, A.L. Luiten, G.W. Van Oosterhout, R.P. Van Stapele, D.L.A. Tjaden, J.S. Van Wieringen, D. Wilkinson and from the Editor of this series E.P. Wohlfarth. Their assistance is gratefully acknowledged here.

I am greatly indebted to my wife for her continuous encouragement and her help in preparing the manuscript.

I also wish to express my appreciation to the management of the Philips Research Laboratories for the facilities granted, to E. Deimel, J. Geel, R. Gersdorf, J.P. Morel and N.F. Verster for permission to mention their unpublished results, to the publishers of Philips Technical Review for permission to reproduce Figs. 3.10 and 3.40, and to Mr. P. Vissers for making the drawings.

H. ZIJLSTRA

# CONTENTS

# LIST OF MOST IMPORTANT SYMBOLS

The symbols may have other meanings, incidentally, than those mentioned below. The list applies to both Parts 1 and 2.

| | |
|---|---|
| $A$ | Area |
| $B$, $B$ | Magnetic induction (flux density) |
| $C$ | Specific heat |
| $C$ | Capacitance |
| $C$ | Curie constant |
| $E$ | Potential energy |
| $E$ | Electric fieldstrength |
| $e$ | Electromotive force |
| $F$, $F$ | Force |
| $f$ | Electric fieldstrength |
| $f$ | Mössbauer fraction |
| $f$ | Frequency |
| $G$ | Shear modulus |
| $G$ | Galvanometer constant |
| $H$, $H$ | Magnetic field |
| $I$, $I$ | Magnetization |
| $i$ | Electric current |
| $J_l$ | Bessel function of order $l$ |
| $J$ | Polar moment of inertia |
| $J$, $J$ | Angular momentum |
| $K$ | Bulk modulus (modulus of compression) |
| $K$ | Anisotropy constant |
| $k$ | Torsion constant |

| | |
|---|---|
| $k$ | Thermal conductivity |
| $L$ | Inductance |
| $l$ | Length |
| $M$ | Mutual inductance |
| $M$ | Molar mass |
| $M$ | Mass |
| $M$ | Torque |
| $\boldsymbol{m}$ | Magnetic moment |
| $N$ | Number of turns |
| $N$ | Number of photons |
| $\|N\|$ | Demagnetization tensor |
| $N_f$ | Fluxmetric or ballistic demagnetization factor |
| $N_m$ | Magnetometric demagnetization factor |
| $n$ | Density of turns |
| $P_l$ | Legendre polynomial |
| $P_l^m$ | Associated Legendre polynomial |
| $p$ | Pressure |
| $p$ | Dipole density |
| $p$ | Volume force density |
| $Q$ | Factor of merit |
| $Q_0$ | Magnetic charge |
| $Q_l$ | Strength of magnetic $2^l$-pole |
| $q$ | Charge density |
| $R$ | Resistance |
| $R_H$ | Hall constant |
| $r$ | Reduced resistivity |
| $\boldsymbol{r}$ | Radius vector |
| $S$ | Stress |
| $s$ | Stress density |
| $\boldsymbol{s}$ | Angular momentum |
| $T$ | Temperature |
| $T$ | Volume |
| $T$ | Torque |
| $t$ | Time |

| | |
|---|---|
| $V$ | Magnetic potential |
| $V$ | Voltage |
| $V$ | Volume |
| $W$ | Power (energy per unit time) |
| $Y$ | Young's modulus of elasticity |
| $Y_l^m$ | Spherical harmonic |
| $Z$ | Impedance |
| $\alpha$ | Dimensional ratio |
| $\alpha$ | Direction cosine |
| $\beta$ | Dimensional ratio |
| $\beta$ | Direction cosine |
| $\gamma$ | Dimensional ratio |
| $\gamma$ | Gyromagnetic ratio |
| $\Delta$ | Laplace operator |
| $\delta$ | Difference operator |
| $\delta$ | Packing density (volume fraction occupied by matter) |
| $\varepsilon$ | Strain |
| $\varepsilon$ | Absorption coefficient |
| $\zeta$ | Dimensional ratio |
| $\zeta$ | Heat transfer coefficient |
| $\eta$ | Electrical resistivity |
| $\theta$ | Polar angle |
| $\theta$ | Debye temperature |
| $\vartheta$ | Reduced temperature |
| $\kappa$ | Efficiency |
| $\lambda$ | Packing density (volume fraction occupied by matter) |
| $\lambda$ | Magnetostriction constant |
| $\mu$ | Absolute permeability |
| $\mu_0$ | Permeability of vacuum |
| $\mu_r$ | Relative permeability (vacuum$=1$) |
| $\xi$ | Surfacial current density |
| $\xi$ | Poisson's ratio of contraction |

| $\xi$ | Lagrange's undetermined multiplier |
|---|---|
| $\rho$ | Radius |
| $\rho_V$ | Verdet's constant |
| $\sigma$ | Area |
| $\sigma$ | Absorbing cross-section |
| $\tau$ | Area |
| $\tau$ | Time constant (relaxation time) |
| $\tau$ | Current density |
| $\Phi$ | Magnetic flux |
| $\varphi$ | Azimuthal angle |
| $\chi$ | Magnetic susceptibility |
| $\psi$ | Electric potential |
| $\omega$ | Angular frequency |
| $\nabla$ | Gradient operator |

# CHAPTER 1

# THE MAGNETIC POTENTIAL

## § 1. INTRODUCTION

Many methods used in the study of magnetic phenomena in solids are based on the observation of the effect of an external magnetic field on the material under investigation. Therefore a great deal of attention will be paid to the generation of magnetic fields and the potential theory connected with it. We shall use the concept of magnetic charges and charge densities and relate these to electrical currents. This approach is made for convenience of calculation and does not imply any judgement on the physical reality of magnetic monopoles.

The quantitative treatment of the theory involves the choice of a unit system. In this book the mksA- or Giorgi-system will be used. However, for convenience of those who are used to other systems a comparison between this and the current cgs-systems is made in the next section.

## § 2. COMPARISON OF UNIT SYSTEMS

For giving a numerical value to a magnetic quantity the electro-magnetic centimeter-gram-second system (emcgs-system) is widely used. Its principal feature is that the magnetic permeability $\mu_0$ of the vacuum is put equal to one. Since

$$\mu_0 \varepsilon_0 c^2 = 1$$

the dielectric constant $\varepsilon_0$ of the vacuum is consequently equal to $c^{-2}$, $c$ being the velocity of light in vacuum.

In the cgs-system of Gauss the permeability and the dielectric constant of the vacuum are both equal to one. The consequence is that a factor $c^{-1}$ appears in the basic formulae. This system is also widely used in magnetism.

The meter-kilogram-second-Ampère system of Giorgi (mksA-system) is very convenient if both electric and magnetic quantities are involved in the calculation. It is rationalized, which means that the factor $4\pi$ that occurs in the relation between electric field-strength and polarization and also between magnetic fieldstrength and magnetization in the cgs-systems, is no longer present in the corresponding relations in the mksA-system. This has been obtained by putting the permeability of the vacuum equal to

$$\mu_0 = 4\pi \times 10^{-7} \text{ H m}^{-1}.$$

The dielectric constant then is

$$\varepsilon_0 = 1/\mu_0 c^2 = 8.855 \times 10^{-12} \text{ F m}^{-1}.$$

A unit charge emits a unit flux in this system rather than a flux $4\pi$ as it does in the cgs-systems.

The mksA-system has become widespread during the last decade, mainly because of its practical possibilities. It is adopted in this book since the measurement of magnetic quantities is very often done by methods based on the interaction between magnetic fields and electric currents.

A comparison between a few basic formulae as they occur in the above mentioned systems, together with a conversion table is given in Appendix 1. A detailed survey on the use of these systems may be found in the book by CORNELIUS [1961].

## § 3. POTENTIAL DUE TO MAGNETIC CHARGE SYSTEMS

### § 3.1. *Single magnetic charge*

Experimenting with long magnetized wires thus simulating free magnetic charges Coulomb showed that the force $F$ between two magnetic charges $Q_0$ and $Q_0'$ is given by

$$F \propto \frac{Q_0 Q_0'}{r^3} r, \tag{1.1}$$

where $r$ is the vector connecting the two charges. From eq. (1.1) it follows directly that along a closed path

$$\oint F \cdot dr = 0, \tag{1.2}$$

which means that the line integral of $F$ from one point to another is irrespective of the path chosen.

In the mksA-system we have

$$F = \frac{1}{4\pi\mu_0} \frac{Q_0 Q_0'}{r^3} r = HQ_0', \tag{1.3}$$

where $H$ is the force per unit charge exerted by $Q_0$ on the charge located at a distance $r$. This force is called the magnetic field-strength at a distance $r$ from the single charge or monopole of strength $Q_0$. The potential $V_A$ at a point $A$ is defined as the work per unit charge required to bring a positive charge from infinity (where $V=0$ by definition) to $A$:

$$V_A = \int_{\infty}^{A} - H \cdot dr = \frac{1}{4\pi\mu_0} \frac{Q_0}{r}, \tag{1.4}$$

where the fieldstrength $H$ at any point is related to the potential $V$ by

$$H = - \operatorname{grad} V. \tag{1.5}$$

The integral of eq. (1.4) does not depend on the path chosen.

The potential difference between two points $A$ and $B$ is

$$V_A - V_B = \int_{A}^{B} H \cdot dr \tag{1.6}$$

and if the integration path is closed

$$\oint \boldsymbol{H} \cdot \mathrm{d}\boldsymbol{r} = 0, \tag{1.7}$$

which also follows directly from eq. (1.2).

Equation (1.7) only holds if the path does not enclose an electric current (see § 4 of this chapter).

### § 3.2. *Additivity of fields and potentials*

If more point charges $Q_i$ are present the force exerted on a positive unit charge at a point $A$ is the resultant of the forces due to each charge individually:

$$\boldsymbol{F} = \sum \boldsymbol{F}_i,$$

where $\boldsymbol{F}_i$ is the force due to the charge $Q_i$. Hence the resultant fieldstrength at any point is

$$\boldsymbol{H} = \sum \boldsymbol{H}_i,$$

where $\boldsymbol{H}_i$ is the fieldstrength due to the charge $Q_i$.

The total potential at the point $A$ is

$$V_A = - \int_{\infty}^{A} \left( \sum \boldsymbol{H}_i \right) \cdot \mathrm{d}\boldsymbol{r} =$$

$$= - \sum \int_{\infty}^{A} \boldsymbol{H}_i \cdot \mathrm{d}\boldsymbol{r} =$$

$$= \sum V_i, \tag{1.8}$$

where $V_i$ is the potential at $A$ due to the charge $Q_i$.

We thus see that the potentials in a point due to several sources separately must be added to give the potential due to the whole system of sources.

### § 3.3. *Laplace's and Poisson's equations*

It can be shown from eq. (1.3) that

$$\oint H \cdot dA = Q_0/\mu_0, \tag{1.9}$$

where $dA$ is a surface element of a closed surface enclosing the point charge $Q_0$.

If the charge is not concentrated in a point but distributed as a charge density $q$ inside the closed surface the right-hand side of eq. (1.9) can be written as

$$\frac{Q_0}{\mu_0} = \frac{1}{\mu_0} \int q \, dv, \tag{1.10}$$

where $dv$ is an element of the volume enclosed by the surface. Application of Gauss' theorem to the left-hand side of eq. (1.9) gives

$$\oint H \cdot dA = \int \text{div} \, H \, dv. \tag{1.11}$$

Since the right-hand sides of eqs. (1.10) and (1.11) are equal for any surface the integrands must be equal which gives

$$\text{div} \, H = q/\mu_0. \tag{1.12}$$

Using eq. (1.5) we have then

$$\text{div grad } V = \Delta V = -q/\mu_0, \tag{1.13}$$

which is called Poisson's equation.

In a region where the charge density equals zero

$$\Delta V = 0, \tag{1.14}$$

which is called Laplace's equation.

Equation (1.14) will be used in Chapter 2 to calculate the magnetic field due to a given system of magnetic charges. The procedure is as follows: The magnetic charges provide a set of boundary conditions that choose one and not more than one solution for $V$ (apart from an undetermined term independent of variables) from the infinite number of solutions that satisfy eq. (1.14). The magnetic fieldstrength then follows uniquely by eq. (1.5).

## § 3.4. *Potential due to multipoles*

Consider a point charge $-Q_0$ at a point $R$ and a charge $+Q_0$ displaced from $R$ by a small vector $d\mathbf{r}_1$ (Fig. 1.1). The potential at a

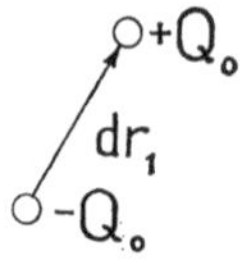

Fig. 1.1.   Dipole consisting of two point charges $-Q_0$ and $+Q_0$ a distance $d\mathbf{r}_1$ apart.

point $S$ due to this charge system will be derived in terms of the potential $V(1)$ due to a positive unit charge located at the origin. The potential at $S$ due to the charge $-Q_0$ at $R$ then is

$$V_a = -Q_0 V(1). \tag{1.15}$$

The potential at $S$ due to the charge $+Q_0$ is to a first approximation

$$V_b = Q_0 \{V(1) - d\mathbf{r}_1 \cdot \text{grad } V(1)\}, \tag{1.16}$$

where grad $V(1)$ is to be taken at the point $S$. If $d\mathbf{r}_1$ is infinitesimal this expression is exact.

The total potential due to the two charges at an infinitesimal distance then is

$$V_1 = V_a + V_b = Q_0(-d\mathbf{r}_1 \cdot \nabla) V(1). \tag{1.17}$$

We replace $d\mathbf{r}_1$ by $\mathbf{n}_1 d r_1$, where $\mathbf{n}_1$ is the unit vector along $d\mathbf{r}_1$.

The two charges form a dipole of strength $Q_1 = Q_0\, dr$ and the potential due to this dipole is

$$V_1 = Q_1(-\mathbf{n}_1 \cdot \nabla) V(1). \tag{1.18}$$

Now consider a quadrupole formed by a dipole of strength $-Q_1$

along the unit vector $n_1$, located at the point $R$ and a dipole of strength $+Q_1$ along $n_1$, displaced from $R$ by an infinitesimal vector $dr_2$ (Fig. 1.2). The potential due to this quadrupole is

$$V_2 = Q_1 (- dr_2 \cdot \nabla) (- n_1 \cdot \nabla) V(1) \qquad (1.19)$$

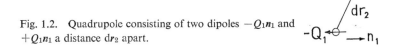

Fig. 1.2.    Quadrupole consisting of two dipoles $-Q_1 n_1$ and $+Q_1 n_1$ a distance $dr_2$ apart.

or, after replacing $dr_2$ by $n_2 \, dr_2$, where $n_2$ is the unit vector along $dr_2$,

$$V_2 = Q_2 (- n_2 \cdot \nabla) (- n_1 \cdot \nabla) V(1), \qquad (1.20)$$

where $Q_2 = Q_1 \, dr_2 = Q_0 \, dr_1 \, dr_2$ is the strength of the quadrupole characterized by $n_1$ and $n_2$. Similarly we find for the general $2^l$-pole

$$V_l = Q_l (- n_l \cdot \nabla) (- n_{l-1} \cdot \nabla) \cdots (- n_1 \cdot \nabla) V(1) \qquad (1.21)$$

where $Q_l$ is the strength of the $2^l$-pole characterized by the unit vectors $n_1, \ldots, n_l$.

### § 3.5. *Potential due to charge and dipole distributions on a surface*

A surface is supposed to be occupied by a non-uniform charge distribution of local density $q$. Consider an element $dA$ of this surface, sufficiently small that $q$ can be considered uniform within the element. The surface element is located at a point R and its total charge is

$$dQ_0 = q \, dA.$$

The potential at a point S due to this charge is, by eq. (1.4),

$$dV = \frac{1}{4\pi\mu_0} \frac{q \, dA}{r},$$

where $r$ is the distance between R and S.

The fieldstrength follows by applying eq. (1.5),

$$dH = \frac{q}{4\pi\mu_0} \frac{r}{r^3} \, dA, \qquad (1.22)$$

where $r$ is the connecting vector from R to S. The fieldstrength due to the whole charged surface is found by integrating this expression.

For a surface occupied by dipoles the procedure is similar. Let a surface be occupied by normal dipoles with a local density $p$. Such a surface is called a magnetic shell. Consider an element $dA$ of this surface located at a point R. The total dipole strength of this element is

$$dQ_1 = p \, dA,$$

and the direction of the dipole is along the unit vector $n$ normal on the surface at R.

The potential at a point S due to this surface element is given by eq. (1.18):

$$dV = p \, dA \left( - n \cdot \nabla \right) V(1) =$$
$$= \frac{1}{4\pi\mu_0} p \, dA \frac{n \cdot r}{r^3},$$

where $r$ is the connecting vector from R to S. We replace $n \, dA$ by $dA$ and find

$$dV = \frac{1}{4\pi\mu_0} p \frac{r \cdot dA}{r^3} = \frac{p}{4\pi\mu_0} \, d\Omega, \qquad (1.23)$$

where $d\Omega$ is the solid angle at S subtended by the surface element $dA$ at R (Fig. 1.3). If we allow point S to approach point R, the angle $d\Omega$ increases to the value $2\pi$ when S meets R. If R approaches R from the other side of the surface the product $r \cdot dA$ has a

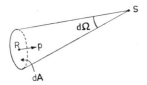

Fig 1.3.   Element of magnetic shell at $R$ subtended by the solid angle $d\Omega$ at $S$.

negative value. The angle $d\Omega$ then is also negative and approaches the value $-2\pi$ at the surface. We thus see that at the surface a potential discontinuity occurs equal to

$$V_+ - V_- = p/\mu_0,\qquad(1.24)$$

where $V_+$ is the potential at R at the positive side of the shell, $V_-$ is the potential at the same point at the negative side of the shell and $p$ is the local dipole density at R. Surface elements not containing R do not contribute to the potential jump since the angle $d\Omega$ for these elements shows no discontinuity when S is approaching $R$.

If we start a line integral of **H** from a point R at the positive side of a shell and follow a path around the edge of the shell to the

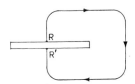

Fig. 1.4.  Finite magnetic shell with integration path. The shell is drawn with finite thickness to show the beginning and end points of the integration path clearly.

corresponding point R′ at the negative side (Fig. 1.4) the value of the integral is

$$\int \boldsymbol{H}\cdot\mathrm{d}\boldsymbol{r} = p/\mu_0,\qquad(1.25)$$

where $p$ is the dipole density at R. However, if we go through the shell the discontinuity given by eq. (1.24) makes the closed integral zero. Similarly an integral along a closed path going twice through the shell at points where the dipole density is $p_1$ and $p_2$, respectively, (Fig. 1.5), equals zero. It contains, however, the jumps $-p_1/\mu_0$ and

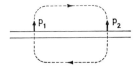

Fig. 1.5.  Non-uniform magnetic shell with integration path (dotted line).

$p_2/\mu_0$, so the line integral of $H$ outside the shell equals

$$\int H \cdot \mathrm{d}r = (p_1 - p_2)/\mu_0 . \tag{1.26}$$

## §4. MAGNETIC POTENTIAL DUE TO ELECTRIC CURRENTS

The magnetic field due to a plane circuit in which a current was flowing was investigated experimentally by Ampère and later more accurately by Weber. It was found that at distances great compared to the size of the circuit the magnetic potential was the same as that due to a magnetic dipole located at the same place as the circuit.

For a circuit of area $A$ and with current $i$ the equivalent dipole has a moment

$$Q_1 = \mu_0 i A . \tag{1.27}$$

The relation between the sense of the current and the direction of $A$ (and $Q_1$) is that of a right-hand screw.

To investigate the potential at a distance not great compared to the size of the circuit we consider some surface bounded by the circuit, which is not necessarily plane. This surface is divided into elements of a size small compared to the distance between the element and the point where the potential is to be determined. This is always possible if the point is not on the circuit, as the surface can then always be chosen so as not to contain the point. Each element is supposed to have a current $i$ of the same sense and magnitude flowing along its edge (Fig. 1.6). Thus the currents of

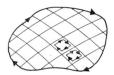

Fig. 1.6. The area enclosed by a current circuit divided into elementary circuits.

two neighbouring elements cancel each other at their common boundary. This results in a current only at those edges where no neighbours are present, i.e. at the circuit bounding the surface. Thus a surface consisting of equal elementary circuits with current $i$ is identical to the surface with the current $i$ flowing along its edge.

The integral $\int \boldsymbol{H} \cdot \mathrm{d}\boldsymbol{r}$ due to such a current is known to be multivalent, being different after each time the current is enclosed by the path of integration. However, a single-valued magnetic potential can be obtained if the surface bounded by the current circuit is excluded from the space where the potential is defined, so that no closed path enclosing the current is possible. Then the potential due to the current circuit can be identified with the potential due to a uniform magnetic shell of density $p$ coinciding with the surface bounded by the current circuit.

We then have by eq. (1.27)

$$p = Q_1/A = \mu_0 i. \tag{1.28}$$

A line integral of $\boldsymbol{H}$ along a path starting from a point at the positive side of the shell and going round its edge to the corresponding point at the negative side has by eq. (1.25) the value

$$\int \boldsymbol{H} \cdot \mathrm{d}\boldsymbol{r} = p/\mu_0 = i, \tag{1.29}$$

which is Maxwell's law for a closed line integral of $\boldsymbol{H}$ around a current $i$. This integral is thus equal to the potential jump at the magnetic shell equivalent with $i$.

This shell may have arbitrary shape provided that its edge coincides with the current circuit. It can always be chosen outside the space where the potential is to be determined.

## § 5. RELATION BETWEEN THE CURRENT DENSITY AND ITS EQUIVALENT DIPOLE DENSITY ON A SURFACE

To calculate the current distribution required for generating a magnetic field of a given geometry it is convenient first to determine the magnetic shell causing the correct magnetic potential and next to relate this shell to an equivalent current distribution. The first procedure will be discussed in Chapter 2, but for the latter a relation will be derived in this section.

Suppose a thin sheet of thickness $\delta$ to contain electric currents parallel to its plane with a non-uniform current density $\tau$. The currents are supposed to have no sources or sinks, so the sheet is equivalent to a magnetic shell with a non-uniform dipole density $p$. A closed integration path is supposed to go twice through the sheet.

Consider the cross-section of the sheet in the plane of the integration path (Fig. 1.7). A unit vector $m$ is supposed to lie in the plane of the sheet and the plane of the path and a unit vector $n$ is supposed to be normal to the sheet.

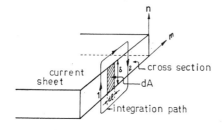

Fig. 1.7. Current sheet with integration path. Only the part of the sheet on the left of the plane of the path has been drawn. Currents flow only parallel to the plane of the sheet.

The line integral of $H$ along the path is by eq. (1.29)

$$\int H \cdot \mathrm{d}r = \int \tau \cdot \mathrm{d}A, \tag{1.30}$$

where $\mathrm{d}A$ is an element of the cross-sectional area of the sheet and integration is performed for the part of the sheet enclosed by the path. This element can be written as

$$\mathrm{d}A = \delta \, \mathrm{d}l(n \times m), \tag{1.31}$$

where $\mathrm{d}l$ is measured in the direction of $m$.

The left-hand side of eq. (1.30) is equal to the potential jumps at the magnetic shell (see the comment to eq. (1.29)), so we have

$$\frac{p_2 - p_1}{\mu_0} = \int \tau \cdot (n \times m) \, \delta \, \mathrm{d}l, \tag{1.32}$$

where $p_1$ and $p_2$ are the dipole densities at the points 1 and 2 in Fig. 1.7 where the path crosses the sheet.

Let the thickness of the sheet approach to zero leaving the product $\tau\delta = \xi$ constant. We further write the left-hand side of eq. (1.32) as an integral to obtain

$$\frac{1}{\mu_0} \int \frac{\partial p}{\partial l} \, \mathrm{d}l = \int \xi \cdot (n \times m) \, \mathrm{d}l. \qquad (1.33)$$

This must be true for any path, so the integrands are identical:

$$\frac{1}{\mu_0} \frac{\partial p}{\partial l} = \xi \cdot (n \times m), \qquad (1.34)$$

where $n \| p$ and $m \| \mathrm{d}l$. This can also be written as

$$\frac{\partial p}{\partial l} = \mu_0 \xi_s, \qquad (1.35)$$

where $\xi_s$ is the current density along the surface and perpendicular to the path along which $p$ is differentiated.

# CHAPTER 2

# EXPANSION OF THE MAGNETIC POTENTIAL
# IN SPHERICAL COORDINATES

## § 1. SPHERICAL HARMONICS

### § 1.1. *Solution of Laplace's equation*

The symmetry of the problems encountered in this book suggests
the use of polar coordinates $r$, $\theta$ and $\varphi$ (Fig. 2.1). Laplace's equation

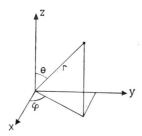

Fig. 2.1.   Spherical polar coordinate system.

then has the form

$$\Delta V = \frac{1}{r^2}\left[\frac{\partial}{\partial r}\left(r^2\frac{\partial}{\partial r}\right) + \frac{1}{\sin\theta}\frac{\partial}{\partial\theta}\left(\sin\theta\frac{\partial}{\partial\theta}\right) + \frac{1}{\sin^2\theta}\frac{\partial^2}{\partial\varphi^2}\right]V = 0. \tag{2.1}$$

This equation can be solved by the method of separation of variables. We assume a solution of the form

$$V = R\Theta\Phi, \tag{2.2}$$

where $R$, $\Theta$ and $\Phi$ are functions of, respectively, $r$, $\theta$ and $\varphi$ ex-

14

clusively. Substitution of this expression in eq. (2.1) and multiplication by $r^2/R\Theta\Phi$ gives

$$\frac{1}{R}\frac{\partial}{\partial r}\left(r^2\frac{\partial}{\partial r}R\right) = \frac{-1}{\Theta\Phi}\left\{\frac{1}{\sin\theta}\frac{\partial}{\partial\theta}\left(\sin\theta\frac{\partial}{\partial\theta}\right)\Theta\Phi + \right.$$
$$\left. + \frac{1}{\sin^2\theta}\frac{\partial^2}{\partial\varphi^2}(\Theta\Phi)\right\}, \qquad (2.3)$$

where the left-hand member is a function of $r$, exclusively, and the right-hand member is a function of $\theta$ and $\varphi$, exclusively. This equality holds for any value of the variables only if both members are a constant, here being denoted by $\lambda$. The right-hand member then becomes after multiplication by $\sin^2\theta$

$$\frac{1}{\Theta}\sin\theta\frac{\partial}{\partial\theta}\left(\sin\theta\frac{\partial\Theta}{\partial\theta}\right) + \lambda\sin^2\theta = -\frac{1}{\Phi}\frac{\partial^2\Phi}{\partial\varphi^2}. \qquad (2.4)$$

Here again a separation of variables is obtained. The two members of this equation are thus a constant, denoted by $m^2$. This leads to a differential equation for $\Phi$:

$$\frac{d^2\Phi}{d\varphi^2} = -m^2\Phi, \qquad (2.5)$$

having as particular solution

$$\Phi_m = e^{im\varphi}. \qquad (2.6)$$

As we are only interested in single-valued solutions $m$ must be an integer. The left-hand member of eq. (2.4) gives a differential equation for $\Theta$:

$$\sin^2\theta\frac{d^2\Theta}{d(\cos\theta)^2} - 2\cos\theta\frac{d\Theta}{d\cos\theta} - \left(\frac{m^2}{\sin^2\theta} - \lambda\right)\Theta = 0. \qquad (2.7)$$

This equation has non-singular and finite solutions for $\Theta$ only if $\lambda$ is an integer. With $\lambda = l(l+1)$ the equation is satisfied by the so-called "associated Legendre polynomials"

$$P_l^m = P_l^{-m} = \frac{\sin^{|m|}\theta}{2^l \, l!} \frac{d^{|m|+l}}{d(\cos\theta)^{|m|+l}} (-\sin^2\theta)^l =$$

$$= \sin^{|m|}\theta \frac{d^{|m|}}{d(\cos\theta)^{|m|}} P_l^0 . \tag{2.8}$$

These polynomials are given in Appendix 2 for several values of $l$ and $m$. They are defined for $l \geqslant 0$ and $|m| \leqslant l$. The radial part of Laplace's equation is found by equating the left-hand member of eq. (2.3) to $\lambda$ and multiplying by $R$:

$$\frac{d}{dr}\left(r^2 \frac{d}{dr} R\right) = \lambda R . \tag{2.9}$$

This can be rewritten as

$$r^2 \frac{d^2(rR)}{dr^2} = \lambda(rR). \tag{2.10}$$

Particular solutions for $rR$ are

$$rR = r^{l+1} \quad \text{and} \quad rR = r^{-l}. \tag{2.11}$$

We thus find the general solution, being regular and finite with respect to $\theta$ and $\varphi$, by substituting eqs. (2.6), (2.8) and (2.11) into eq. (2.2) and summing with respect to $l$ and $m$:

$$V = \sum_{l=0}^{\infty} \sum_{m=-l}^{l} \left(a_{lm}r^l + b_{lm}r^{-(l+1)}\right) P_l^{|m|} e^{im\varphi} =$$

$$= \sum_{l=0}^{\infty} \sum_{m=-l}^{l} \left(a_{lm}r^l + b_{lm}r^{-(l+1)}\right) Y_l^m, \tag{2.12}$$

where $a_{lm}$ and $b_{lm}$ are coefficients to be determined by the boundary conditions. These coefficients are generally complex quantities and can be written as

$$a_{lm} = a'_{lm} + ia''_{lm};$$
$$b_{lm} = b'_{lm} + ib''_{lm},$$

where $a'$, $a''$, $b'$ and $b''$ are real and $i = \sqrt{-1}$. The potential, however, is real which implies the following relations $(m \neq 0)$

$$
\begin{aligned}
a'_{lm} &= \quad a'_{l\bar{m}} = \quad \tfrac{1}{2}s_{lm}; \quad a'_{l0} = s_{l0}; \\
a''_{lm} &= - a''_{l\bar{m}} = - \tfrac{1}{2}t_{lm}; \quad t_{l0} = 0; \\
b'_{lm} &= \quad b'_{l\bar{m}} = \quad \tfrac{1}{2}u_{lm}; \quad b'_{l0} = u_{l0}; \\
b''_{lm} &= - b''_{l\bar{m}} = - \tfrac{1}{2}v_{lm}; \quad v_{l0} = 0,
\end{aligned}
\tag{2.13}
$$

where $\bar{m}$ is written for $-m$ and the coefficients $s$, $t$, $u$ and $v$ are introduced for convenience. With these coefficients eq. (2.12) is real and can be written as

$$
V = \sum_{l=0}^{\infty} \sum_{m=0}^{l} \left( s_{lm} r^{l} + u_{lm} r^{-(l+1)} \right) P_{l}^{m} \cos m\varphi +
$$
$$
+ \sum_{l=0}^{\infty} \sum_{m=0}^{l} \left( t_{lm} r^{l} + v_{lm} r^{-(l+1)} \right) P_{l}^{m} \sin m\varphi, \tag{2.14}
$$

where $l \geq 0$ and $0 \leq m \leq l$. By this, eq. (2.14) has the same number of mutually independent terms as eq. (2.12), namely $2l+1$ for each value of $l$.

At a large distance from a finite system of sources causing the potential field, only terms with negative powers of $r$ can be present to ensure finiteness of the potential at infinity. On the other hand only terms with positive powers of $r$ can describe the potential near the origin, if no singularity (a point charge, for instance) is present there.

§ 1.2. *Uniqueness and orthogonality*

The functions $Y_{l}^{m}$ have two important properties. The first is that any function $F$ of $\theta$ and $\varphi$ satisfying Laplace's equation can be expanded as a series of $Y_{l}^{m}$:

$$
F = \sum_{l=0}^{\infty} \sum_{m=-l}^{l} f_{lm} Y_{l}^{m}.
$$

Such an expansion is unique, which means that only one set of coefficients $f_{lm}$ can be found to describe the function $F$. The other property is that the integral

$$\int_{\text{sphere}} \bar{Y}_l^m Y_{l'}^{m'} \, d\omega = 0 , \tag{2.15}$$

if either $l \neq l'$ or $m \neq m'$ or both, and

$$\int_{\text{sphere}} \bar{Y}_l^m Y_{l'}^{m'} \, d\omega = \frac{4\pi (l + m)!}{(2l + 1)(l - m)!} , \tag{2.16}$$

if $l = l'$ and $m = m'$, where $\bar{Y}_l^m$ is the complex conjugate of $Y_l^m$ and integration is performed over the entire surface of the sphere with unit radius. Functions that have these two properties are said to form a complete and orthogonal set.

The orthogonality provides a simple means to determine the coefficients $f_{lm}$ when a function $F$ is given: Consider the integral

$$\int_{\text{sphere}} \bar{Y}_{l'}^{m'} F \, d\omega = \int_{\text{sphere}} \bar{Y}_{l'}^{m'} \left( \sum f_{lm} Y_l^m \right) d\omega .$$

The right-hand integral has vanishing terms for all $l$ and $m$, except when $l = l'$ and $m = m'$. We thus obtain

$$f_{lm} = \frac{(2l + 1)(l - m)!}{4\pi (l + m)!} \int_{\text{sphere}} \bar{Y}_l^m F \, d\omega . \tag{2.17}$$

The integral can sometimes be evaluated analytically but in many cases must be approximated by numerical and computer methods, especially when $F$ is given as a graph or a table. These methods will not be considered here.

## § 1.3. *Multipole fields and spherical harmonics*

The potential outside a finite system of charges is described by eq. (2.14) with only terms with negative powers of $r$:

$$V_e = \sum_{l=0}^{\infty} \sum_{m=0}^{l} \left( u_{lm} \cos m\varphi + v_{lm} \sin m\varphi \right) r^{-(l+1)} P_l^m , \tag{2.18}$$

where the subscript e stands for "external". Each term of this series can be identified with the potential of one of the $2^l$-poles discussed in Ch. 1, § 3.4.

For instance, the dipolar term

$$V_{10} = u_{10} \cos \theta / r^2 \tag{2.19}$$

is the same as

$$V_1 = Q_1 (-\boldsymbol{n}_1 \cdot \nabla) V(1)$$

(eq. 1.18), with $Q_1 = 4\pi\mu_0 u_{10}$, $V(1) = 1/(4\pi\mu_0 r)$ and the unit vector $\boldsymbol{n}_1$ along the $z$-axis.

As there are $2l+1$ mutually independent terms possible for each value of $l$, the general $2^l$-pole can be decomposed into $2l+1$ mutually independent components. For instance, the three components of a general dipole are

$$\frac{u_{10} \cos \theta}{r^2} = \frac{u_{10} z}{r^3},$$

$$\frac{u_{11} \sin \theta \cos \varphi}{r^2} = \frac{u_{11} x}{r^3},$$

$$\frac{v_{11} \sin \theta \sin \varphi}{r^2} = \frac{v_{11} y}{r^3}.$$

We now consider the potential energy $E_l$ of a $2^l$-pole in a field described by the potential $V$. This energy is evaluated in a similar way as has been done with the potential of a multipole in Ch. 1, § 3.4:

The potential energy of a monopole ($l=0$) in the field is

$$E_0 = Q_0 V,$$

where $Q_0$ is the strength of the monopole. The potential energy of a dipole along $\boldsymbol{n}_1$ is

$$E_1 = Q_1 \boldsymbol{n}_1 \cdot \nabla V, \tag{2.20}$$

where $Q_1$ is the strength of the dipole and $\boldsymbol{n}_1$ is a unit vector.

The potential energy of a $2^l$-pole, characterized by the unit vectors $\boldsymbol{n}_1, \boldsymbol{n}_2, ..., \boldsymbol{n}_l$ is

$$E_l = Q_l (\boldsymbol{n}_l \cdot \nabla)(\boldsymbol{n}_{l-1} \cdot \nabla) \cdots (\boldsymbol{n}_1 \cdot \nabla) V, \tag{2.21}$$

where $Q_l$ is the strength of the $2^l$-pole. Thus $E_l$ is found by $l$ times differentiating $V$. In the special case that $V$ is a homogeneous function of the coordinates of degree $l$ the potential energy $E_l$ is a constant. A field having this potential is described by the terms with $r^l$ of eq. (2.14):

$$V_l = \sum_{m=0}^{l} (s_{lm} \cos m\varphi + t_{lm} \sin m\varphi) \, r^l \, P_l^m. \tag{2.22}$$

Such homogeneous terms are called "spherical harmonics of degree $l$". We thus have the following theorem:

*The potential energy of a $2^l$-pole in a field, the potential of which is a spherical harmonic of degree $l$, is independent of the position of the multipole, provided that its orientation is retained.*

A consequence of this theorem is that such a field may exert a torque upon the multipole, but no translational forces.

As an example we consider the general quadrupole ($l=2$). Its external potential can be expressed as the sum of the terms with $l=2$ of eq. (2.18):

$$\begin{aligned}
V_e = \; & u_{20} \, P_2^0/r^3 + \\
& + u_{21} \, P_2^1 \cos \varphi/r^3 + \\
& + u_{22} \, P_2^2 \cos 2\varphi/r^3 + \\
& + v_{21} \, P_2^1 \sin \varphi/r^3 + \\
& + v_{22} \, P_2^2 \sin 2\varphi/r^3 .
\end{aligned} \tag{2.23}$$

This quadrupole has a position-independent potential energy in a field described by eq. (2.22) with $l=2$. The potential of this field can be decomposed in five mutually independent components:

$$\begin{aligned}
s_{20} \, r^2 \, P_2^0 &= \tfrac{1}{2} s_{20} (2z^2 - x^2 - y^2); \\
s_{21} \, r^2 \, P_2^1 \cos \varphi &= 3 s_{21} xz ; \\
s_{22} \, r^2 \, P_2^2 \cos 2\varphi &= 3 s_{22} (x^2 - y^2); \\
t_{21} \, r^2 \, P_2^1 \sin \varphi &= 3 t_{21} yz ; \\
t_{22} \, r^2 \, P_2^2 \sin 2\varphi &= 6 t_{22} xy .
\end{aligned} \tag{2.24}$$

The magnetic fieldstrength is found by applying eq. (1.5) to the sum of these terms resulting in

$$H = \begin{Vmatrix} s_{20} - 6s_{22} & -6t_{22} & -3s_{21} \\ -6t_{22} & s_{20} + 6s_{22} & -3t_{21} \\ -3s_{21} & -3t_{21} & -2s_{20} \end{Vmatrix} r. \tag{2.25}$$

This fieldstrength depends linearly on coordinates and thus has a uniform gradient.

## § 2. APPLICATIONS

### § 2.1. *Charge distribution on a spherical surface*

The coefficients of the expansion of the potential are determined by the boundary conditions. These boundary conditions may consist of a certain fixed potential distribution along certain lines or surfaces, but may also be formulated as a certain charge distribution, the relation between charge density and potential being given by Poisson's equation.

In this section the potential due to an arbitrary charge distribution on a spherical surface will be considered. Let the charge density $q$ at the point $(\theta_0, \varphi_0)$ on a spherical surface with radius $r_0$ be

$$q = \sum_{l=0}^{\infty} \sum_{m=-l}^{l} q_{lm} Y_l^m(\theta_0, \varphi_0). \tag{2.26}$$

Owing to the completeness of the set of functions $Y_l^m$, any physically interesting function of $\theta_0$ and $\varphi_0$ can be expressed in this series form.

The potential $V_i$ inside the sphere only contains terms with positive powers of $r$ (including zero):

$$V_i = \sum_{l=0}^{\infty} \sum_{m=-l}^{l} a_{lm} r^l Y_l^m, \tag{2.27}$$

and the potential $V_e$ outside the sphere only contains terms with negative powers of $r$:

$$V_e = \sum_{l=0}^{\infty} \sum_{m=-l}^{l} b_{lm} r^{-(l+1)} Y_l^m. \tag{2.28}$$

As there are no double layers present at the surface the potential must be continuous there:

$$V_i(r_0) = V_e(r_0),$$                    (2.29)

which, owing to the uniqueness of the expansions (2.27) and (2.28), requires the term by term equality:

$$a_{lm} r_0^l Y_l^m = b_{lm} r^{-(l+1)} Y_l^m.$$                    (2.30)

We substitute

$$a_{lm} = c_{lm} r_0^{-(l+1)},$$
$$b_{lm} = c_{lm} r_0^l,$$                    (2.31)

which satisfies eq. (2.30) and provides a new set of coefficients $c_{lm}$ that can be related to the charge distribution coefficients $q_{lm}$.

To find this relation we apply Gauss' theorem to an element $\delta\sigma$ of the spherical surface. We describe a flat box with its bottom inside the sphere, its top outside the sphere and of which $\delta\sigma$ is the median section (Fig. 2.2). The charge enclosed by the box is equal to $q\,\delta\sigma$.

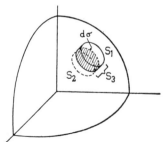

Fig. 2.2. Application of Gauss' theorem to a charged surface.

We integrate Poisson's equation over the volume of the box

$$\int \Delta V \, dv = \int -\frac{q}{\mu_0} \, dv = -\frac{q}{\mu_0} \, \delta\sigma,$$                    (2.32)

and apply Gauss' theorem to the left-hand member:

$$\int \text{grad } V \cdot d\mathbf{s} = -\frac{q}{\mu_0} \, \delta\sigma,$$                    (2.33)

where $dv$ is a volume element and $ds$ is a surface element of the box. The surface integral of eq. (2.33) is divided into three parts:

$$\int \operatorname{grad} V \cdot ds = \int_{S_1} \operatorname{grad} V \cdot ds + \int_{S_2} \operatorname{grad} V \cdot ds + \int_{S_3} \operatorname{grad} V \cdot ds,$$

where $S_1$ is the top, $S_2$ the bottom and $S_3$ the curved wall connecting top and bottom of the box. The height of the box can be taken arbitrarily small without interfering with eq. (2.33). In the limiting case, when this height approaches to zero to a higher degree than $S_1$ and $S_2$, the integral over $S_3$ vanishes. Then $S_1$ and $S_2$ are equal to $\delta\sigma$ and we can write

$$n \cdot \operatorname{grad} V_e - n \cdot \operatorname{grad} V_i = - q/\mu_0, \qquad (2.34)$$

where $n$ is the unit vector normal to the charged surface pointing outwards.

Using eq. (1.5) this equation can be rewritten as

$$(H_e - H_i)_n = q/\mu_0, \qquad (2.35)$$

which is the difference between the normal components of the fieldstrengths on either side of a surface with a local charge density $q$. This equation is generally valid as in its derivation we did not use the fact that the surface is spherical. In our case of the spherical surface eq. (2.34) becomes

$$\frac{\partial V_e}{\partial r} - \frac{\partial V_i}{\partial r} = - \frac{q}{\mu_0}, \qquad (2.36)$$

which after substitution of eqs. (2.26), (2.27) and (2.28) and term by term equation gives

$$c_{lm} = \frac{r_0^2}{2l + 1} \frac{q_{lm}}{\mu_0}. \qquad (2.37)$$

Substituting this into eqs. (2.31) and the result into eqs. (2.27) and (2.28) gives the potential due to a charge distribution on a spherical surface

$$V_i = \frac{1}{\mu_0} \sum_{l=0}^{\infty} \sum_{m=-l}^{l} q_{lm} \frac{r_0^{-(l-1)}}{(2l+1)} r^l Y_l^m, \tag{2.38}$$

$$V_e = \frac{1}{\mu_0} \sum_{l=0}^{\infty} \sum_{m=-l}^{l} q_{lm} \frac{r_0^{l+2}}{(2l+1)} r^{-(l+1)} Y_l^m, \tag{2.39}$$

where the coefficients $q_{lm}$ are those mentioned in eq. (2.26). The conditions of eqs. (2.13) applied to the coefficients $q_{lm}$ for a real charge distribution automatically lead to real potentials $V_i$ and $V_e$.

The equations for $V_i$ and $V_e$ have an interesting property. When we contract the sphere under conservation of the products $q_{lm}r_0^{l+2}$ the external potential $V_e$ will remain unchanged even when the sphere is contracted to a point at the origin. Similarly we find an unchanging internal potential if the products $q_{lm}r_0^{-(l-1)}$ are kept constant.

Consider for instance the special case of the dipolar term ($l=1$, $m=0$) for which

$$V_i = \frac{1}{3\mu_0} q_{10} r \cos\theta. \tag{2.40}$$

This potential describes a homogeneous field along the $z$-direction. The potential and thus the field remains unchanged if $q_{10}$ is kept constant. This is obtained by keeping the local charge density on the surface constant when the sphere is contracted or expanded. The external potential is

$$V_e = \frac{1}{3\mu_0} q_{10} r_0^3 r^{-2} \cos\theta, \tag{2.41}$$

which is unchanged if the product $q_{10}r_0^3$ is kept constant.

§ 2.2. *Dipole distribution on a spherical surface*

The potential due to a current circuit can be identified with the potential due to a uniform dipole layer bounded by the current circuit and assuming any arbitrary surface (Ch. 1, § 4). Let that surface be that of a sphere of radius $r_0$. Then a distribution of closed currents on that surface has the same potential as a corresponding non-uniform dipole layer, the dipoles being normal to the surface. The relation between the dipole distribution and the current distribution is treated in Ch. 1, § 5. In the present chapter the potential due to a general distribution of normal dipoles on a spherical surface will be derived. This distribution is composed of a general charge distribution on a spherical surface of radius $r_0$ and a similar charge distribution of opposite sign on a spherical surface of radius $r_0 + \delta r$, to form a dipole layer. To obtain this the absolute values of the total charges of the two surfaces must be equal.

Let the charge density on the inner surface be

$$q_1 = - \sum_{l=0}^{\infty} \sum_{m=-l}^{l} q_{lm} Y_l^m (\theta_0, \varphi_0).$$

The charge density on the outer surface then is

$$q_2 = \frac{- r_0^2}{(r_0 + \delta r)^2} q_1,$$

forming with $q_1$ a layer of normal dipoles of density

$$p = - q_1 \, \delta r = \delta r \sum \sum q_{lm} Y_l^m (\theta_0, \varphi_0),$$

where the positive direction of $p$ is taken outwards. The potential due to this general dipole layer is the sum of the potentials due to each charged surface (eqs. (2.38) and (2.39)) which for infinitesimal $\delta r$ results in

$$V_i = \frac{1}{\mu_0} \sum_{l=0}^{\infty} \sum_{m=-l}^{l} \frac{-(l+1)}{2l+1} p_{lm} r_0^{-l} r^l Y_l^m, \tag{2.42}$$

$$V_e = \frac{1}{\mu_0} \sum_{l=0}^{\infty} \sum_{m=-l}^{l} \frac{l}{2l+1} p_{lm} r_0^{l+1} r^{-(l+1)} Y_l^m, \tag{2.43}$$

where $p_{lm}$ is written for $q_{lm} \, \delta r$.

The density of normal dipoles on the surface producing these potentials is then given by

$$p = \sum_{l=0}^{\infty} \sum_{m=-l}^{l} p_{lm} Y_l^m(\theta_0, \varphi_0), \quad (r = r_0), \qquad (2.44)$$

where the coefficients $p_{lm}$ must satisfy conditions analogous to eqs. (2.13) for reality of $p$ and $V$. It is worth noting that the difference between the potentials on either side of the dipole layer is

$$V_e - V_i = \frac{1}{\mu_0} \sum_{l=0}^{\infty} \sum_{m=-l}^{l} p_{lm} Y_l^m, \qquad (2.45)$$

which is just the dipole density at the surface divided by the permeability of the vacuum, in agreement with eq. (1.24).

## § 3. POTENTIAL DUE TO CURRENT DISTRIBUTIONS

### § 3.1. *Distribution of surface currents equivalent to the general spherical magnetic shell*

In Ch. 1, § 4 the equivalence of a closed current circuit and a uniform magnetic shell of any shape enclosed by the circuit is discussed. In this section we shall derive the distribution of currents on the spherical surface to give the same internal and external potentials as does the general spherical magnetic shell. This shell can be considered as a superposition of small uniform shells each being equivalent to a small current circuit. Thus any non-uniform shell can be considered as equivalent to a superposition of current circuits distributed on the shell surface. As all circuits are closed no current sources are present on the surface. When $\boldsymbol{\xi}$ is the current density along the surface with $\xi_\theta$ the polar component and $\xi_\varphi$ the azimuthal component (Fig. 2.3), the continuity of the current is expressed by

$$\frac{\partial(\xi_\theta \sin\theta)}{\partial\theta} + \frac{\partial\xi_\varphi}{\partial\varphi} = 0. \qquad (2.46)$$

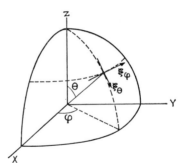

Fig. 2.3. Components of a surface current distribution in polar coordinates.

The relation between the current density $\xi$ along the surface and the equivalent magnetic shell is derived in Ch. 1, § 5 and is given by eq. (1.35). Using the polar and azimuthal components of $\xi$ this equation becomes

$$\frac{1}{r_0}\frac{\partial p}{\partial \theta_0} = -\mu_0 \xi_\varphi \tag{2.47}$$

and

$$\frac{1}{r_0 \sin\theta_0}\frac{\partial p}{\partial \varphi_0} = \mu_0 \xi_\theta. \tag{2.48}$$

These equations will be used to calculate the current distribution which is equivalent to the dipole distribution given by eq. (2.44). Substitution of the expression for $p$ into eq. (2.47) gives

$$\mu_0 \xi_\varphi = \frac{-1}{r_0}\frac{\partial}{\partial \theta_0}\left\{\sum_{l=0}^{\infty}\sum_{m=-l}^{l} p_{lm}Y_l^m(\theta_0, \varphi_0)\right\}. \tag{2.49}$$

Using the definition of the associated Legendre polynomial (eq. (2.8)) it can easily be shown that

$$\frac{\partial}{\partial \theta}P_l^{|m|} = \frac{|m|\cos\theta}{\sin\theta}P_l^{|m|} - P_l^{|m|+1}. \tag{2.50}$$

Substituting this into eq. (2.49) gives

$$\mu_0 \xi_\varphi = \frac{1}{r_0}\sum_{l=0}^{\infty}\sum_{m=-l}^{l} p_{lm}\left(P_l^{|m|+1} - \frac{|m|\cos\theta}{\sin\theta}P_l^{|m|}\right)e^{im\varphi}. \tag{2.51}$$

Similarly we find by substituting eq. (2.44) into eq. (2.48)

$$\mu_0 \xi_\theta = \frac{1}{r_0 \sin \theta_0} \sum_{l=0}^{\infty} \sum_{m=-l}^{l} im p_{lm} Y_l^m, \tag{2.52}$$

where $i = \sqrt{-1}$.

If $p_{lm}$ satisfies the conditions analogous to eqs. (2.13), thus ensuring the reality of $p$, $\xi_\theta$ and $\xi_\varphi$ are also real quantities as can easily be verified.

## § 3.2. *Current distribution on a spherical surface to generate a homogeneous field inside the sphere*

As an example we shall use eqs. (2.51) and (2.52) to calculate the current distribution required for a homogeneous field along the z-axis. The potential of this field is the term with $l=1$ and $m=0$:

$$V = a_{10} r P_1 \tag{2.53}$$

and the fieldstrength is

$$H_z = -\frac{\partial V}{\partial z} = -a_{10}. \tag{2.54}$$

The corresponding term of eq. (2.42) is

$$V = \frac{1}{\mu_0} \frac{2}{3} p_{10} r_0^{-1} r P_1. \tag{2.55}$$

The identity of the two potentials relates $p_{10}$ to $a_{10}$ by

$$p_{10} = -\tfrac{3}{2} \mu_0 r_0 a_{10}. \tag{2.56}$$

We substitute this into eq. (2.51) with the result

$$\xi_\varphi = -\tfrac{3}{2} a_{10} \sin \theta = \tfrac{3}{2} H_z \sin \theta. \tag{2.57}$$

This is a spherical coil with a constant current per unit of z-axis. This distribution can be approximated to by winding a coil-former as shown in Fig. 2.4 with wire of a constant diameter.

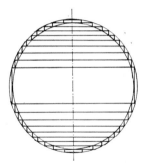

Fig. 2.4. Coil-former for generating approximately a homogeneous field. The steps are confined between two concentric spheres and are closely wound with wire of a constant diameter in a single layer.

### § 3.3. Current distribution on a spherical surface to generate a homogeneous fieldgradient inside the sphere

The potential describing a homogeneous fieldgradient only contains terms with $l=2$ (see § 1.3 of this chapter):

$$V_i = r^2 \sum_{m=-2}^{2} a_{2m} Y_2^m, \qquad (2.58)$$

where the conditions of eqs. (2.13) must be satisfied for real $V$. Using the coefficients $s_{lm}$ and $t_{lm}$ as they appear in these equations and substituting

$$x = r \sin \theta \cos \varphi,$$
$$y = r \sin \theta \sin \varphi,$$
$$z = r \cos \theta,$$

we find (see eqs. (2.24))

$$V = 3s_{21}xz + 3t_{21}yz + 6t_{22}xy + 3s_{22}(x^2 - y^2) + \\ + \tfrac{1}{2}s_{20}(2z^2 - x^2 - y^2). \qquad (2.59)$$

The fieldstrength is given by eq. (2.25) which shows that the fieldstrength is a linear function of the coordinates and that the gradient is a constant. The corresponding terms of eq. (2.42) are

$$V_i = \frac{3}{5\mu_0} r_0^{-2} r^2 \sum_{m=-2}^{2} p_{2m} Y_2^m, \qquad (2.60)$$

which must be identical with eq. (2.58) thus giving the relations between $a_{2m}$ and $p_{2m}$:

$$p_{2m} = \tfrac{5}{3}\mu_0 r_0^2 a_{2m}.\tag{2.61}$$

Substituting this into eq. (2.51) gives the azimuthal current density

$$\xi_\varphi = 5r_0 \left[\sin 2\theta \left(\tfrac{1}{2}s_{20} - s_{22}\cos 2\varphi - t_{22}\sin 2\varphi\right) \right.$$
$$\left. - \cos 2\theta \left(s_{21}\cos\varphi + t_{21}\sin\varphi\right)\right].\tag{2.62}$$

The polar current density follows by substitution of eq. (2.61) into eq. (2.52):

$$\xi_\theta = 5r_0 \left[\cos\theta \left(t_{21}\cos\varphi - s_{21}\sin\varphi\right) + \right.$$
$$\left. + 2\sin\theta \left(t_{22}\cos 2\varphi - s_{22}\sin 2\varphi\right)\right],\tag{2.63}$$

where the coefficients $s$ and $t$ are those occurring in eq. (2.25).

In Fig. 2.5 the current lines are schematically indicated for the

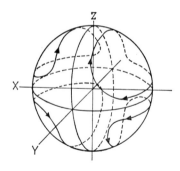

Fig. 2.5.  Schematic indication of the current distribution on a spherical surface to generate a homogeneous gradient $\partial H_z/\partial x$.

case that only the coefficient $s_{21}$ is different from zero. We then have

$$\frac{\partial H_z}{\partial x} = \frac{\partial H_x}{\partial z} = -3s_{21},\tag{2.64}$$

and

$$\xi_\varphi = \frac{5}{3}\frac{\partial H_x}{\partial z} r_0 \cos 2\theta \cos\varphi,\tag{2.65}$$

$$\xi_\theta = \frac{5}{3}\frac{\partial H_x}{\partial z} r_0 \cos\theta \sin\varphi.\tag{2.66}$$

## § 4. ROTATIONAL SYMMETRY

### § 4.1. *Potentials with rotational symmetry*

If rotational symmetry about the $z$-axis is assumed, the azimuthal dependence vanishes and the expressions for the potentials reduce to

$$V_i = \frac{1}{\mu_0} \sum_{l=0}^{\infty} \frac{1}{2l+1} q_l r_0^{-(l-1)} r^l P_l, \quad (r < r_0), \qquad (2.67)$$

$$V_e = \frac{1}{\mu_0} \sum_{l=0}^{\infty} \frac{1}{2l+1} q_l r_0^{l+2} r^{-(l+1)} P_l, \quad (r > r_0), \qquad (2.68)$$

for a charge distribution on the spherical surface with radius $r_0$, given by

$$q(\theta_0) = \sum_{l=0}^{\infty} q_l P_l(\theta_0), \quad (r = r_0), \qquad (2.69)$$

and to

$$V_i' = \frac{1}{\mu_0} \sum_{l=0}^{\infty} \frac{l+1}{2l+1} p_l r_0^{-l} r^l P_l, \quad (r < r_0), \qquad (2.70)$$

$$V_e' = \frac{1}{\mu_0} \sum_{l=0}^{\infty} \frac{-l}{2l+1} p_l r_0^{l+1} r^{-(l+1)} P_l, \quad (r > r_0), \qquad (2.71)$$

for a distribution of dipoles normal to the spherical surface with radius $r_0$, given by

$$p(\theta_0) = \sum_{l=0}^{\infty} p_l P_l(\theta_0), \quad (r = r_0). \qquad (2.72)$$

These equations are found by putting $m$ equal to zero in eqs. (2.26), (2.38), (2.39), (2.42), (2.43) and (2.44).

Similarly the current distribution at the spherical surface required to generate the magnetic shell given by eq. (2.72) is found by putting

$m=0$ in eqs. (2.51) and (2.52):

$$\mu_0 \xi_\varphi = \frac{1}{r_0} \sum_{l=0}^{\infty} p_l P_l^1 (\theta_0),\tag{2.73}$$

$\xi_\theta$ being zero for $m=0$.

## § 4.2. Expansion of the potential for rotational symmetry

Assume that the $z$-axis is the axis of rotational symmetry and that no singularities are present on this axis. The potential then is generally

$$V = \sum_{l=0}^{\infty} a_l r^l P_l,\tag{2.74}$$

which on the axis reduces to

$$V = \sum_{l=0}^{\infty} a_l z^l,\tag{2.75}$$

as for $\theta=0$ all Legendre polynomials become unity. We compare this with Maclaurin's series

$$V = \sum_{l=0}^{\infty} \frac{z^l}{l!} \left( \frac{\partial^l V}{\partial z^l} \right)_{z=0}.\tag{2.76}$$

Since the expansion of eq. (2.74) and thus of eq. (2.75) is unique we equate eqs. (2.75) and (2.76) term by term to obtain

$$a_l = \frac{1}{l!} \left( \frac{\partial^l V}{\partial z^l} \right)_{z=0}.\tag{2.77}$$

By substituting this into eq. (2.74) we have

$$V = \sum_{l=0}^{\infty} \frac{1}{l!} \left( \frac{\partial^l V}{\partial z^l} \right)_{z=0} r^l P_l.\tag{2.78}$$

The procedure followed for $V$ can be applied to any function satisfying Laplace's equation (1.14), for instance the axial component

$H_z$ of the fieldstrength

$$H_z = \sum_{l=0}^{\infty} \frac{1}{l!} \left( \frac{\partial^l H_z}{\partial z^l} \right)_{z=0} r^l P_l, \tag{2.79}$$

where $(\partial^l H_z / \partial z^l)_{z=0}$ is the $l^{\text{th}}$ derivative of $H_z$ at the origin.

Using

$$H_z = - \partial V / \partial z$$

we obtain another series for $H_z$ by differentiating eq. (2.74)

$$H_z = \sum_{l=0}^{\infty} - a_l \frac{\partial}{\partial z} (r^l P_l). \tag{2.80}$$

It can be shown that

$$\frac{\partial}{\partial z} (r^l P_l) = l r^{l-1} P_{l-1},$$

so that eq. (2.80) becomes

$$H_z = \sum_{l=1}^{\infty} - a_l l r^{l-1} P_{l-1}, \tag{2.81}$$

which can be rewritten as

$$H_z = \sum_{l=0}^{\infty} - a_{l+1} (l + 1) r^l P_l. \tag{2.82}$$

The $n^{\text{th}}$ derivative of $H_z$ with respect to $z$ is generally

$$H_z^{(n)} = \sum_{l=0}^{\infty} - a_{l+n+1} \frac{(l + n + 1)!}{l!} r^l P_l, \tag{2.83}$$

as can easily be seen by further differentiating eq. (2.81). The coefficients of this series are given by eq. (2.77) which can also be written as

$$a_{l+1} = \frac{1}{(l + 1)!} \left( \frac{\partial^l H_z}{\partial z^l} \right)_{z=0}. \tag{2.84}$$

Substituting this into eq. (2.83) gives

$$H_z^{(n)} = \sum_{l=0}^{\infty} \frac{-1}{l!} H_z^{(l+n)}(0) \, r^l P_l, \qquad (2.85)$$

where $H_z^{(l+n)}(0)$ is the $(l+n)$-th derivative of $H_z$ with respect to $z$ at the origin. We thus have in eq. (2.85) series expansions of all axial derivatives of $H_z$ when the derivatives of $H_z$ at the origin are known.

### § 4.3. *Potential of a single circular current circuit*

The coil systems we discuss in this book are usually composed of circular windings. Their field is calculated by superposing the field contributions of all turns. For this purpose the potential due to a single circular current is required, which will be calculated here.

Consider a circular current of infinitesimal thickness, located on a spherical surface of radius $r_0$ with the centre as origin of the coordinate system. The plane of the current is perpendicular to the $z$-axis and its constant polar coordinate is $\theta_0^*$ (Fig. 2.6). If the

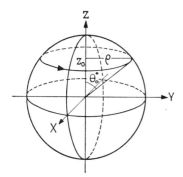

Fig. 2.6.    Single circular current.

strength of the current is $i$ the part of the spherical surface where $0 < \theta_0 < \theta_0^*$ can be considered as being occupied by a uniform magnetic shell with dipole density $\mu_0 i$. The remaining part where

$\theta_0 > \theta_0^*$ is not occupied. This dipole distribution is expanded in a series as eq. (2.72), where the coefficients $p_l$ are determined by using eq. (2.17) which in this case of rotational symmetry reduces to

$$f_l = \tfrac{1}{2}(2l + 1) \int\limits_{-1}^{1} F(\theta_0)\, P_l(\theta_0)\, \mathrm{d}(\cos\theta_0). \qquad (2.86)$$

Substituting $p(\theta_0)$ for $F(\theta_0)$ we have

$$p_l = \tfrac{1}{2}(2l + 1)\, \mu_0 i \int\limits_{1}^{\cos\theta_0^*} P_l(\theta_0)\, \mathrm{d}(\cos\theta_0),$$

and by substituting this into eq. (2.70)

$$V = \sum_{l=0}^{\infty} a_l r^l P_l,$$

where

$$a_l = \tfrac{1}{2} i(l + 1)\, r_0^{-l} \int\limits_{1}^{\cos\theta_0^*} P_l(\theta_0)\, \mathrm{d}(\cos\theta_0).$$

These coefficients are calculated here for $l$ ranging from 0 to 4:

$$\begin{aligned}
a_0 &= \tfrac{1}{2} i(\cos\theta_0^* - 1); \\
a_1 &= -i \sin^2\theta_0^* / 2r_0; \\
a_2 &= -3i \sin^2\theta_0^* \cos\theta_0^* / 4r_0^2; \\
a_3 &= i \sin^2\theta_0^* (1 - 5\cos^2\theta_0^*) / 4r_0^3; \\
a_4 &= 5i \sin^2\theta_0^* \cos\theta_0^* (3 - 7\cos^2\theta_0^*) / 16r_0^4.
\end{aligned} \qquad (2.87)$$

These coefficients are connected by

$$\frac{\partial}{\partial z_0} a_l = -(l + 1)\, a_{l+1}, \qquad (2.88)$$

where $z_0 = r_0 \cos\theta^*$.

As an example we calculate the axial field at the origin due to the circular current. Using eq. (2.82) we observe that at the origin only the term with $l=0$ is different from zero, so that

$$H_z(0) = -a_1 = + \frac{i}{2r_0} \sin^2\theta_0^* = \frac{i\rho^2}{2(z_0^2 + \rho^2)^{\frac{3}{2}}}, \qquad (2.89)$$

where $\rho$ is the radius of the circular current and $z_0$ is the distance of its plane from the origin (see Fig. 2.6). This formula is known as Ampère's law.

## § 5. SYSTEMS OF CIRCULAR COILS

### § 5.1. *Approximation to the homogeneous field*

Consider $H_z$, the $z$-component of a field due to a circular current $i$ of radius $\rho_0$ lying in the $xy$-plane. The fieldstrength $H_z$ is given by eq. (2.79) where, owing to the symmetry with respect to the $xy$-plane, only terms with $l$ even are present. Thus $\partial H_z/\partial z$ is zero at the origin and hence $\partial H_x/\partial x$ and $\partial H_y/\partial y$ are also zero.

After the constant term $(l=0)$ representing a homogeneous field in eq. (2.79) the first term to appear is thus the second derivative $\partial^2 H_z/\partial z^2$. In this case we speak of "second order inhomogeneity". In order to generate a field having no second order inhomogeneity we combine two circular circuits, one at $\theta_0 = \theta_0^*$ and the other at $\theta_0 = \pi - \theta_0^*$ (Fig. 2.7). These two circuits which are fed by the current $i$ having the same sense in both, again form a system sym-

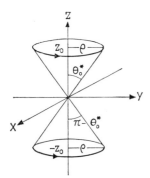

Fig. 2.7.   System of two coaxial circular currents.

metrical in $z$. Thus at the origin the first derivative of the field is automatically zero. But now we have freedom to vary $\theta_0^*$ in order to make the second derivative or the term with $l=2$ equal to zero ($a_3=0$ in eq. (2.82)).

We see from eqs. (2.87) that

$$a_3 = \frac{i}{4r_0^3} \sin^2\theta_0^* (1 - 5\cos^2\theta_0^*),$$

which is zero if

$$1 - 5\cos^2\theta_0^* = 0. \tag{2.90}$$

This condition is fulfilled if

$$\rho = 2z_0, \tag{2.91}$$

where $\rho$ is the radius of the circuits and $2z_0$ the distance between their planes. Such a coil system is known as a Helmholtz pair. Since, owing to symmetry, the third derivative is also zero ($a_4=0$) its field is a field with only fourth and higher order inhomogeneity. The fieldstrength at the centre is

$$H_z(0) = -2a_1 = \frac{4i}{5r_0} = 0.7155\,\frac{i}{\rho}, \tag{2.92}$$

where the factor 2 is due to the presence of two circular currents.

The performance of such a coil pair may be improved by slightly increasing the distance between the coils. The effect is that the term next to the last vanishing one (here the term with $l=4$) is decreased. The price to be paid for this is that the term which initially was made zero by the choice of $\theta_0^*$ now contributes once more, but the resulting performance may be better. This is illustrated schematically in Fig. 2.8 where the value of $H_z$ along the $z$-axis is shown.

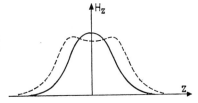

Fig. 2.8. Field distribution along the $z$-axis for exact fourth-order compensation (drawn curve) and for a slightly increased distance between the coils (dotted curve).

The solid curve applies to the situation where $a_3 = 0$ and the broken curve to coils with a slightly increased distance.

Better approximations to the homogeneous field can be obtained by coil systems consisting of more than two coils located at proper distances to make higher derivatives of the field at the origin equal to zero.

## § 5.2. *Approximation to the homogeneous gradient* $\partial H_z / \partial z$

Consider the coil system of Fig. 2.7 but now with a current $i$ in the upper circuit and a current $-i$ in the lower circuit. The field-gradient due to these two currents is conveniently described by eq. (2.83) with $n = 1$

$$H_z' = \sum_{l=0}^{\infty} - 2a_{l+2}(l+1)(l+2) r^l P_l, \qquad (2.93)$$

where the coefficients $a_l$ are those of eqs. (2.87) and the factor 2 is due to the presence of two circular currents. The two opposed currents produce opposed fields that cancel each other exactly at the origin. The fieldgradient $H_z'$ is symmetric with respect to the $xy$-plane which implies that only terms with $l$ even are present. The first derivative of $H_z'$ is thus zero. The second derivative of $H_z'$ can be made zero by a proper choice of $\theta_0^*$ which makes $a_4 = 0$. We see from eqs. (2.87) that this is obtained if

$$\cos^2\theta_0^* = \tfrac{3}{7}. \qquad (2.94)$$

This condition is fulfilled if

$$z_0 = \tfrac{1}{2}\rho\sqrt{3}, \qquad (2.95)$$

where $\rho$ is the radius of the circular currents and $2z_0$ is the distance between their planes. The fieldgradient along the $z$-axis at the origin then is

$$H_z'(0) = - 4a_2 = 0.6413i/\rho^2. \qquad (2.96)$$

The first, second and third derivatives of $H_z'$ are zero at the origin so we have a fieldgradient with only fourth and higher order inhomogeneity.

## § 5.3. *Approximation to the homogeneous gradient $\partial H_z/\partial x$*

The potential describing the field with a homogeneous gradient $\partial H_z/\partial x$ is given by the second of eqs. (2.24). The current distribution required to obtain this potential (see Fig. 2.5) suggests placing two coil pairs on the spherical surface with the lines $x=z$ and $x=-z$ as axis, respectively (Fig. 2.9). The sense of the current through the

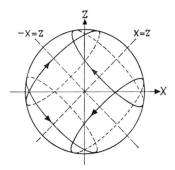

Fig. 2.9. Four-coil system for generating approximately a homogeneous gradient $\partial H_z/\partial x$.

coils is taken according to Fig. 2.5. The coils are for the present supposed to consist of one turn of infinitesimal thickness. To find the potential of such a coil system we start with a single coil pair with its axis along the $z$-axis. The current in the upper coil has a positive sense and in the lower coil a negative sense. The potential due to this coil pair is given by eq. (2.74) with only even values of $l$ present:

$$V = 2a_0 + 2a_2 r^2 P_2 + 2a_4 r^4 P_4 + \cdots, \qquad (2.97)$$

where the factor 2 is due to the presence of two coils and the coefficients $a_l$ are those of eqs. (2.87).

Now we rotate the coil system by an angle $\pm \pi/4$ about the $y$-axis. The new axis of the coil pair is then the line $x=z$ or $x=-z$ and the rotation is performed formally by substituting

$$\begin{aligned}
\sin\theta\cos\varphi &\to 2^{-\frac{1}{2}}(\sin\theta\cos\varphi \pm \cos\theta), \\
\cos\theta &\to 2^{-\frac{1}{2}}(\cos\theta \mp \sin\theta\cos\varphi),
\end{aligned} \qquad (2.98)$$

where the choice between $+$ or $-$ is to be made in the sense that the upper sign corresponds with a positive and the lower sign with a negative rotation.

Rotation of the coil system will replace the harmonics of eq. (2.97) by sums of harmonics of the same degree:

$$V_{tr} = 2a_0 + 2a_2 r^2 \sum_{m=0}^{2} k_{2m} Y_2^m + 2a_4 r^4 \sum_{m=0}^{4} k_{4m} Y_4^m, \qquad (2.99)$$

where $V_{tr}$ denotes the potential after rotation and $k_{lm}$ are coefficients independent of coordinates.

In the present case $P_2$ transforms to (see JEANS [1923] p. 241)

$$P_2 \to \tfrac{1}{4} \{ Y_2^0 + \tfrac{1}{4} (Y_2^2 + Y_2^{-2}) + (Y_2^1 + Y_2^{-1}) \},$$

for negative rotation by $\pi/4$. This is the contribution from one coil pair. The contribution from the other pair is found by reversing the currents and rotating by $+\pi/4$:

$$-P_2 \to -\tfrac{1}{4} \{ Y_2^0 + \tfrac{1}{4} (Y_2^2 + Y_2^{-2}) - (Y_2^1 + Y_2^{-1}) \}.$$

These two contributions are added to give

$$\tfrac{1}{2} (Y_2^1 + Y_2^{-1}) = 3 \cos \theta \sin \theta \cos \varphi.$$

We thus obtain

$$V_{tr} = 2a_0 + 6a_2 r^2 \cos \theta \sin \theta \cos \varphi + 2a_4 r^4 \sum_{m=0}^{4} k_{4m} Y_l^m + \cdots,$$
$$(2.100)$$

where the constant term is of no importance since we are only interested in derivatives of the potential. The term with $a_4$ is the first to cause deviations from the homogeneous gradient. It can be made zero by a proper spacing between the coils of each pair, as discussed in the previous section (see eq. (2.95)). The result after transformation into Cartesian coordinates then is

$$V_{tr} = 6a_2 xz + \text{terms of 6}^{\text{th}} \text{ degree} + \cdots, \qquad (2.101)$$

describing a gradient

$$\frac{\partial H_z}{\partial x} = \frac{\partial H_x}{\partial z} = -6a_2 = 0.9619 \frac{i}{\rho^2},\qquad(2.102)$$

having only fourth and higher order inhomogeneity:

$$\frac{\partial^2 H_z}{\partial x^2} = \frac{\partial^3 H_z}{\partial x^3} = 0.$$

Applications of coil systems of this type are discussed in Part 2, Ch. 3.

## § 6. BIBLIOGRAPHY

The basic ideas outlined in this and the previous chapter have been quoted from the book by MAXWELL [1873]. The method of spherical harmonics, already used by Maxwell has been generally treated by JEANS [1923] and more specifically by GARRETT [1951] for axially symmetric systems. Another textbook on mathematical methods used by the author is that by MARGENAU and MURPHY [1956].

CHAPTER 3

# AIR-CORE SOLENOIDS

### § 1. CURRENT DISTRIBUTION AND EFFICIENCY

### § 1.1. *Thick solenoids with uniform current density*

In the previous chapter we considered thin coils consisting of one wire or a current sheet. Except for superconductors, which will be treated later, these thin coils are incapable of carrying the strong currents that are often needed to generate the fields we require. Therefore we shall use solenoids with large cross-section in order to keep the current density below the limit set by the supplied power and the cooling capacity.

Let a cylindrical coil of rectangular cross-section be wound from thin wire (Fig. 3.1). The density of turns is the same at any point of

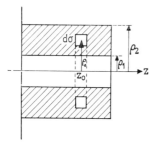

Fig. 3.1. Thick solenoid with winding element.

the cross-section, so we may attribute a current density $\tau$ to such a point, which is also uniform throughout the cross-section.

We require the field $H_z$ and its derivatives at a point on the $z$-axis which we shall take as the origin. The $z$-axis is the axis of

42

rotational symmetry of the coil. We remember from Ch. 2, § 4.2 that if we know $H_z$ and its derivatives at the origin, we know the field at any point, at least within the sphere with the origin as centre and which excludes the coil. The potential at the origin may be evaluated as we did in Ch. 2, § 4.2, by using the relation

$$V = \sum_l a_l z^l. \tag{3.1}$$

The contribution $da_l$ to the coefficient $a_l$ caused by the circular current $\tau \, d\sigma$ flowing through the element $d\sigma$ of the cross-section is found from eqs. (2.87):

$$da_1 = -\tfrac{1}{2}\tau \, \frac{\rho^2 \, d\rho \, dz_0}{(z_0^2 + \rho^2)^{\frac{3}{2}}};$$

$$da_2 = -\tfrac{3}{4}\tau \, \frac{\rho^2 z_0 \, d\rho \, dz_0}{(z_0^2 + \rho^2)^{\frac{5}{2}}};$$

$$da_3 = \tfrac{1}{4}\tau \, \frac{(\rho^4 - 4\rho^2 z_0^2) \, d\rho \, dz_0}{(z_0^2 + \rho^2)^{\frac{7}{2}}}; \tag{3.2}$$

$$da_4 = \tfrac{5}{16}\tau \, \frac{(3\rho^4 z_0 - 4\rho^2 z_0^3) \, d\rho \, dz_0}{(z_0^2 + \rho^2)^{\frac{9}{2}}}.$$

Here $\rho$ is the distance of the element $d\sigma$ from the $z$-axis or the radius of the circular current. The $z$-coordinate of the element $d\sigma$ is denoted by $z_0$, in order to distinguish it from the $z$-coordinate of the potential $V$. The quantities $da_l$ are integrated for a coil with rectangular cross-section and with inner radius $\rho_1$, outer radius $\rho_2 = \alpha \rho_1$ and extending axially from $z_0 = 0$ to $z_0 = \beta \rho_1$. This leads to the following expressions for the fieldstrength $H_z$ and its derivatives at the origin by using eq. (2.84) which is rewritten as

$$\left( \frac{\partial^{l-1} H_z}{\partial z^{l-1}} \right)_{z=0} = l! a_l: \tag{3.3}$$

$$H_z(0) = \frac{\tau}{2} \rho_1 \beta \ln \frac{\alpha + (\alpha^2 + \beta^2)^{\frac{1}{2}}}{1 + (1 + \beta^2)^{\frac{1}{2}}}, \tag{3.4}$$

$$H_z'(0) = \frac{\tau}{2} \left[ \frac{\alpha}{(\alpha^2 + \beta^2)^{\frac{1}{2}}} - \frac{1}{(1 + \beta^2)^{\frac{1}{2}}} - \ln \frac{\alpha + (\alpha^2 + \beta^2)^{\frac{1}{2}}}{\alpha \{1 + (1 + \beta^2)^{\frac{1}{2}}\}} \right], \tag{3.5}$$

$$H_z''(0) = -\frac{\tau}{2} \frac{1}{\rho_1 \beta} \left[ \frac{\alpha^3}{(\alpha^2 + \beta^2)^{\frac{3}{2}}} - \frac{1}{(1 + \beta^2)^{\frac{3}{2}}} \right], \tag{3.6}$$

$$H_z'''(0) = -\frac{\tau}{2} \frac{1}{\rho_1^2} \left[ \frac{\alpha^3(\alpha^2 + 4\beta^2)}{\beta^2(\alpha^2 + \beta^2)^{\frac{5}{2}}} - \frac{1 + 4\beta^2}{\beta^2(1 + \beta^2)^{\frac{5}{2}}} - \frac{3}{2\alpha^2} + \frac{3}{2} \right], \tag{3.7}$$

where $H_z'(0)$ is written for $(\partial H_z/\partial z)_{z=0}$, etc. This may be rewritten in the form:

$$H_z(0) = \tau \rho_1 F_1 ; \qquad H_z'(0) = \tau F_2 ;$$

$$H_z''(0) = \frac{\tau}{\rho_1} F_3 ; \qquad H_z'''(0) = \frac{\tau}{\rho_1^2} F_4 . \tag{3.8}$$

The functions $F_1$, etc. are tabulated in Appendix 3 for $\alpha$ ranging from 1 to 30 and $\beta$ from 0 to 50. The use of these tables is obvious if one considers that the field of any coil of rectangular cross-section may be determined by adding and subtracting the fields of other coils of rectangular cross-section, which may be found in the tables. For instance, the value of $F$ for a coil with inner diameter $2\alpha_1\rho_1$, outer diameter $2\alpha_2\rho_1$, and axially bounded between $\beta_1\rho_1$ and $\beta_2\rho_1$, can be found by taking from the appropriate table the value of $F$ for $(\alpha_2, \beta_2)$, subtracting the two values of $F$ for $(\alpha_1, \beta_2)$ and $(\alpha_2, \beta_1)$, respectively, and adding the value of $F$ for $(\alpha_1, \beta_1)$. The common factor $\rho_1$ enables us to enlarge or reduce the coil on scale and calculate the field. This is illustrated by a worked-out example in Appendix 3. By using this method the spacing to form a Helmholtz pair of two thick coils of square cross-section is calculated. This is done by calculating $F_3$ for a coil, the cross-sectional sides of which are given by $\alpha - 1$ and $\beta_2 - \beta_1$ (where these two quantities are equal in order to make the cross-section of the coil square) and shifting the coil along the $\beta$-axis until $F_3$ is zero. The second derivative of the field is then zero, and since owing to symmetry the first and third derivatives also vanish, we have compensated the field inhomogeneity to the third order. Figure 3.2 shows the relation thus found between the quantities $z_0/\rho_0 = (\beta_1 + \beta_2)/(1 + \alpha)$ and $d/\rho_0 = (\alpha - 1)/(1 + \alpha)$, being the half-distance between the centres of the coils and their half-width, respectively (see Fig. 3.3), both reduced with the average radius $\rho_0$ of the coils as a unit.

Similarly we find a system of two thick coils with rectangular cross-section which generates a gradient field with its inhomogeneity

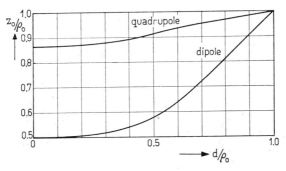

Fig. 3.2. Reduced half-distance between coils as a function of the reduced half-width of the square winding cross-section, both with the average coil radius as a unit, to approximate a homogeneous field (curve denoted by "dipole") or a homogeneous gradient (curve denoted by "quadrupole"). The coil system is shown in Fig. 3.3.

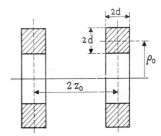

Fig. 3.3. Pair of circular coils with square winding cross-section.

compensated to the third order. Here we find the proper reduced half-distance $z_0/\rho_0 = (\beta_1 + \beta_2)/(1+\alpha)$ by shifting the coil in the table of Appendix 3 until $F_4$ is zero. This reduced distance is also given in Fig. 3.2 as a function of the reduced half-width $d/\rho_0 = (\alpha-1)/(\alpha+1)$ of the coils, again with the average radius $\rho_0$ as a unit. We can increase the volume in which the field or gradient is homogeneous within a certain tolerance, by slightly increasing the distance between the coils, as we did in Ch. 2, § 5.1.

The homogeneity in the centre plane perpendicular to the $z$-axis is examined by considering eq. (2.82) for the given symmetry (i.e. only terms with $l$ even are present)

$$H_z = - a_1 - 3a_3 r^2 P_2 - 5a_5 r^4 P_4 - \cdots . \tag{3.9}$$

At the $z$-axis this equation reduces to

$$H_z = - a_1 - 3a_3 z^2 - 5a_5 z^4 - \cdots , \tag{3.10}$$

and in the centre plane $(\theta = \pi/2)$ to

$$H_z = - a_1 + \tfrac{3}{2}a_3\rho^2 - \tfrac{15}{8}a_5\rho^4 + \cdots . \tag{3.11}$$

By comparing these two expressions we see that the homogeneity of a field with rotational symmetry is about two times better along a radial direction than along the axis. A similar treatment applied to the field gradient generated by an antisymmetric coil pair shows that in this case the same rule holds for the uniformity of the gradient.

## § 1.2. *Thick solenoids with current density proportional to $\rho^{-1}$*

Let us construct a solenoid of thin disks with inner diameter $2\rho_1$, and outer diameter $2\rho_2$. The disks are cut along a radius and stacked together so as to form a helix (Fig. 3.4).

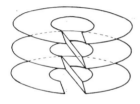

Fig. 3.4. Principle of a Bitter solenoid.

Coils of this type were first constructed by BITTER [1939]. The current density $\tau$ in such a coil is inversely proportional to the radius:

$$\tau = \frac{\tau_0}{\rho}\,\rho_1 = \frac{\tau_0}{\gamma}, \tag{3.12}$$

where $\tau_0$ is the current density at the inner edge of the disks and $\gamma = \rho/\rho_1$, the reduced radius. The coil, which consists of thin conducting plates with thin interlayers of insulating material, will be treated here as a continuous body with a current distribution according to eq. (3.12). If we substitute this expression for $\tau$ into eqs. (3.2) and integrate for a coil with inner diameter $\rho_1$, outer diameter $\alpha\rho_1$, and extending axially from $z_0 = 0$ to $z_0 = \beta\rho_1$, by using eq. (2.84) we find for the fieldstrength $H_z(0)$ and its derivatives $H_z'(0)$, etc. at the origin

$$H_z(0) = \tfrac{1}{2}\tau_0\rho_1 \ln \frac{\alpha\{\beta + (1+\beta^2)^{\frac{1}{2}}\}}{\beta + (\alpha^2 + \beta^2)^{\frac{1}{2}}}, \tag{3.13}$$

$$H_z'(0) = \tfrac{1}{2}\tau_0 \left\{ \frac{1}{(\alpha^2+\beta^2)^{\frac{1}{2}}} - \frac{1}{(1+\beta^2)^{\frac{1}{2}}} - \frac{1}{\alpha} + 1 \right\}, \tag{3.14}$$

$$H_z''(0) = \frac{1}{2}\frac{\tau_0}{\rho_1}\left\{ \frac{\beta}{(1+\beta^2)^{\frac{3}{2}}} - \frac{\beta}{(\alpha^2+\beta^2)^{\frac{3}{2}}} \right\}, \tag{3.15}$$

$$H_z'''(0) = \frac{1}{2}\frac{\tau_0}{\rho_1^2}\left\{ \frac{\alpha^2 - 2\beta^2}{(\alpha^2+\beta^2)^{\frac{5}{2}}} - \frac{1 - 2\beta^2}{(1+\beta^2)^{\frac{5}{2}}} - \frac{1}{\alpha^3} + 1 \right\}, \tag{3.16}$$

where $\tau_0$ is the current density at the inner boundary of the coil. These expressions are rewritten as

$$\begin{aligned}
H_z(0) &= \tau_0\rho_1 K_1, \\
H_z'(0) &= \tau_0 K_2, \\
H_z''(0) &= \frac{\tau_0}{\rho_1} K_3, \\
H_z'''(0) &= \frac{\tau_0}{\rho_1^2} K_4.
\end{aligned} \tag{3.17}$$

The functions $K_1$, etc. are tabulated in Appendix 4 for $\alpha$ ranging from 1 to 30 and $\beta$ from 1 to 50. These tables are to be used in the same way as the tables of $F$ in Appendix 3. It should be noted here that if the field of a coil with inner radius $\rho^* = \alpha^* \rho_1$ is calculated, the value of $\tau_0$ to be substituted in eqs. (3.17) is

$$\tau_0 = \tau_0^*/\alpha^*, \tag{3.18}$$

where $\tau_0^*$ is the current density at the actual inner boundary $\alpha^* \rho_1$, of the coil.

The spacing required to form a Helmholtz pair with two of these coils is found by using the tables of Appendix 4 as explained in the previous section, by making $K_3 = 0$.

Similarly we find the spacing of an antisymmetric pair of Bitter-type coils, to generate a gradient field compensated for second order inhomogeneity by making $K_4 = 0$.

## § 1.3. *Power consumption*

A certain amount of energy has to be fed into the solenoid to generate a magnetic field. This energy will be partly used to build up the magnetic field and, after the field has become stationary, entirely to maintain the current at a constant value. In this state the supplied energy is entirely dissipated as Joule heat, due to the electrical resistance of the coil, and this heat has to be carried off by some cooling provision. The amount of heat may be consider-able if strong fields are to be generated. It is therefore important to know how much power will be consumed by a given coil design, in order to be able to provide a suitable cooling and eventually find an optimal construction. Suppose that the coil treated in Ch. 3, § 1.1 (Fig. 3.1) is wound from wire with a specific resistance $\eta$ and that the body of the coil is filled to a fraction $\lambda$ with conducting material, the remaining part being used for insulation and cool-ing provisions. The coil will still be treated as a homogeneous body.

The coil contains $N$ turns in total. The density of the turns then is

$$\frac{dN}{d\sigma} = \frac{N}{(\alpha - 1)\,\beta\rho_1^2}, \tag{3.19}$$

where $dN$ is the number of turns contained by an element $d\sigma$ of the cross-section of the coil. The resistance of the coil element of which $d\sigma$ is the cross-section, is

$$dR = \frac{2\pi\eta\rho\,dN}{\lambda(d\sigma/dN)} = \frac{2\pi\eta N^2}{\lambda(\alpha - 1)^2\beta^2\rho_1^4}\,\rho\,d\rho\,dz_0, \tag{3.20}$$

where $\rho$ is the radius of the coil element and $d\rho\,dz_0$ is written for $d\sigma$.

The resistance of the whole coil follows by integration:

$$R = \frac{\pi\eta N^2(\alpha + 1)}{\lambda\beta\rho_1(\alpha - 1)}. \tag{3.21}$$

Now we are able to express the current density in terms of electrical power. The current density $\tau$ is

$$\tau = \frac{iN}{(\alpha - 1)\,\beta\rho_1^2} \tag{3.22}$$

and the power consumption $W$ when the field is stationary

$$W = i^2 R. \tag{3.23}$$

Elimination of $i$ from eqs. (3.22) and (3.23) and substitution of $R$ by eq. (3.21) gives

$$\tau = \frac{1}{\rho_1}\left(\frac{W\lambda}{\eta\rho_1}\right)^{\frac{1}{2}}\left(\frac{1}{\pi\beta(\alpha^2 - 1)}\right)^{\frac{1}{2}}. \tag{3.24}$$

When we substitute this into eq. (3.4) we have

$$H_z(0) = \frac{1}{2\pi}\left(\frac{W\lambda}{\eta\rho_1}\right)^{\frac{1}{2}}\left(\frac{\pi\beta}{\alpha^2 - 1}\right)^{\frac{1}{2}}\ln\frac{\alpha + (\alpha^2 + \beta^2)^{\frac{1}{2}}}{1 + (1 + \beta^2)^{\frac{1}{2}}}, \tag{3.25}$$

which is rewritten as

$$H_z(0) = G_1\left(\frac{W\lambda}{\eta\rho_1}\right)^{\frac{1}{2}}. \tag{3.26}$$

This relation between magnetic field and power consumption can be derived for any coil with any current distribution. The dimensionless factor $G_1$ depends on the shape of the coil and the current distribution. FABRY [1898] was the first to derive eq. (3.26) and to discuss its validity. The factor $G_1$ is tabulated in Appendix 5 for values of $\alpha$ ranging from 1 to 30 and $\beta$ from 0 to 50. Its maximum value for a coil of rectangular cross-section and uniform current density is 0.142, the maximum being obtained at the centre of a coil with $\alpha = 3$ and extending from $\beta = -2$ to $\beta = 2$.

Next we calculate this factor for the coil treated in Ch. 3, § 1.2. This coil is built up of thin disks of inner radius $\rho_1$, outer radius $\alpha\rho_1$, and width $h$ (Fig. 3.5). The resistance $r$ of such a disk is

$$r = \left( \int_{\rho_1}^{\alpha\rho_1} \frac{h\, \mathrm{d}\rho}{2\pi\rho\eta} \right)^{-1} = \frac{2\pi\eta}{h \ln \alpha}. \tag{3.27}$$

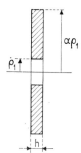

Fig. 3.5.   Solid disk of a Bitter solenoid.

The coil contains $N$ disks, occupying a fraction $\lambda$ of the body of the coil. The remaining part is occupied by insulation, etc. in such a way that the coil still may be considered as a continuous body. This is the case if the inter-layers of insulating material are thin compared with the inner diameter of the coil. The width $h$ of a disk is related to the length $\beta\rho_1$ of the coil by

$$h = \frac{\lambda\beta\rho_1}{N}. \tag{3.28}$$

The total resistance of the coil is

$$R = Nr = \frac{2\pi N^2 \eta}{\lambda \beta \rho_1 \ln \alpha}.$$ 
(3.29)

Using the relation $i = (W/R)^{\frac{1}{2}}$ we find

$$i = \frac{\rho_1}{N} \left(\frac{W\lambda}{\eta \rho_1}\right)^{\frac{1}{2}} \left(\frac{\beta \ln \alpha}{2\pi}\right)^{\frac{1}{2}},$$ 
(3.30)

where $W$ is the supplied power and $i$ the current flowing through the disks. This current is related to the current density $\tau$ by

$$i = \frac{\beta \rho_1}{N} \int\limits_{\rho_1}^{\alpha \rho_1} \tau \, \mathrm{d}\rho.$$ 
(3.31)

Substitution of eq. (3.12) and integration gives

$$i = \frac{\tau_0 \beta \rho_1^2 \ln \alpha}{N}.$$ 
(3.32)

By eliminating $i$ from eqs. (3.30) and (3.32) and substituting $\tau_0$ into eq. (3.13) we find

$$H_z(0) = \frac{1}{2\pi} \left(\frac{W\lambda}{\eta \rho_1}\right)^{\frac{1}{2}} \left(\frac{\pi}{2\beta \ln \alpha}\right)^{\frac{1}{2}} \ln \frac{\alpha \{\beta + (1 + \beta^2)^{\frac{1}{2}}\}}{\beta + (\alpha^2 + \beta^2)^{\frac{1}{2}}},$$ 
(3.33)

which is rewritten as

$$H_z(0) = G_2 \left(\frac{W\lambda}{\eta \rho_1}\right)^{\frac{1}{2}}$$ 
(3.34)

which is again Fabry's formula.

The value of $G_2$ for these coils with radial current-distribution and rectangular cross-section, is tabulated in Appendix 6 for $\alpha$ ranging from 1 to 30 and $\beta$ from 0 to 50. The maximum value of $G_2$ for this type of coil is 0.166, obtained if $\alpha = 6$ and $\beta$ goes from $-2$ to 2.

§ 1.4. *The Gaume coil*

A further development of the coil with current density inversely proportional to radius was performed by GAUME [1958] in order to improve the efficiency. He made a pile of conducting disks, the same as Bitter used for his coil (see Ch. 3, § 1.2). But Gaume's disks were of varying thickness, the thinnest being located at the centre of the coil and the thickest at the ends (Fig. 3.6). By this he not

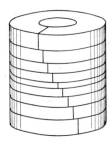

Fig. 3.6.   Principle of the Gaume solenoid.

only took advantage of the favourable radial current-distribution that made Bitter's coil 17% more efficient compared with the coil with uniform current-density, but he also optimized the axial current-distribution. He found maximum efficiency for a current distribution given by

$$\tau = \frac{\tau_0}{\gamma} \left\{ \frac{1}{(\zeta^2 + 1)^{\frac{1}{2}}} - \frac{1}{(\zeta^2 + \alpha^2)^{\frac{1}{2}}} \right\} \frac{\alpha}{\alpha - 1}, \qquad (3.35)$$

where $\gamma = \rho/\rho_1$ and $\zeta = z_0/\rho_1$. The quantity $\tau_0$ is the current density at $\rho = \rho_1$ and $z_0 = 0$.

The constant $G$ of eq. (3.26) for this coil is

$$G = 0.185, \qquad (3.36)$$

obtained if $\alpha = 8$ and $\beta$ goes from $-8$ to $+8$, which means a gain in efficiency of 11% over Bitter's coil. Instead of varying the thickness of the disks the desired axial current-distribution can also be obtained by varying the overlap angle between disks of constant thickness. This possibility makes coils of this type very suitable for generating fields meeting special requirements. For instance, the current density of eq. (3.35) can be obtained by letting the overlap angle follow the same $\zeta$-dependence as $\tau$ does.

These possibilities are further analyzed in another article by GAUME [1962].

## § 1.5. *Optimum current distribution*

We have seen that for a coil to generate as strong a field as possible with a given amount of power, the efficiency is higher for the coil with a current density inversely proportional to the radius, than for the coil with uniform current-density. The Gaume coil performs even better. It might be interesting to determine the optimum current-distribution for a cylindrical coil of maximum efficiency. Therefore we make only one condition, namely that the inner boundary of the coil is a cylinder of radius $\rho_1$, in order to make the field to be generated accessible for instruments. The coil is allowed to be infinitely long and infinitely thick and the current density $\tau$ may be any function of $\rho$ and $z_0$.

We have to find the function $\tau$ of $\rho$ and $z_0$ which maximizes the following integral

$$\int A_1 \, d\sigma = \frac{1}{2} \int\limits_{\rho_1}^{\infty} d\rho \int\limits_{-\infty}^{\infty} dz_0 \, \frac{\tau \rho^2}{(z_0^2 + \rho^2)^{\frac{3}{2}}} = \text{maximum}, \qquad (3.37)$$

and at the same time conserves the value of

$$\int A_2 \, d\sigma = \int\limits_{\rho_1}^{\infty} d\rho \int\limits_{-\infty}^{\infty} dz_0 \tau^2 \rho = \text{constant}. \qquad (3.38)$$

The integrand of eq. (3.37) is the first of eqs. (3.2) giving the field of one circular coil-element, of which $d\sigma$ is the cross-section, and the integral (3.38) is the power dissipated in the coil, the latter irrespective of constant factors. We use Lagrange's method of undetermined multipliers by stating that, if $\int A_1 \, d\sigma$ is a maximum, then

$$\int (A_1 - \xi A_2) \, d\sigma, \tag{3.39}$$

where $\xi$ is a factor independent of coordinates, is a maximum too. This new integrand has to satisfy Euler's equation, which in this case leads to the condition

$$\frac{\partial}{\partial \tau}(A_1 - \xi A_2) = 0, \tag{3.40}$$

since derivatives of $\tau$ do not occur in the integrands of eqs. (3.37) and (3.38). So

$$\frac{\rho^2}{2(z_0^2 + \rho^2)^{\frac{3}{2}}} - 2\xi\tau\rho = 0 \tag{3.41}$$

and

$$\tau = \frac{1}{4\xi} \frac{\rho}{(z_0^2 + \rho^2)^{\frac{3}{2}}}. \tag{3.42}$$

The factor $\xi$ is determined by considering that

$$\int_{\rho_1}^{\infty} d\rho \int_{-\infty}^{\infty} dz_0 \tau^2 \rho = \frac{W\lambda}{2\pi\eta}, \tag{3.43}$$

which, after substitution of eq. (3.42) and integration, leads to

$$\xi = \frac{\sqrt{3}}{8}\left(\frac{\eta}{W\lambda\rho_1}\right)^{\frac{1}{2}}. \tag{3.44}$$

Substitution of this into eq. (3.42) and the result into eq. (3.37) gives after integration

$$H_z(0) = 0.217\left(\frac{W\lambda}{\eta\rho_1}\right)^{\frac{1}{2}}, \tag{3.45}$$

which is Fabry's formula for an infinite coil with an inner axial bore of radius $\rho_1$ and having an optimum current-distribution. Such a coil is called a Maxwell coil after Maxwell who was the first to derive this current distribution.

If we drop the condition of axial accessibility the absolute maximum of $G = 0.230$ is obtained at the centre of a sphere, the current density outside the sphere being proportional to $\rho/\{z_0(z_0^2 + \rho^2)\}$.

The values of $G$ as derived in these sections are valid if we perform our calculations using the mksA-system of units. In practice we shall often use a mixed system of units when considering the fields generated by electric currents. Then, $H_z$ will be expressed in oersteds, $W$ in watts, $\rho$ in cm and $\eta$ in ohm cm. The numerical value of $G$ is then multiplied by $0.4\pi$, so that the maximum value of $G$ for a coil with uniform current-density becomes $G = 0.179$ and for a coil with a current density inversely proportional to the radius $G = 0.209$, etc.

## § 2. MECHANICAL CONSIDERATIONS

### § 2.1. *Forces on the coil*

Consider a circular winding of cross-sectional area $d\sigma$ and radius $\rho$, being an element of a thick cylindrical solenoid. A current $\tau\, d\sigma$ flows through the winding ($\tau$ being the current density) thus generating a magnetic shell of strength $\mu_0\tau\, d\sigma$ per unit area (see Ch. 1, § 4). The potential energy of an element of area $ds$ of this shell in the field $\boldsymbol{H}$ of the solenoid is

$$d e = \mu_0\tau\, d\sigma\, \boldsymbol{H}\cdot d\boldsymbol{s}. \tag{3.46}$$

The potential energy $e$ of the whole magnetic shell and thus of the winding in the field of the coil follows by integration (considering that $\mu_0 H = B$):

$$e = \tau\, d\sigma \int \boldsymbol{B}\cdot d\boldsymbol{s} = \tau\, d\sigma\, \Phi, \tag{3.47}$$

where $\Phi$ is the magnetic flux enclosed by the winding. Let the elementary winding contain $dn$ turns. The current through one turn of the coil is $i$ and so the current through the elementary winding is

$$\tau \, d\sigma = i \, dn. \tag{3.48}$$

The mutual inductance $M$ between one turn and the rest of the coil is defined by

$$\Phi = Mi, \tag{3.49}$$

where $\Phi$ is the magnetic flux from the rest of the coil enclosed by the turn under consideration.

Substitution of eqs. (3.48) and (3.49) into eq. (3.47) then gives

$$e = \tau^2 M \frac{d\sigma}{dn} \, d\sigma. \tag{3.50}$$

The potential energy per unit area of the cross-section of the coil then is

$$E = \frac{\tau^2}{n} M, \tag{3.51}$$

where $n$ is the number of turns per unit area of the cross-section of the coil. Owing to axial symmetry, only radial and axial forces on the winding are possible.

They are found by taking the gradient of $E$

$$F_\rho = 2\pi\rho p_\rho = -\frac{\partial E}{\partial \rho} = -\frac{\tau^2}{n} \frac{\partial M}{\partial \rho}, \tag{3.52}$$

$$F_z = 2\pi\rho p_z = -\frac{\partial E}{\partial z} = -\frac{\tau^2}{n} \frac{\partial M}{\partial z}, \tag{3.53}$$

where $p_\rho$ and $p_z$ are the radial and axial components, respectively, of the force on a unit volume of the solenoid. It should be noted here that for a turn at a given location in a coil of given dimensions $M$ is proportional to the density $n$ of the turns, so that $F_\rho$ and $F_z$ are in fact independent of $n$, as should be expected.

Graphs of $M$ between a cylindrical coil and a single turn in its endplane are given by COCKCROFT [1928] as a function of the dimensions of the coil and the radial position of the turn.

As an example $p_\rho$ will be calculated here for an infinitely long coil with uniform current density. It is obvious that in this case $p_z = 0$ everywhere. Consider a cylindrical current-sheet of thickness $d\rho$ and radius $\rho$, being an element of the coil. The flux due to this infinitely long current-sheet is

$$d\Phi = \pi\rho^2 \, dB = -\pi\mu_0\rho^2\tau \, d\rho, \qquad (3.54)$$

where $dB$ is the homogeneous induction inside the current sheet, which can easily be calculated by integrating the first of eqs. (3.2) from $z_0 = -\infty$ to $z_0 = +\infty$. The field due to the current sheet is zero on its outside, so the flux is simply the product of $B$ and the area of the sheet normal to its axis.

Now we consider a single turn of radius $\rho^*$ which encloses a part $(\rho^*/\rho)^2$ of the flux due to a current sheet of radius $\rho > \rho^*$, and the whole flux due to a current sheet of radius $\rho < \rho^*$. The total flux enclosed by this turn then is

$$\Phi(\rho^*) = \int_{\rho^*}^{\rho_2} (\rho^*/\rho)^2 \, d\Phi + \int_{\rho_1}^{\rho^*} d\Phi \qquad (3.55)$$

for a coil of inner radius $\rho_1$ and outer radius $\rho_2$. This becomes after substitution of eq. (3.54) and integration

$$\Phi(\rho^*) = -\tfrac{1}{3}\mu_0\pi\tau(3\rho_2\rho^{*2} - 2\rho^{*3} - \rho_1^3). \qquad (3.56)$$

After substitution of eq. (3.49) and differentiation to $\rho^*$ we find by using eq. (3.48)

$$\frac{\partial M}{\partial \rho^*} = -2\pi\mu_0 n (\rho_2\rho^* - \rho^{*2}). \qquad (3.57)$$

For convenience we write $\rho$ for $\rho^*$. Then by combining eqs. (3.52) and (3.57) we obtain

$$p_\rho = \mu_0\tau^2 (\rho_2 - \rho). \qquad (3.58)$$

## § 2.2. *Stresses in the coil*

The body forces $p_\rho$ and $p_z$ given by eqs. (3.52) and (3.53) give rise to a stress distribution in the coil such that each volume element is in static equilibrium. We use cylindrical coordinates and the stress per unit area will be called stress-intensity.

Figure 3.7 shows a volume element bounded by the radial surfaces $\rho$ and $(\rho+\mathrm{d}\rho)$, the axial surfaces $z$ and $(z+\mathrm{d}z)$ and the azimuthal surfaces $\varphi$ and $(\varphi+\mathrm{d}\varphi)$. The components $s$ of the stress-intensity tensor have as first index the surface on which they act ($\rho$ for radial,

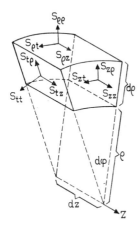

Fig. 3.7. Element of a thick solenoid with surface stresses.

$z$ for axial and $t$ for azimuthal) and as second index the line along which they act. They are drawn in Fig. 3.7 in the direction of their positive sense. So a stress component with like indices is a normal stress and with unlike indices a shear stress. The volume forces $p_\rho$ and $p_z$ are not drawn in the figure. Their positive sense is along the positive $\rho$- and $z$-direction, respectively.

Owing to the rotational symmetry of the problem the azimuthal or tangential component $p_t$ of the volume force is zero and so are the shear stress-intensities $s_{zt}$, $s_{tz}$, $s_{t\rho}$ and $s_{\rho t}$.

Translational equilibrium is obtained by the condition that the

sum of all forces acting on the volume element be zero. This leads
to the radial equilibrium equation

$$\frac{\partial}{\partial \rho}(\rho s_{\rho\rho}) + \rho \frac{\partial s_{z\rho}}{\partial z} - s_{tt} + \rho p_\rho = 0 \qquad (3.59)$$

and the axial equilibrium equation

$$\frac{\partial}{\partial \rho}(\rho s_{\rho z}) + \rho \frac{\partial s_{zz}}{\partial z} + \rho p_z = 0. \qquad (3.60)$$

Rotational equilibrium is ensured by the symmetry of the stress
tensor; in other words $s_{\rho z} = s_{z\rho}$, etc.

Now we suppose that the coil behaves elastically as an isotropic
body. This assumption is a reasonable one for a coil whose turns
are cemented together to form a solid block. This is a common
technique of making coils for the production of very strong pulsed
fields, where the stresses in the coil become considerable. The theory
of elasticity which will be applied here is treated extensively by
LOVE [1927].

We apply Hooke's law for isotropic bodies, which relates the
stress distribution to the strain distribution:

$$\begin{aligned}
Y\varepsilon_{\rho\rho} &= s_{\rho\rho} - \xi(s_{tt} + s_{zz}), \\
Y\varepsilon_{tt} &= s_{tt} - \xi(s_{\rho\rho} + s_{zz}), \\
Y\varepsilon_{zz} &= s_{zz} - \xi(s_{\rho\rho} + s_{tt}), \\
G\varepsilon_{\rho z} &= s_{\rho z}.
\end{aligned} \qquad (3.61)$$

Here $\varepsilon_{\rho\rho}$, $\varepsilon_{tt}$ and $\varepsilon_{zz}$ are relative elongations of the volume element
along a radius, tangential to a circle and along the $z$-axis, respective-
ly. The strain component $\varepsilon_{\rho z}$ is a shear in the $z$-direction along a
radial surface. The constants in eqs. (3.61) are Young's modulus of
elasticity $Y$, the torsion- or shear-modulus $G$ and Poisson's ratio of
contraction $\xi$. The following relation exists between these constants:

$$Y = 2(1 + \xi)G. \qquad (3.62)$$

The strain distribution may be described by a distribution of displacements $u$ with radial component $u_\rho$, and axial component $u_z$. The displacement vector $u$ is defined as the vector from the position of a point in the elastic body before the stress is applied, to the position of the same point after application of the stress.

Owing to the rotational symmetry the displacement has no tangential component. It can easily be shown that the following relations exist between the stresses and the displacements:

$$\varepsilon_{\rho\rho} = \frac{\partial u_\rho}{\partial \rho}, \qquad \varepsilon_{zz} = \frac{\partial u_z}{\partial z},$$

$$\varepsilon_{tt} = \frac{u_\rho}{\rho}, \qquad \varepsilon_{\rho z} = \frac{\partial u_\rho}{\partial z} + \frac{\partial u_z}{\partial \rho}. \tag{3.63}$$

Now we have by eqs. (3.59), (3.60), (3.61) and (3.63), a set of ten equations with ten unknowns, namely four stress-intensity components, four strain components and two displacement components. The volume forces $p_\rho$ and $p_z$ are given by eqs. (3.52) and (3.53) and the elastic constants are determined by the material used.

The solution of the stress components (the tangential stress-intensity $s_{tt}$, which is a tensile stress, is of special importance) from these equations is not easy, and has generally to be performed by numerical methods. The stress distribution in a short cylindrical coil will tend to contract the coil in the axial direction and to expand it radially. A compressive hoop around the circumference of the coil will therefore provide adequate reinforcement. Another point, that may be important for short, thick, wire – or tape – wound solenoids is the stability of the windings. The magnetic field at the outer circumference will be opposite to the field at the centre. The sense of the current, however, is the same anywhere in the coil, which means that the outer turns are subjected to a compressive tangential stress, instead of a tensile one. Though in equilibrium, these turns will collapse if not properly supported by the inner turns and the reinforcement: the equilibrium is unstable. The stress distribution in short, thick solenoids and the stability of the turns is extensively analyzed by DANIELS [1953] and also by KUZNETSOV [1960].

## § 2.3. Stress distribution in an infinitely long solenoid

To give an idea of the magnitude of the stresses we shall calculate them for an infinitely long coil of inner radius $\rho_1$ and outer radius $\rho_2$. The stress distribution in such a coil is rather simple, since, owing to symmetry,

$$p_z = 0 \quad \text{and} \quad s_{\rho z} = 0. \tag{3.64}$$

Then it follows from eq. (3.60) that

$$\frac{\partial s_{zz}}{\partial z} = 0, \tag{3.65}$$

so that, if the coil is not supported at its endfaces (at infinity), $s_{zz}$ is zero everywhere.

Obviously the axial strain $\varepsilon_{zz}$ has to be uniform in this very long coil. So it follows from the third of eqs. (3.61) that

$$s_{\rho\rho} + s_{tt} = 2C, \tag{3.66}$$

where $C$ is a constant to be determined afterwards. Substitution into eq. (3.59) gives

$$\rho \frac{\mathrm{d}s_{\rho\rho}}{\mathrm{d}\rho} + 2(s_{\rho\rho} - C) + \rho p_\rho = 0, \tag{3.67}$$

where $p_\rho$ is given by eq. (3.58). Hence we find for the radial stress distribution

$$\rho \frac{\mathrm{d}s_{\rho\rho}}{\mathrm{d}\rho} + 2(s_{\rho\rho} - C) + \mu_0 \tau^2 (\rho_2 \rho - \rho^2) = 0. \tag{3.68}$$

With the boundary conditions

$$s_{\rho\rho} = 0 \quad \text{for} \quad \rho = \rho_1 \quad \text{and} \quad \rho = \rho_2, \tag{3.69}$$

which determine both $C$ and the integration constant, we find for

$s_{\rho\rho}$ the following solution

$$s_{\rho\rho} = \frac{\mu_0\tau^2}{12}\left\{3\rho^2 - 4\rho_2\rho + \rho_2^2 - \rho_1^2\left(\frac{3\rho_1 - \rho_2}{\rho_1 + \rho_2}\right)\left(1 - \frac{\rho_2^2}{\rho^2}\right)\right\},$$

$$(3.70)$$

and by eq. (3.66)

$$s_{tt} = -\frac{\mu_0\tau^2}{12}\left\{3\rho^2 - 4\rho_2\rho - \rho_2^2 - \rho_1^2\left(\frac{3\rho_1 - \rho_2}{\rho_1 + \rho_2}\right)\left(1 + \frac{\rho_2^2}{\rho^2}\right)\right\}.$$

$$(3.71)$$

The total tangential stress $S_t$ per unit length of the coil, trying to tear it apart radially, follows by integration of $s_{tt}$ over the radial thickness of the coil:

$$S_t = \int_{\rho_1}^{\rho_2} s_{tt}\,d\rho = \tfrac{1}{6}\mu_0\tau^2(2\rho_1^3 - 3\rho_1^2\rho_2 + \rho_2^3).\qquad(3.72)$$

We know by integration of eq. (3.54) that

$$B = \int_{\rho_1}^{\rho_2} dB = -\mu_0\tau(\rho_2 - \rho_1),\qquad(3.73)$$

where $B$ is the homogeneous induction inside the thick solenoid.

Substitution of $\tau$ into eq. (3.72) gives

$$S_t = \tfrac{1}{2}HB(2\rho_1 + \rho_2)/3.\qquad(3.74)$$

If the solenoid consists of only a thin layer of turns of radius $\rho_1$ this reduces to

$$S_t(\text{single layer coil}) = \tfrac{1}{2}HB\rho_1.\qquad(3.75)$$

We compare this with the total tangential tensile stress in a thin-walled tube under internal pressure $P$

$$S_t = P\rho_1.\qquad(3.76)$$

This equation is easily derived by dividing the circular cross-section of the tube in two by a diameter and equating the force due to the internal pressure pushing the two halves apart and the force due to the tensile stress in the tube wall keeping them together.

Now we see that the magnetic field $H$ gives rise to a tangential stress in its generating coil equal to the stress caused by an effective magnetic pressure $P_m$ of

$$P_m = \tfrac{1}{2}HB. \tag{3.77}$$

A fieldstrength of $3 \times 10^7$ A m$^{-1}$ which is quite common in pulse techniques is thus equivalent to a pressure of 5600 atm.

It should be noted here that, although we may consider the total stress as being caused by a magnetic pressure, the radial stress-distribution is entirely different from that in a tube under pressure. To see this we consider eq. (3.71). We see that for both $\rho = \rho_1$ and $\rho = \rho_2$ the value of $s_{tt}$ is

$$s_{tt} = \frac{\mu_0 \tau^2}{6} \frac{\rho_2^3 + \rho_1 \rho_2^2 + \rho_1^2 \rho_2 - 3\rho_1^3}{\rho_1 + \rho_2} \tag{3.78}$$

and that it is positive for any value of $\rho$, $\rho_1$ and $\rho_2$. Hence $s_{tt}$ is always a tensile stress. This stress reaches a maximum value for $\rho$ somewhere between $\rho_1$ and $\rho_2$. For instance, if $\rho_2 = 3\rho_1$, the maximum stress intensity occurs at $\rho = 2\rho_1$, with a value

$$s_{tt}(\text{max}) = \tfrac{7}{4}\mu_0 \tau^2 \rho_1^2 = \tfrac{7}{8}P_m, \tag{3.79}$$

to be compared with the stress intensities at the inner and the outer surface

$$s_{tt} = \tfrac{3}{2}\mu_0 \tau^2 \rho_1^2 = \tfrac{3}{4}P_m. \tag{3.80}$$

The tensile stress in a thick-walled tube, also with $\rho_2 = 3\rho_1$, falls steadily from

$$s_{tt}(\rho_1) = \tfrac{5}{4}P_m \quad \text{to} \quad s_{tt}(\rho_2) = \tfrac{1}{4}P_m, \tag{3.81}$$

where $P_m$ is the internal pressure. These values are to be compared with eqs. (3.79) and (3.80) and follow from eq. (3.67) for $p_\rho = 0$ and with boundary conditions $s_{\rho\rho} = P_m$ for $\rho = \rho_1$ and $s_{\rho\rho} = 0$ for $\rho = \rho_2$.

We see that the stress distribution in the magnetic coil is much more uniform than in the equivalent pressure tube. Consequently the maximum stress intensity in the magnetic coils stays well below the maximum value occurring in the pressure tube. In this case the favourable difference is 30% of the value in the pressure tube (Fig. 3.8).

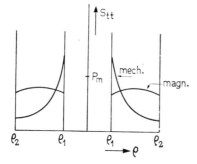

Fig. 3.8. Comparison of the stress distributions in a thick solenoid (magn.) and in a thick-walled pressure tube (mech.).

A long solenoid with outer radius three times the inner radius and generating a field of $3 \times 10^7$ A m$^{-1}$ ($\approx 3.8 \times 10^5$ Oe) will thus endure a stress intensity of more than $5 \times 10^8$ N m$^{-2}$, which exceeds the tensile strength of copper wire which is about $2.5 \times 10^7$ N m$^{-2}$. Thus an unsupported copper solenoid will explode in this case, thereby releasing its magnetic potential energy which is $\frac{1}{2}HB$ or $5.6 \times 10^8$ J m$^{-3}$. This is quite comparable with the explosive power of T.N.T. which is $6 \times 10^9$ J m$^{-3}$. Some safety precautions are therefore to be recommended when working with these fields.

The limiting factor is clearly the yield strength of the conducting material, which must not be exceeded by the tensile stress anywhere in the coil body. There is some advantage in using copper alloys that have a considerably higher yield strength than pure copper, their resistivity being of the same order of that of copper. A comparative survey is given in Table 3.1.

In addition to the compressive circumferential support of the coil it might be useful to have a reinforcement at the radius where the

TABLE 3.1

TABLE 3.1

Electrical and mechanical properties of various constructional materials for coils

| Composition | State | $\eta$ ($\times 10^8$) | $Y$ ($\times 10^{-11}$) | $G$ ($\times 10^{-11}$) | $s_{max}$ ($\times 10^{-8}$) | $s_{0.1}$ ($\times 10^{-8}$) |
|---|---|---|---|---|---|---|
| | | $\Omega$ m | N m$^{-2}$ | | | |
| Cu (OFHC) | annealed | 1.7 | 1.1 | 0.4 | 2.0 | 0.4 |
| | hard drawn | 1.8 | | | 4.2 | 3.6 |
| Cu + 0.8 % Cd | annealed | 1.8 | 1.2 | 0.4 | 2.9 | 0.7 |
| | hard drawn | 2.1 | | | 6.5 | 5.1 |
| Cu + 0.6 % Cr | precip. hardened | 2.1 | 1.1 | 0.4 | 3.8 | 2.5 |
| Cu + 2.5 % Be | precip. hardened | 7.6 | 1.3 | | 11 | 7.3 |

$\eta$ = electrical resistivity $\qquad$ $s_{max}$ = tensile strength
$Y$ = Young's modulus of elasticity $\qquad$ $s_{0.1}$ = yield stress for 0.1 % plastic
$G$ = torsion modulus $\qquad\qquad\qquad\qquad$ deformation

Data are taken from:
High Conductivity Copper Alloys (Publ. 51); Copper and its Alloys in Engineering and Technology (Publ. 43), (Copper Development Association, London [1956]). C. J. Smithells, Metals Reference Handbook, 2nd ed. (Butterworths Scientific Publications, London [1955]).

maximum tensile stress occurs, for instance by incorporating an interlayer of some strong material. Such a reinforcement will only be effective, if its Young's modulus of elasticity is considerably superior to that of the winding, since it is meant to influence the stress distribution by its elastic properties, rather than prevent breaking by its ultimate strength. It may be added here that a radial temperature gradient due to inhomogeneous cooling, gives rise to additional stresses which may become considerable and thus cause the coil to give way at a much lower fieldstrength than follows from this calculation. Also a short coil will endure a higher stress than a long coil at the same fieldstrength, since the former requires a greater current to generate the field as compared to the latter, so that the volume forces and thus the stresses will be greater.

## § 2.4. *Force-free coils*

The force on the coilwindings as expressed in eqs. (3.52) and (3.53) may also be written as

$$p_\rho = \mu_0 \tau H_z, \tag{3.82}$$

and

$$p_z = \mu_0 \tau H_\rho, \tag{3.83}$$

by making use of the following equations:

$$\frac{\partial M}{\partial \rho} = \frac{\tau}{n} \frac{\partial \Phi}{\partial \rho} = \mu_0 \frac{\tau}{n} 2\pi\rho H_z, \tag{3.84}$$

and

$$\frac{\partial M}{\partial z} = \frac{\tau}{n} \frac{\partial \Phi}{\partial z} = \mu_0 \frac{\tau}{n} 2\pi\rho H_\rho. \tag{3.85}$$

These equations can easily be verified for the coil treated in Ch. 3, § 2.1.

The eqs. (3.82) and (3.83) can be written vectorially

$$p = \tau \times B = \mu_0 \tau \times H, \tag{3.86}$$

which is Biot-Savart's law.

It is interesting to investigate the possibility of making $p$ equal to zero everywhere.

For this the field $H$ has to satisfy the condition

$$\text{curl } H \times H = 0 \tag{3.87}$$

or

$$\text{curl } H = \alpha H, \tag{3.88}$$

where $\alpha$ is a scalar quantity. The current density is replaced by curl $H$ in accordance with Maxwell's law, and has to be parallel to the field vector $H$. In a thick cylindrical solenoid this might be accomplished by superposing an axial current density $\tau_z$, dependent on $\rho$ and $z$, on the tangential current density $\tau_t$, that now is also allowed to be a function of $\rho$ and $z$. The axial current component can be obtained by winding the layers of the solenoid with a certain pitch, corresponding to the required ratio $\tau_z/\tau_t$ (see Fig. 3.9).

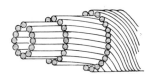

Fig. 3.9. Principle of a stress-reduced coil. Successive layers are partly cut away.

This method of winding excludes a radial current density. We shall confine our treatment to this type of coil, having only axial and tangential current. The axial current gives rise to a tangential fieldstrength $H_t$ and the tangential current to an axial fieldstrength $H_z$. In a short coil both give rise to a radial field component $H_\rho$. We shall try to find the spatial dependence of $\tau_t$ and $\tau_z$ required to generate a field that satisfies eq. (3.88). The fact that $\tau_\rho$ is zero for the type of coil under consideration also implies that $H_\rho$ is zero everywhere. Any derivative to the azimuthal angle $\varphi$ is zero, owing to rotational symmetry. Then eq. (3.88) becomes

$$-\frac{\partial H_z}{\partial \rho} = \alpha H_t , \tag{3.89}$$

$$\frac{1}{\rho} \frac{\partial}{\partial \rho} (\rho H_t) = \alpha H_z , \tag{3.90}$$

$$\frac{\partial H_t}{\partial z} = 0 . \tag{3.91}$$

Equation (3.91) can only be satisfied by the field of an infinitely long solenoid. For such a solenoid any derivative to $z$ is zero. The factor $\alpha$ may be any function of $\rho$.

The solution of the differential equations will in general be difficult and often only possible by numerical methods, except if $\alpha$ is a constant; then the analytical solution is simple. However, such a coil is not practical, because the constant proportionality factor between fieldstrength and current density implies the presence of conductors at any place where the field is different from zero. We shall see that, to fulfil eq. (3.88) the entire space has actually to be filled with conductors.

With $\alpha$ constant we can rewrite eqs. (3.89) and (3.90) as

$$\alpha \tau_t = -\frac{\partial \tau_z}{\partial \rho}, \tag{3.92}$$

$$\alpha \tau_z = \frac{1}{\rho} \frac{\partial}{\partial \rho} (\rho \tau_t). \tag{3.93}$$

Elimination of $\tau_z$ gives

$$\rho^2 \frac{\partial^2 \tau_t}{\partial \rho^2} + \rho \frac{\partial \tau_t}{\partial \rho} + (\alpha^2 \rho^2 - 1) \tau_t = 0. \tag{3.94}$$

This is Bessel's equation (see for instance MARGENAU and MURPHY [1956] p. 74). A solution remaining finite for $\rho = 0$ is

$$\tau_t = C_1 J_1 (\alpha \rho),$$

where $J_1 (\alpha \rho)$ is a Bessel function of order one and with argument $\alpha \rho$; $C_1$ is a factor, independent of variables. Elimination of $\tau_t$ from eqs. (3.92) and (3.93) gives

$$\rho^2 \frac{\partial^2 \tau_z}{\partial \rho^2} + \rho \frac{\partial \tau_z}{\partial \rho} + \alpha^2 \rho^2 \tau_z = 0, \tag{3.95}$$

which is again Bessel's equation with solution

$$\tau_z = C_2 J_0 (\alpha \rho),$$

where $J_0 (\alpha \rho)$ is a Bessel function of order zero and $C_2$ is a factor, independent of variables.

The properties of the Bessel functions give us the following information

$$\tau_t = 0 \quad \text{for} \quad \rho = 0,$$
$$\tau_z = C_2 \quad \text{for} \quad \rho = 0,$$
$$\tau_t = \tau_z = 0 \quad \text{for} \quad \rho = \infty,$$
$$\tau_z/\tau_t = 0 \quad \text{for} \quad \rho = \infty.$$

So the current and consequently the fieldstrength have only an axial component at the axis. At large distances from the axis the current density and fieldstrength become purely tangential.

The convergence to zero of the current density at large distances from the axis implies the possibility of making finite coils with reduced stress densities. In fact calculations like this enable us to transport the forces from regions where reinforcement of the coil is difficult to regions where an adequate support can be made. This is treated by FURTH, LEVINE and WANIEK [1957], LEVINE [1962], WELLS and MILLS [1962] and WAKEFIELD [1962], the latter indicating how calculations can be adapted for use on an electronic computer. Solutions of the axially symmetric problem with $\alpha$ constant are presented by LÜST and SCHLÜTER [1954] and CHANDRASEKHAR [1956]. Such solutions are of interest for the production of stable high temperature plasmas, which have to satisfy eq. (3.87), the plasma not being allowed to contain tensile stresses or to be in material contact with a wall.

The impossibility of making a finite coil system with zero force can be proved generally by considering that the body forces in the coil are forces between current-carrying conductors, which obey the inverse-square law of distance. We can therefore write the potential energy due to these forces as

$$E_{\text{mech}} = \int r \cdot p \, \mathrm{d}v, \tag{3.96}$$

where $r$ is the radius vector to the point where the body force is $p$. The integration is performed over that space occupied by conductors. This mechanical potential energy is equal to the magnetic potential energy $E_{\text{magn}}$, due to the same currents:

$$E_{\text{magn}} = \tfrac{1}{2}\mu_0 \int H^2 \, dv, \tag{3.97}$$

where the integration is performed over the entire space. So if $E_{\text{mech}}$ be zero, $E_{\text{magn}}$ has also to be zero, and the latter is only possible if $H$ vanishes identically. Alternatively, if a field is present in some region, there are also forces to be balanced. The only thing we can do is to shift them to a more convenient region, thereby inevitably reducing the efficiency of the coil system.

## § 3. HEAT DISSIPATION AND COOLING

Fields up to a few times $10^4$ A m$^{-1}$ can usually be generated by copper coils without requiring special cooling provisions. The heat dissipated can easily be handled by natural convection and conduction. Experience obtained in the fabrication of small transformers has shown that a current density of about $3 \times 10^6$ A m$^{-2}$, equivalent to about $2 \times 10^5$ W m$^{-3}$, is quite safe for copper coils at room temperature. Cooling by forced air may provide some improvement, but the thermal conductivity of coils wound of insulated wire is commonly too low to allow the transport of appreciable amounts of heat to the surface of the coil. The thermal conductivity which for normal compounded coils is of the order of 0.1 W m$^{-1}$ $^\circ$C$^{-1}$, can be improved by a special method of winding called orthocyclic winding (LENDERS [1961/62]). The wire is wound by layers, the turns of the next layer being made to lie exactly in the grooves of the previous one. This is done by letting the wire jump from one groove to the next at the axial line through the point where the layer has been commenced (Fig. 3.10).

The misfit is thus limited to a line that shifts from one layer to the next, so that an intimate contact between neighbouring wires is ensured. The fraction of the volume filled by copper is 70–85%, depending on wire diameter to be compared to the theoretical value

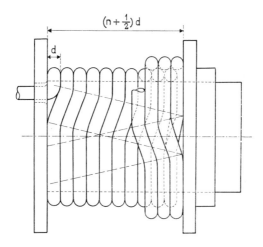

Fig. 3.10.  Principle of orthocyclic winding of coils. The plane of the turns is exactly perpendicular to the coil axis, the transition from one turn to the next being made by a short jump. The turns of each layer lie in the grooves between the turns of the previous layer. (After LENDERS [1961/62].)

for cylindrical wire of 91%. The wire is coated with a thermosetting enamel that is cured after winding the coil. In this way a free-bearing coil is obtained with a thermal conductivity of about 1 W $m^{-1} \, °C^{-1}$ and a considerable mechanical strength. This is still low compared to the thermal conductivity of pure copper which is 400 W $m^{-1} \, °C^{-1}$, but the advantage over normal coils is obvious and we have additional profit from the high copper-filled volume-fraction and the mechanical strength which makes coil formers etc. unnecessary.

Next we consider forced cooling by fluids, distinguishing between low-power coils where the heat is transported by conduction through the coil body and removed by a liquid stream at the surface, and high-power coils where the cooled surface is located through-out the coil body and where the heat resistance of the coil material is unimportant compared to the heat resistance at the interface be-

tween coil and liquid. An example of the first type of coil is given
in Fig. 3.11, where disks of wire (orthocyclic) or copper tape are
confined between copper plates which are watercooled at their
periphery. The insulation between coil and cooling plate is obtained by mylar sheet coated with silicone grease for better thermal

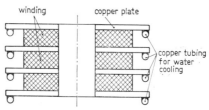

Fig. 3.11.   Cooling of flat coil-disks by inserting water-cooled copper plates.

contact. In this way it is possible to have a heat flux of about 500
$W \, m^{-2}$ across the interface, which means an allowable load of about
$6 \times 10^5 \, W \, m^{-3}$ for the orthocyclic coil and about $2.5 \times 10^6 \, W \, m^{-3}$
for the tape coil where the tape width extends from the median
plane of a coil disk to the cooling plates. Tape coils are made by
AHERN [1961] and by ISHIKAWA and CHIKAZUMI [1962] for exciting
iron-yoke magnets.

The high-power type of coil has its cooling surface dispersed in
the coil body. Now the problem has two aspects.

First, we have to force a sufficient quantity of coolant through
the coil in order to transport the heat from the coil to the heat exchanger or the drain thereby not overheating the coolant. If $T_m$ is
the maximum permissible temperature of the coolant and $T_0$ the
temperature at which it is pumped into the coil, the minimum permissible flow is

$$Q = \frac{W}{C_c(T_m - T_0)},$$

where $Q$ is the volume of coolant pumped through the coil per unit
time, $W$ is the power supplied to the coil and $C_c$ is the specific heat
per unit volume of the coolant.

Second, we have to ensure that the heat transfer from the coil body to the coolant is sufficient to prevent overheating of the coil. If the temperature gradients in the coil body may be considered small compared to the temperature jump at the solid-liquid interface (which is typically the case in high-power solenoids), the coil may be said to have an average temperature which is subject to a maximum permissible value $T_n$. The required heat transfer coefficient per unit area is given by

$$\zeta = \frac{W}{A(T_n - T_a)},$$

where $A$ is the total amount of cooling interface and $T_a$ is the average temperature of the coolant. For simplicity $\zeta$ is considered as being constant throughout the coil and $T_n - T_a$ is identified with the temperature jump at the solid-liquid interface.

The heat transfer coefficient for turbulent flow is given by the empirical relation (see McADAMS [1954])

$$\zeta = 0.023 \frac{k}{D_e} (Pr)^{0.4} (Re)^{0.8}, \tag{3.98}$$

where $k$ is the thermal conductivity of the coolant and $D_e$ is the hydrodynamic diameter of the passage through which the coolant is flowing. $Pr$ and $Re$ are the dimensionless Prandtl- and Reynolds-number, respectively. The hydrodynamic diameter is defined as

$$D_e = \frac{4a}{c},$$

where $a$ is the cross-sectional area and $c$ the circumference of the cooling passage. The Prandtl-number applies to the coolant and is given by

$$Pr = \frac{C_c \mu}{\rho k},$$

where $\mu$ is the viscosity, $C_c$ is the specific heat per unit volume, $\rho$ is the density and $k$ is the thermal conductivity of the coolant. The

Reynolds-number applies to the flow conditions and is given by

$$Re = \frac{D_e v \rho}{\mu},$$

where $v$ is the flow velocity in units length per unit time and the other symbols are as given above.

Equation (3.98) can be rewritten as

$$\zeta = 0.023 \frac{v^{0.8}}{D_e^{0.2}} \left(\frac{C_c \rho k^{\frac{3}{2}}}{\mu}\right)^{0.4} = 0.023 \frac{v^{0.8}}{D_e^{0.2}} U, \qquad (3.99)$$

where the factor between brackets applies to the coolant exclusively. Obviously it has to be as great as possible. The factor $U$ was calculated by DE KLERK [1962] for various fluids and listed in Table 3.2.

TABLE 3.2

Quality number $U$ of coolant in $J\ s^{-0.2}\ m^{-2.6}\ °C^{-1}$

| Coolant | Temp. °C | $U \times 10^{-4}$ |
|---|---|---|
| Water | 25 | 9 |
| | 50 | 11 |
| | 75 | 13 |
| | 100 | 16 |
| Kerosene | 25 | 1.8 |
| | 50 | 2.1 |
| | 75 | 2.4 |
| | 100 | 2.6 |
| Orthodichlorobenzene | 25 | 2.2 |
| | 50 | 2.6 |
| | 75 | 2.7 |
| | 100 | 3.0 |

We see that water is the best coolant, but the other two fluids are electric insulators which makes them more suitable for cooling high-voltage coils.

When using the data from Table 3.2, $v$ should be expressed in m s$^{-1}$ and $D_e$ in m. The heat transfer coefficient is then obtained in W m$^{-2}$ °C$^{-1}$. Equations (3.98) and (3.99) apply to tubes with a smooth inner surface. If the surface is not smooth the value of the heat transfer coefficient will be lower.

The pressure difference $\Delta p$ required to maintain a flow velocity $v$ through a passage is given by

$$\Delta p = \left( \frac{0.32l}{Re^{\frac{1}{4}}D_e} + 1 \right) \tfrac{1}{2}\rho v^2 ,$$

where $l$ is the length of the passage and $v$ the flow velocity in units length per unit time (McADAMS [1954]). This formula is applicable to turbulent flow only, i.e. if the value of $Re$ is well above 1000.

The cooling capacity increases with increasing velocity of the coolant along the surface to be cooled. The coil may consist of coaxial layers of copper-wire or -tape with interspace between the layers through which the coolant can flow. Alternatively the coil may consist of disks with radial interspace. Such coils are not very strong and do not allow for high velocities (and thus high pressure gradients) of the coolant. The specific heat transfer will be of the order of $10^5$ W m$^{-2}$, but owing to the large amount of cooling surface the specific load may be appreciable, $50–75 \times 10^6$ W m$^{-3}$ for a water-cooled solenoid.

The use of de-ionized water is to be recommended in order to avoid electrocorrosion of the conductors. For the same reason the voltage across the coil should not exceed 150 V.

A coil made of copper tubing, through which water is forced, will give about the same performance. Such a coil may be made rather strong mechanically, but the high length to diameter ratio of the tubing means a high flow resistance, even when the coil is divided into sections connected in parallel for the water cooling. Thus only a moderate water velocity will be possible at a pressure that will not burst the copper tubing. This type of coil is frequently used for exciting iron-yoke electromagnets.

A special case is the Bitter-type coil described in Ch. 3, § 1.2. The passages for the cooling water are axial, thus they are short and moreover they do not decrease the mechanical strength of the structure. The distribution of the passages should be made in accordance with the local heat production and preferably in a hexagonal pattern. The performance of these coils is described by BITTER [1939] and BRECHNA and MONTGOMERY [1962]. Heat transfer coefficients of more than $10^7$ W m$^{-2}$ have been obtained at a specific load between $10^9$ and $10^{10}$ W m$^{-3}$ of the coil. This already very high thermal flux at the solid-liquid interface might be improved still more by letting the water boil locally at the interface. However, this state of nucleate boiling is essentially unstable, since a local and temporary increase of the heat flux may cause a transition from the state of nucleate boiling in which a large amount of small vapour bubbles is formed at the interface, to the state of film boiling in which the interface is covered by a continuous vapour film, accompanied by a sharp increase of the thermal resistance. Thus the film will quickly increase its area and owing to its thermal insulating properties, lead to a burn-out of the coil. The phenomenon of nucleate boiling and the obtainable heat fluxes are treated by ROHSENOW [1954]. Water flows of 10–15 m s$^{-1}$ are used in the above mentioned coils. To obtain these velocities is technically not simple. The power required for pumping the coolant may be quite comparable to the power consumed to sustain the field-generating current through the coil. For megawatt-consuming solenoids it will be useful to take the pumping power into account when optimizing the system for maximum efficiency.

For instance, a coil with wide passage for coolant circulation, will require little pumping power, but the low copper-filled volume-fraction decreases the field-generating efficiency with respect to the electrical power. On the other hand, a dense coil may show a high field-generating efficiency, but requires a great deal of pumping power to force sufficient coolant through the narrow cooling holes. The optimization of fluid-cooled coils has been treated by KRONAUER

[1962] who came to the conclusion that for a magnet with uniform current density, minimization of the total power (i.e. the sum of electrical and pumping power) leads to the condition that the pumping power should be one quarter of the total power.

A practical solution for the provision of such huge pumping power has been found by BERGLES [1963] who used compressed air to force a stock of about 1200 l of distilled water through a coil at a rate of about $250 \, l \, s^{-1}$. During the few seconds of cooling, the coil, placed inside a larger continuously cooled coil, was excited to generate more than $3 \times 10^7 \, A \, m^{-1}$. A survey of the cooling methods discussed in this section is given in Table 3.3. It should be noted

TABLE 3.3

Performance of cooling methods

| Method | $W_s$ $10^4 W \, m^{-2}$ | $W_v$ $10^6 W \, m^{-3}$ | $\tau$ $10^4 A \, m^{-2}$ | $\Delta T$ $°C$ | $H$ $A \, m^{-1}$ |
|---|---|---|---|---|---|
| Natural convection and conduction | – | 0.2 | 300 | 50 | $10^4$ |
| Orthocyclic coils with cooling plates | 5 | 0.6 | 500 | 60 | $10^5$ |
| Tape coils with cooling plates | 20 | 2 | 1000 | 60 | $10^6$ |
| Water flow between windings or through hollow conductors | 10 | 30 | 5000 | 10 | $10^6$ |
| Axial flow through Bitter-type coils | 900 | $10^4$ | – | 70 | $10^7$ |

$W_s$ = heat flux through interface,

$W_v$ = specific load per unit volume of coil,

$\tau$ = density of current in copper,

$\Delta T$ = temperature difference between copper and coolant,

$H$ = order of magnitude of fieldstrength.

that the data given in this table are quoted from existing designs that usually do not satisfy optimal conditions, especially in the low-power cases. They are only mentioned to give the order of magnitude of the various quantities. Any new design may deviate somewhat from these data.

§ 4. PULSED FIELDS

§ 4.1. *Coils for pulsed fields*

In the previous section we have seen that one of the limiting factors for obtaining strong magnetic fields is the increasing difficulty of draining the Joule heat from the coil. In this section we shall treat coils whose Joule heat is not removed but stored in their own heat capacity. The field of such magnets cannot be maintained for long periods, since the temperature of the coil will increase steadily. Therefore the current must be switched on for only a short time and the field will thus occur as a short pulse. The total amount of dissipated energy has to be kept below the maximum amount that the coil can contain without damage:

$$\int_{t_0}^{t_1} \eta(T)\,\tau^2\,\mathrm{d}t < \int_{T_0}^{T_1} C(T)\,\mathrm{d}T, \qquad (3.100)$$

where $\eta(T)$ = resistivity of the coil at temperature $T$,

$\tau$ = current density in the coil,

$C(T)$ = specific heat per unit volume of the coil at temperature $T$.

The pulse starts at time $t_0$ and ends at time $t_1$. The temperature rises from $T_0$ to $T_1$ during the pulse, where $T_1$ is the maximum permissible temperature, for instance the melting point of the coil material. Equation (3.100) may be applied to coils with uniform current density (for instance, wire-wound coils). In other coils eq. (3.100) has to be applied locally and the exchange of heat between parts of the coil has to be taken into account. We see from eq.

(3.100) that for pulses sufficiently short, arbitrarily high currents and correspondingly str ong fields are possible. Of course, the field-strength will still be limi ted by the maximum stress permitted by the yield point of the coil material. However, here lies another ad-vantage. If the pulse is of the order of one microsecond, the coil material, although stressed beyond its yield point, will not have time enough to be strained appreciably. Then the limiting stress will be the ultimate tensile strength, at which a brittle rupture will occur. The latter stress is sometimes appreciably higher than the former as will be observed from Table 3.1.

Another conclusion to be made from eq. (3.100) is that a low starting temperature allows more heat to be stored in the coil. An additional advantage is the decrease in resistivity of pure metals at low temperatures, the power required to sustain a given current being proportionally small. We return to these cryogenic coils in Ch. 3, § 5.

Since both heat capacity and electrical resistivity are temperature-dependent, it is n ot easy to make predictions about the suitability of a material for the construction of a pulsed coil. Therefore F. C. Ford has ap plied the following testmethod quoted by FURTH [1962]. He placed in a coil a long cylindrical bar of the material to be tested and applied a pulse of peak value $H$ and a duration so short that the field at the centre of the bar remained zero, owing to eddy currents at the bar's surface, the field being along the axis of the bar.

By increasing the value of $H$ he found a maximum fieldstrength beyond which the bar's surface was damaged either by melting or fracture. He thus compared several materials in terms of permissible fieldstrength. A short analysis of the method will be given here.

The eddy currents are considered as being confined within a "skin" of a thickness small compared to the radius of the bar. The "skin"-thickness is calculated in Part 2, Ch. 2, § 4.1 to be approxi-mately

$$\delta\rho \approx 500 \left( \frac{\eta}{f \mu_r} \right)^{\frac{1}{2}}, \tag{3.101}$$

where $\eta$ = electrical resistivity,

$\mu_r$ = relative magnetic permeability (vacuum = 1),

$f$ = frequency of Fourier-component of field pulse.

The "skin"-thickness is well-defined if a sinusoidally alternating field of a fixed frequency is applied. In copper it is about 70 $\mu$m for $f = 10^6$ Hz at room temperature. For a pulse the "skin"-thickness is a somewhat vague concept, but if no Fourier-components of low frequency occur we may say that the eddy currents are flowing only near the surface of the bar. So we have the situation of a current sheet flowing in the material to be tested and generating a field of strength $-H$, thus cancelling the external field $H$ at the interior of the bar. The heat developed by the current pulse will cause the temperature to rise locally and by increasing the value of $H$ the bar will melt at the surface, where the current density is highest.

If the pulse duration is multiplied by a factor $a$ without changing the pulse height and relative pulse shape, the Fourier-components all shift in frequency by a factor $1/a$ and the "skin"-thickness by a factor $a^{\frac{1}{2}}$. The total current in the "skin" remains the same while generating the same field, so the current density is multiplied by $a^{-\frac{1}{2}}$. The local Joule heat per unit time is then multiplied by $1/a$ and, since the pulse duration was multiplied by $a$, the time integral of the heat developed locally is independent of pulse duration. If pulse duration is still so short that heat transfer in the bar may be neglected (this condition is certainly satisfied by the requirement that the "skin"-thickness should be small compared to the bar radius), the temperature rise is also independent of pulse duration. A similar reasoning reveals that the temperature rise is also independent of electrical resistivity and magnetic permeability.

The mechanical stress caused by the external field acting on the current-carrying "skin" will remain the same by eq. (3.75), but the stress intensity will be multiplied by $a^{-\frac{1}{2}}$, the "skin"-thickness itself being proportional to $a^{\frac{1}{2}}$. While considering the field- and current-directions it should be noted that this stress is compressive, and tends to elongate the bar along its axis. This is exactly what we see when applying this test until failure of the bar occurs. Illustrations may be found in Furth's article. The bar radius also has an influence on the result of this test, as may be seen from eq. (3.75). If the length of the exciting coil is not great compared to the radius of the bar, the thermal limit found by this test will be radius-dependent as well.

To recapitulate we may say that Ford's test is applicable for the comparison of materials if it is properly standardized as regards pulse shape, pulse duration and bar radius. The result of such a test is given by FURTH [1962] and shows a series of rods of about 1.9 cm diameter tested in a 20 $\mu$s pulse of $5 \times 10^7$ A m$^{-1}$. It appears that aluminum, copper and brass showed superficial melting and plastic flow (the aluminum rod even to fracture), whereas hard steel showed no damage at all. A tungsten rod, which is considered to be highly resistent to this test, showed brittle fracture, presumably due to mechanical faults in the bar. These results are in good agreement with estimations made by FURTH, LEVINE and WANIEK [1957] from mechanical and thermal properties.

If the uniformity of the current density is not ensured by the coil construction (as it is for the wire-wound coil) we have to deal with the phenomenon of the skin effect. We saw already when discussing Ford's test that for short pulses of the order of microseconds the magnetic field is prevented from penetrating into the conducting material of the coil. For instance, a Bitter-type coil (see Ch. 3, § 1.2) of infinite conductivity can only have a current flowing along its inner circumference. If the conductivity is not infinite, the field will diffuse into the conductor in correspondence with eq. (3.101).

The "skin"-thickness will be greater the longer the pulse duration and the higher the resistivity. For direct current and finite resistivity the current distribution will finally be that as given by eq. (3.12).

If the skin effect is dominant the current is confined to a thin sheet at the inner boundary of the coil. The Biot-Savart forces consequently then act at the inner boundary of the coil so that now we have the situation of a thick-walled tube with a (magnetic) pressure $P_m$ inside. The stress distribution in a long coil is then found by putting $p_\rho$ equal to zero in eq. (3.67) and solving for $s_{\rho\rho}$ using the boundary conditions $s_{\rho\rho} = -P_m$ for $\rho = \rho_1$ and $s_{\rho\rho} = 0$ for $\rho = \rho_2$:

$$s_{\rho\rho} = P_m \frac{\rho_1^2}{\rho_2^2 - \rho_1^2} \left( 1 - \frac{\rho_2^2}{\rho^2} \right). \tag{3.102}$$

Using eq. (3.66) we find for the tangential stress intensity

$$s_{tt} = P_m \frac{\rho_1^2}{\rho_2^2 - \rho_1^2} \left( 1 + \frac{\rho_2^2}{\rho^2} \right). \tag{3.103}$$

The diffusion of the field into the conductor changes the inductance of the coil. This will occur during a pulse, owing to the temperature rise and the consequent increase of resistivity. So when investigating the efficiency of the coil we have to take this into account.

In general when operating a pulse-field system, we have a tank containing a certain amount of stored energy (see Ch. 3, § 4.2) which is fed into the coil in a short time and thereby converted into magnetic energy. In some designs this is reabsorbed from the coil into the tank at the end of the pulse. During this process a part of the energy is lost as Joule heat owing to the finite resistance $R$ of the circuit. Thus the peak value of the magnetic energy will be somewhat lower than the energy we initially had at our disposal in the tank. To analyze this we divide the initial amount of tank energy $E_t$ into two parts

$$E_t = \int_{t_0}^{t_m} R i^2 \, dt + \int_{t_0}^{t_m} \frac{d\Phi}{dt} i \, dt, \tag{3.104}$$

where $R$ is the resistance in the circuit, $i$ the current at time $t$ through the circuit and $\Phi$ the flux enclosed by the coil. The integration is performed from $t = t_0$, when the pulse is started, to $t = t_m$, when the current $i$ reaches its maximum value $i_m$. At the latter time the potential energy in the tank is partly converted into magnetic energy, the rest being lost as Joule heat.

The magnetic flux in the coil may be rewritten as

$$\Phi = Li, \tag{3.105}$$

where $L$ is the inductance of the coil. Eq. (3.104) then becomes

$$E_t = \int_{t_0}^{t_m} Ri^2 \, dt + \int_0^{i_m} Li \, di + \int_{t_0}^{t_m} \frac{dL}{dt} i^2 \, dt. \tag{3.106}$$

The third term of the right-hand side is zero, if the coil is rigid and the relative current-distribution is time-independent.

The second term is then equal to $\frac{1}{2}Li_m^2$ and the efficiency $\kappa$ of the energy conversion is

$$\kappa = \frac{\frac{1}{2}Li_m^2}{\frac{1}{2}Li_m^2 + \int_{t_0}^{t_m} Ri^2 \, dt}. \tag{3.107}$$

If, however, the skin effect is dominant and the heating of the coil considerable, part of the energy is consumed by the field diffusion into the conductor already mentioned, where it is converted into heat. If, moreover, the coil is not rigid another part of the energy is spent in accelerating the conductors mechanically, thus being converted into kinetic energy. In both cases the inductance of the coil will be increased, the current being forced to follow a circular path of increasing radius. Thus $dL/dt$ is positive and the efficiency $\kappa$ of the energy conversion can be written as

$$\kappa = \frac{\frac{1}{2}Li_m^2}{\frac{1}{2}Li_m^2 + \int_{t_0}^{t_m} (R + dL/dt) \, i^2 \, dt}. \tag{3.108}$$

The efficiency depends on $R$, $L$ and the time $t_m$ required to reach the current maximum, this time also depending on $R$ and $L$. This will be treated further in Ch. 3, § 4.2 for a rigid coil without skin effect.

Next we shall investigate the relation between the energy contained by the coil and the fieldstrength at its centre. The energy content $E_m$ is

$$E_m = \frac{1}{2}Li^2 = \frac{1}{2} \int HB \, dv = \frac{\mu_0}{2} \int H^2 \, dv, \tag{3.109}$$

where the integration is performed over the entire space. We see that the fieldstrength $H_0$ at the centre of the coil is proportional to the square root of the magnetic energy per unit volume

$$H_0 = S \left( \frac{1}{2\mu_0} Li^2/U \right)^{\frac{1}{2}}, \qquad (3.110)$$

where $U$ is the internal volume of the coil (for instance) and $S$ is a factor depending on the geometrical dimensional ratios and the current distribution of the coil. This was calculated by CHAMPION [1950] from whose calculations the graphs given in Fig. 3.12 are quoted. The long narrow coil is most favourable in this respect.

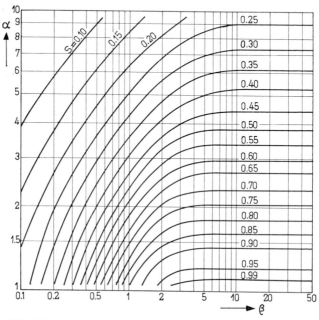

Fig. 3.12. The quantity $S$ of eq. (3.110) plotted as a function of the reduced external diameter $\alpha$ and the reduced length $\beta$, both with the internal diameter of the coil as a unit. (After CHAMPION [1950].)

The last term of eq. (3.106) presents another interesting aspect. Normally $dL/dt$ is positive as we have seen. If, however, a current is flowing and, after short-circuiting, the coil is compressed by an externally applied force the flux will be compressed resulting in an increase of the fieldstrength. This is easily seen by writing eq. (3.106) without integral signs:

$$Ei = Ri^2 + Li\frac{di}{dt} + \frac{dL}{dt}i^2, \tag{3.111}$$

which equation is valid at any time $t$.

Short-circuiting of the coil makes $E$ equal to zero, so that (neglecting the term with $R$)

$$L\frac{di}{dt} = -\frac{dL}{dt}i. \tag{3.112}$$

Compression of the coil gives $dL/dt$ a negative value so that $di/dt$ is positive which means an increase of the fieldstrength. FOWLER et al. [1960] have done this by initially generating a field of several times $10^6$ A m$^{-1}$ in a conducting cylinder and then compressing it by an explosive charge, thus obtaining a fieldstrength of more than $10^9$ A m$^{-1}$.

This behaviour follows also directly from eq. (3.104) where for $E=0$ and neglecting $R$ it follows that the flux $\Phi$ enclosed by the conducting cylinder is time-independent. Reduction of the enclosed area therefore results in an increase of fieldstrength.

The energy supplied by this process is found by writing the magnetic energy as

$$E_m = \Phi^2/2L \tag{3.113}$$

by using eq. (3.105).

The increase of energy per unit time then is

$$\frac{dE}{dt} = -\frac{\Phi^2}{2L^2}\frac{dL}{dt}, \tag{3.114}$$

which is positive for $dL/dt$ negative.

The pressure required for compressing the flux is at least equal to the magnetic pressure mentioned in Ch. 3, § 2.3. The $10^9$ A m$^{-1}$ field of FOWLER *et al.* [1960] thus requires a compressive pressure of $6 \times 10^6$ atm, a pressure that only can be obtained by explosives during a very short time of the order of one microsecond.

The miniature coils made by DEBLOIS [1961] deserve special attention owing to the simplicity and relative cheapness of the design. He generated fields of about $10^7$ A m$^{-1}$ during microseconds in coils of about one mm diameter and three mm length. The required energy of only a few Joules was supplied by a small capacitor storage-unit and switched by a thyratron. The advantage lies in the small diameter of the coil that reduces both the mechanical stresses (eq. (3.75)) and the required energy (eq. (3.109)). Thus space-consuming support of the coil is unnecessary and the development of heat is small, which makes the coils suitable for incorporation inside a helium-dewar or a pressure cell (DEBLOIS [1962]).

## § 4.2. *Energy storage and efficiency of energy conversion*

The energy to be converted into magnetic energy can be stored by several methods. KAPITZA [1924], who was the first to use pulsed fields, started his experiments by using a lead storage battery of special design, thus storing his energy chemically. The battery was made to release a great part of its energy content within a few milliseconds. By this Kapitza obtained a fieldstrength of $4 \times 10^7$ A m$^{-1}$ in a coil of one millimeter inside diameter. A special difficulty inherent in this dc-method is the problem of breaking the current at the end of the experiment. A common switch would fail owing to arcing. Kapitza solved this by leading the current through a length of copper wire of such diameter that it acted as a fuse with proper time constant. In later experiments KAPITZA [1927] used a fly-wheel coupled to a single-phase ac-generator, thus storing his energy kinetically. The coil was connected to the generator during half a cycle of the current, the circuit being made when the generator-emf was just zero. The current then rises to a maximum value and drops again to zero, at which moment the break was made. During this cycle kinetic energy is converted into magnetic energy and vice versa, apart from the energy lost as Joule heat. The maximum fieldstrength thus obtained was $2.6 \times 10^7$ A m$^{-1}$ in a coil with 1 cm inner diameter. Large amounts of energy can be stored in this way. BLAMEY and SMITH [1962] used a homopolar generator to store $5 \times 10^8$ J that could be released in two seconds.

A third method of storage is the inductive one. Let two coils be wound coaxially so that they are closely coupled by their mutual inductance. One of the coils, called the primary, is fed by a direct current, and the second coil, called the secondary, is connected to the load (Fig. 3.13). Now if the switch is opened the primary current

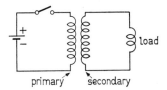

Fig. 3.13. Principle of energy storage and transfer using a mutual inductance.

is broken and a voltage is induced in the secondary coil thus giving rise to a current that distributes the magnetic energy, initially present in the primary coil, over the secondary coil and the load. By utilizing special networks the entire energy can be transferred into the load. Details are given by CARRUTHERS [1962] in his survey of methods for the storage of energy. A $2 \times 10^8$ J inductor appears to be possible but has a diameter of about 10 m and contains more than 100 tons of copper.

The fourth method is widely used and will be treated here in more detail. By this method the energy is stored as electrostatic energy in a capacitor. Such capacitors are the cheapest means of storage if the energy has to be released within a few milliseconds (CARRUTHERS [1962]). The principle of the circuit used is given in Fig. 3.14. The capacitor $C$ is charged to a voltage $V$, its energy content then being

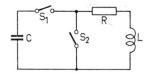

Fig. 3.14. Generation of a pulsed field by discharging a capacitor through a solenoid. The switch $S_2$ is closed a quarter-period after closing the switch $S_1$ to conserve the energy in the coil.

$\frac{1}{2}CV^2$. When the switch $S_1$ is closed ($S_2$ is open), a current $i$ flows through the coil according to the differential equation

$$L\frac{d^2i}{dt^2} + R\frac{di}{dt} + \frac{i}{C} = 0,\qquad (3.115)$$

where $R$ is the total resistance of the circuit. The capacitor $C$ is supposed to be free of inductance. This can be obtained to a high approximation by special design. The capacitor should also be capable of carrying a high current. The inductance $L$ of the coil is supposed to be independent of time. This is the case if the coil is rigid and the relative current distribution is constant.

With the boundary conditions of $i$ being zero and $C$ being charged to a voltage $V$ when $t=0$ (the instant that the pulse starts), the solution of $i$ is

$$i = \frac{V}{L}\,e^{-tR/2L}\,\frac{\sin \omega t}{\omega},\qquad (3.116)$$

where

$$\omega = \sqrt{\frac{1}{LC} - \frac{R^2}{4L^2}}.\qquad (3.117)$$

Eq. (3.117) can be rewritten as

$$\omega = (LC)^{-\frac{1}{2}}(1-d)^{\frac{1}{2}},\qquad (3.118)$$

where $d = R^2C/4L$, the damping constant.

If $d<1$, $\omega$ is real and the current $i$ oscillates as a function of time. If $d>1$, $\omega$ is imaginary and the current rises to a maximum and decreases to zero again without becoming negative (Fig. 3.15).

In the latter case it is convenient to substitute $\omega$ by $k\sqrt{-1}$.

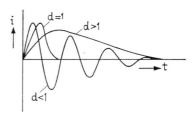

Fig. 3.15. Comparison of an underdamped $(d < 1)$, a critically damped $(d = 1)$ and an over-damped $(d > 1)$ discharge.

Eq. (3.116) then becomes

$$i = \frac{V}{L} e^{-tR/2L} \frac{\sinh kt}{k}, \tag{3.119}$$

where

$$k = (LC)^{-\frac{1}{2}} (d - 1)^{\frac{1}{2}}. \tag{3.120}$$

The maximum fieldstrength occurs at $t = t_m$, when $i$ reaches its first maximum. It is easy to derive that for $d < 1$

$$t_m = \frac{1}{\omega} \arctan \frac{2\omega L}{R}, \tag{3.121}$$

and

$$i_m = \frac{V}{L} D(d) \frac{\sin \omega t_m}{\omega}, \tag{3.122}$$

where

$$D(d) = \exp \left\{ -\left( \frac{d}{1 - d} \right)^{\frac{1}{2}} \arccos d^{\frac{1}{2}} \right\}. \tag{3.123}$$

In the overdamped case where $d > 1$ these equations become

$$t_m = \frac{1}{k} \operatorname{arctanh} \frac{2kL}{R} \tag{3.124}$$

and

$$i_m = \frac{V}{L} D(d) \frac{\sinh kt_m}{k}, \tag{3.125}$$

where

$$D(d) = \exp \left\{ -\left( \frac{d}{d - 1} \right)^{\frac{1}{2}} \operatorname{arccosh} d^{\frac{1}{2}} \right\}. \tag{3.126}$$

The factor $D(d)$ is plotted in Fig. 3.16 for $d$ ranging from $10^{-3}$ to $10^2$. If $d=1$, the circuit is said to be critically damped. Then $\omega=0$ and $t_m=2L/R$. The maximum current then becomes

$$i_m = \frac{2V}{R}\frac{1}{e} = 0.736\frac{V}{R}. \tag{3.127}$$

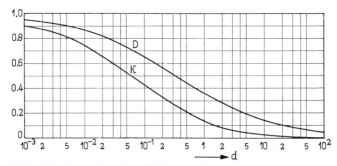

Fig. 3.16.   The factor $D$ and the efficiency $\kappa$ of energy conversion, as a function of the damping constant $d$.

To investigate the efficiency of the energy conversion we rewrite eq. (3.121) using eq. (3.117):

$$\tan \omega t_m = \left(\frac{1-d}{d}\right)^{\frac{1}{2}}. \tag{3.128}$$

Then

$$\sin \omega t_m = (1-d)^{\frac{1}{2}}. \tag{3.129}$$

Substitution into eq. (3.122) then gives

$$i_m = \left(\frac{V^2C}{L}\right)^{\frac{1}{2}} D(d). \tag{3.130}$$

The magnetic energy at the current maximum is

$$\tfrac{1}{2}Li_m^2 = \tfrac{1}{2}CV^2\{D(d)\}^2, \tag{3.131}$$

where $\frac{1}{2}CV^2$ is the energy initially contained by the capacitor. The efficiency of the energy conversion

$$\kappa = \{D(d)\}^2 \tag{3.132}$$

is also plotted in Fig. 3.16.

We see that the efficiency is high if the damping constant $d$ is small. We shall consider this case for a rigid coil with uniform current density and rectangular cross section. If the damping of the circuit is small $(d \ll 1)$ the damping factor can be approximated to by

$$d = \frac{R^2 C}{4L} \approx \left(\frac{R}{2L}\frac{1}{\omega}\right)^2. \tag{3.133}$$

The time for maximum current $t_m$ is then

$$t_m \approx \frac{\pi}{2\omega} \approx \frac{\pi}{2}\sqrt{LC}. \tag{3.134}$$

We suppose that the resistance $R$ of the circuit is entirely due to the coil. It follows by eq. (3.21) that

$$R = \frac{\pi \eta N^2 (\alpha + 1)}{\lambda \rho_1 \beta (\alpha - 1)},$$

where $N$ is the number of turns, $\eta$ the resistivity, $\lambda$ the filling factor, $\rho_1$ the inner radius, $\alpha$ the ratio of outer and inner diameter and $\beta$ the length-to-inner-diameter ratio of the coil.

The inductance $L$ is also supposed to be entirely due to the coil. It is given by

$$L = N^2 \rho_1 \Lambda \times 10^{-9}, \tag{3.135}$$

where $\Lambda$ is a factor dependent on $\alpha$ and $\beta$ exclusively. It is plotted in Fig. 3.17, quoted from CHAMPION [1950]. With $R$ and $L$ substituted into eq. (3.133) we find

$$d = \frac{\eta^2}{\lambda^2 \rho_1^4 \omega^2} f(\alpha, \beta), \tag{3.136}$$

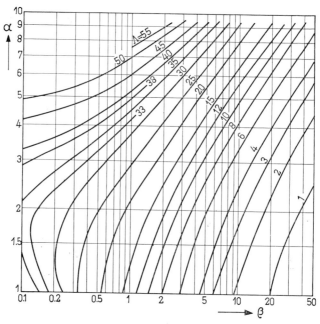

Fig. 3.17. Form factor $\Lambda$ for the calculation of the self-inductance of cylindrical coils as a function of their reduced external diameter $\alpha$ and length $\beta$, both with the internal diameter as a unit. (After CHAMPION [1950].)

where $f(\alpha, \beta)$ is a function dependent on $\alpha$ and $\beta$ exclusively and which for short thick solenoids is of the order of $10^{12}$. Considering that $\lambda$ is of the order of one, $\eta^2$ is of the order of $10^{15}$ for normal conductors at room temperature and that $\rho_1^4$ is of the order of $10^{-7}$ for most applications we may distinguish between two cases:

*a) Pulses of short duration*

When $t_m$ is shorter than one millisecond $(\omega > 10^3)$, $d$ is smaller than $10^{-2}$ and we see from Fig. 3.16 that the efficiency $\kappa$ approaches unity. So there is little to be gained from the use of high-conductivity materials or cooling to low temperatures. Instead of this we can use high-strength materials (see Table 3.1) and allow a low $\lambda$ in favor of reinforcing structures. A high value of $\omega$ is obtained by using low $C$ and $L$. A high voltage $V$ is then required to store sufficient energy.

*b) Pulses of long duration*

When $t_m$ is longer than 10 ms $(\omega < 10^2)$, $d$ is greater than one and the efficiency $\kappa$ is low. Thus there is much to be gained from the use of pure metals, that are cooled down to low temperatures in order to reduce their resistivity. Also a high filling factor $\lambda$ is important. The factor $f(\alpha, \beta)$ becomes smaller for increasing $\alpha$ and $\beta$. Although this may reduce the factor $S$ of eq. (3.110) an optimum may be found. We return to this point when treating cryogenic coils (Ch. 3, § 5.1).

At the end of the first half cycle of the oscillatory discharge the current through the coil is zero again and the capacitor contains its initial energy, apart from Joule loss. However, we may use this energy to lengthen the pulse duration by closing the switch $S_2$ (Fig. 3.14) at time $t = t_m$ when the current is a maximum. The current $i$ then decays according to

$$L\frac{di}{dt} + Ri = 0, \tag{3.137}$$

or

$$i = i_m \exp\left\{-\frac{R}{L}(t - t_m)\right\}. \tag{3.138}$$

The switches $S_1$ and $S_2$ may be mechanical or ignitrons, $S_2$ being triggered by a suitable time-delay circuit. It is also possible to replace $S_2$ by a rectifying cell (Fig. 3.18), that prevents the capacitor from being charged the opposite way. These means not only lengthen the pulse but also prevent the current from reversing. The current

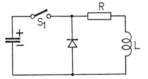

Fig. 3.18. Application of a rectifier cell to prevent the discharge from being oscillatory.

reversal can also be prevented by using a wire fuse similar to Kapitza's that blows immediately after $t = t_m$. The energy content of the coil is then to a large extent converted into shockwave energy radiating from the exploding wire. The energy content of these installations is mostly of the order of $10^4$ J so some safety precautions are to be recommended!

When the capacitor is charged to several kilovolts we may use a triggered spark gap for $S_1$. The spark gap consists of two electrodes in air a few millimetres apart. An initiating discharge of, say, 15 000 V is made between one of these electrodes and a third one (Fig. 3.19) by means of, for example, an ordinary automotive

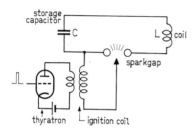

Fig. 3.19. Principle of a discharge circuit with a triggered spark-gap.

ignition coil whose primary is supplied with a pulse of 300 V (FONER and KOLM [1957]). This triggers the main discharge which is oscillatory if the damping of the circuit is sufficiently small, the ionization left by the spark of the previous half cycle initiating the spark of the next one.

Foner and Kolm obtained $6 \times 10^7$ A m$^{-1}$ ($7.5 \times 10^5$ Oe) in a copper-beryllium helix with inner diameter of 4.8 mm. Their capacitor bank contained 9000 J to be released in a pulse of 120 $\mu$s duration.

A special case of storage of chemical energy is the explosive used by FOWLER et al. [1960] to compress mechanically a conducting cylinder enclosing a magnetic flux (see Ch. 3, § 4.1). The energy content of one gram T.N.T. is about $3.5 \times 10^3$ J.

## § 4.3. *Flux concentrators*

In Ch. 3, § 4.1 we have seen, when treating Ford's test method, that a static conductor placed in a pulsed field will influence the field distribution owing to eddy currents induced by the rapidly changing magnetic field. This can be used to increase the fieldstrength in some region, thereby reducing it in other regions.

Consider a thin solenoid surrounding a slotted conducting cylinder (Fig. 3.20). When a short field pulse is applied by the

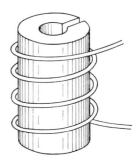

Fig. 3.20.   Principle of a flux concentrator. No appreciable increase of fieldstrength will occur in this cylindrical arrangement.

solenoid, eddy currents will be induced in the outer surface of the cylinder such that the field does not enter the conducting body.

It will be assumed that the pulse is sufficiently short to confine the eddy currents to a thin "skin" at the surface of the cylinder. The solenoid is considered as a current sheet of strength $Ni$, where $N$ is the number of turns and $i$ the current strength. The current induced in the outer surface of the cylinder will form a current sheet of about the same strength (depending on the measure of coupling between the primary solenoid and the secondary cylinder).

This current sheet will find its way along the slot to the inner cylindrical surface and back again, thus generating a field at the centre of the system. The configuration of Fig. 3.20 will obviously give no increase of the fieldstrength if the outer diameter of the system is small compared to its length. The only effect is that the field is restricted to a smaller region, the current density per unit of length of the solenoid, of the outer surface and of the inner surface being the same. The inductance of the solenoid is lowered correspondingly by the presence of the conducting body. In fact the body behaves as being diamagnetic.

The efficiency of conversion of the supplied electrical energy to the magnetic energy of the field due to the inner cylindrical surface is reduced by two kinds of losses (KIM and PLATNER [1959]):

*a) Inductive losses*

The system of solenoid and conductive cylinder may be considered as a pulse transformer (Fig. 3.21). The primary $L_1$ is the solenoid,

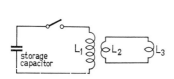

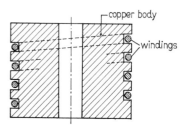

Fig. 3.21. The flux concentrator considered as a matching transformer.

Fig. 3.22. Flux concentrator with stress-reduced primary winding.

the secondary $L_2$ the outer surface of the cylinder and $L_3$ the inner surface of the cylinder. If the coupling between $L_1$ and $L_2$ is not perfect, part of the electrical energy is lost as leakage flux. The coupling therefore should be as close as possible, which may be attained by embedding the turns of the solenoid in a helical groove, machined in the outer surface of the cylinder; see Fig. 3.22 (HOW-LAND and FONER [1962]). An additional advantage of this construction is that the force between solenoid and cylinder trying to increase the area between them is directed inwards, because the secondary current flows mainly along the crests of the grooves. This makes an external support of the solenoid superfluous. The slot connecting $L_3$ to $L_2$ contains some inductance, leading also to a loss. This can

be minimized by making the gap narrow. However, if the gap is too
narrow arcing will occur.

*b) Resistive losses*

We saw already that the solenoid with conducting cylinder can be
considered as a coil with the same number of turns but on a smaller
radius. The system therefore has a smaller inductance, but the
resistance remains that of the primary coil with large radius
augmented by the resistance of the secondary circuit. So it will be
clear that the efficiency of the system under consideration is less
than that of a comparable single coil. The advantage, however, lies
in the mechanical strength of the solid body, the easy adaptability
of its impedance to that of the energy source, and in the possibility
of shaping the central field by giving the inner surface a suitable
profile, as we shall see.

We now replace the cylinder of Fig. 3.20 by a body with the same
outer surface, but having an inner cylindrical surface of a much
smaller length. The endfaces are conically recessed (Fig. 3.23).

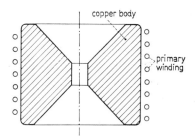

Fig. 3.23.   Flux concentrator with
conical end faces to increase the
fieldstrength at the centre.

Considering the geometry of the body we see that a great part of
the secondary current will be concentrated on the inner cylindrical
surface, thus following the shortest path. We now have an increase
of the fieldstrength, the current density being much greater at the
inner surface. If the length-to-diameter ratio of the solenoid and of
the inner cylindrical surface are the same, and further conditions
are ideal, then the increase of fieldstrength owing to the presence of

the conducting body is the ratio of the radius of the solenoid (= outer cylindrical radius) to the radius of the inner cylindrical surface. This follows easily by integration of the first of eqs. (3.2) for a thin coil. If conditions are not ideal, e.g. the secondary current is not entirely concentrated on the inner cylindrical surface, but flows partly on the conical surfaces, the gain in fieldstrength is smaller. The quantitative treatment of the problem involves highly complicated boundary conditions and needs numerical methods that go beyond the scope of this book. The concentration of the current to the inner surface can be improved by making corrugations on the slotsurfaces along the required current path. This makes the pathlength, and thus the resistance, less favourable for currents flowing perpendicular to the desired direction (HOWLAND and FONER [1962]).

The difference in efficiency between a coil with a flux concentrator and a comparable single coil may be illustrated by the following examples:

HOWLAND and FONER [1962] obtained a fieldstrength of $2.2 \times 10^7$ A m$^{-1}$ in a flux concentrator with inner diameter of 1.3 cm. When using an insert, reducing the inner diameter to 0.5 cm, they obtained $3.6 \times 10^7$ A m$^{-1}$. Using the same energy source FONER and KOLM [1957] obtained $2.9 \times 10^7$ A m$^{-1}$, in a single coil with inner diameter of 1.6 cm, which compares favourably with the results obtained by using a flux concentrator.

The fact that the fields obtained by Howland and Foner do not obey the inverse proportionality relation with the inner diameter may be partly due to the slight change in inductance of the coil due to the insert, but rather indicates that the secondary current is not entirely constricted within the inner cylindrical surface but partly flows along the conical surfaces.

A principal condition for the proper functioning of flux concentrators is a pulse duration so short that the "skin-effect" is dominant in the conducting body. This restricts the application of the method to pulses of less than 100 $\mu$s duration, when using normal conductors at room temperature (see eq. (3.101)). By using pure metals at low temperatures (see Ch. 3, § 5.1), pulses up to one millisecond duration may be obtained. By using superconductors even a static flux concentration might be possible. However, other phenomena limit this possibility, as we shall see in Ch. 3, § 5.3.

## § 5. CRYOGENIC COILS

### § 5.1. *Continuously-cooled cryogenic coils*

In general, pure metals have a positive temperature coefficient of resistivity, which means that the resistance of a coil can be reduced by cooling it to a low temperature. The Joule heat developed by a current is then proportionally lower. For continuously operated coils the gain is evident from eq. (3.26) where the power to maintain a field is proportional to the resistivity of the coil conductors. The resistivity of a metal is made up of two parts if no magnetic field is present:

$$\eta(T) = \eta_G(T) + \eta_0, \tag{3.139}$$

where $\eta(T)$ is the resistivity of the metal as a function of temperature $T$, $\eta_G(T)$ is the part of the resistivity due to thermal lattice vibrations and $\eta_0$ is the resistivity due to chemical and physical impurities. The latter part is called residual resistivity and is independent of temperature. The part $\eta_G(T)$ was analyzed theoretically by GRÜNEISEN [1933] who introduced a reduced resistivity $r(T) = \eta(T)/\eta(\theta)$ and a reduced temperature $\vartheta = T/\theta$ where $\theta$ is the Debye temperature. The resulting curve is generally applicable to pure metals and is in excellent agreement with experiment. It is given in Fig. 3.24 together with two curves of $r(\vartheta)$ for residual resistivities $r_0 = 10^{-2}$ and $r_0 = 10^{-3}$, respectively.

The residual resistivity depends on the purity of the metal. Copper, for instance, can be purified on a technical scale to a residual resistivity of about $10^{-2}$ times the resistivity at the Debye temperature (330 °K).

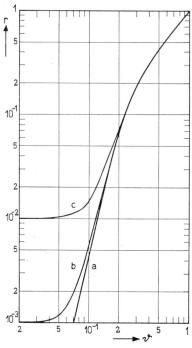

Fig. 3.24. Reduced resistivity $r$ as a function of reduced temperature $\vartheta$. The Debye temperature is the unit of the temperature-axis and the resistivity at this temperature is the unit of the resistivity-axis. Curve a applies to pure metals (GRÜNEISEN [1933]), curves b and c apply to metals with a residual resistivity of $10^{-3}$ and $10^{-2}$ times the resistivity at the Debye temperature, respectively.

The impurities still present may be made less effective by heat treatment in a slightly oxidizing atmosphere. By this the solute atoms are oxidized internally and precipitated, the precipitates being less active in scattering the electrons. From this it will be clear that the use of OFHC-copper is not to be recommended. The process of internal oxidation is described by MEIJERING [1952/53]. Aluminum is in a more favourable position, since the solubility of most impurities is very low, so that a simple heat treatment at about 300 °C suffices to precipitate them. This heat treatment should be carried out after winding the coil, thus also removing the physical impurities, such as stresses and dislocations introduced by the winding procedure. A residual resistivity of $10^{-3}$ times the resistivity at the Debye temperature (395 °K) is readily obtained.

The resistivity of a metal is increased by the presence of a magnetic field. The Lorentz-force on the electrons tends to curve the path along which they are travelling, thus increasing the number of collisions with scattering centres. This curving will be more pronounced, the longer the mean free path of the electrons, i.e. the lower the concentration of scattering centres. Hence the relative increase of resistivity $\Delta\eta/\eta$ will be higher, the lower the resistivity for a given fieldstrength. It appears that for a given metal $\Delta\eta/\eta$ is a single-valued function of $H/\eta$. The plot of $\Delta\eta/\eta$ against $H\eta(\theta)/\eta$ is called a Kohler diagram (KOHLER [1949]). A Kohler diagram for aluminum and copper in a transverse magnetic field is given in Fig. 3.25 after experiments by LÜTHI [1960].

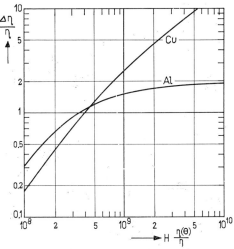

Fig. 3.25.  Kohler diagram for aluminum and copper in a transverse magnetic field. (After LÜTHI [1960].)

It is interesting to note that aluminum shows saturation of the magneto-resistance whereas the resistance of copper increases indefinitely. Sodium is also an interesting material since it shows a saturating magneto-resistance and it can be obtained in a very pure form by vacuum distillation. Besides it can be annealed at room temperature to remove strains that might increase the residual resistance. However, it is not very suitable for laboratory magnets due to its reactivity with moisture and air. Therefore it will not be considered here.

Since a conductor in a transverse magnetic field is just the

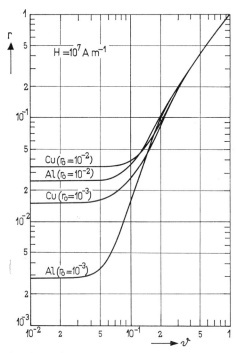

Fig. 3.26. Reduced resistivity $r$ as a function of reduced temperature $\vartheta$ (see caption of Fig. 3.24) for copper and aluminum of various purity, in a transverse field of $10^7$ A m$^{-1}$.

situation we have in a solenoid, we apply the data of Fig. 3.25 to the curves of Fig. 3.24 for a fieldstrength $H = 10^7$ A m$^{-1}$. The result is given in Fig. 3.26. It should be noted here that the magnetic field acting on the conductors of a solenoid is not homogeneous. To calculate its influence needs elaborate integration. Roughly we may say that for a short thick solenoid with uniform current density, the field in the centre is two or three times the effective field causing the increase in resistance. For Bitter-type coils the magneto-resistive effect reduces the field to current ratio and makes it also field-dependent.

The design of large cryogenic coils for nuclear fusion experiments, where large refrigeration power is required, is treated by POST and TAYLOR [1960]. They took the refrigerating power into account when optimizing their design and found an optimum operating temperature for copper at about 20 °K and for sodium at about 10 °K.

Considering the residual resistance and the magneto-resistance we see from Fig. 3.26 that cooling below 20 °K gives no further gain both for copper and aluminum. So cooling with liquid hydrogen seems practical. Cooling with liquid nitrogen makes less use of the drop in resistivity but the coolant is cheaper and easier to handle. Another coolant with attractive properties is liquid neon. It is expensive so it has to be used in a closed circuit with a liquid-hydrogen heat exchanger (LAURENCE et al. [1962]). The relevant physical properties of the three coolants are listed in Table 3.4. Their performance is limited by the phenomenon of film boiling when the temperature difference between coolant and coil surface becomes too great (see also Ch. 3, § 3). However, nucleate boiling could be used to cool the coil by a stationary coolant. The heat fluxes obtainable by using hydrogen or nitrogen are given in Fig. 3.27 quoted from data measured by WEIL [1951].

LAQUER and HAMMEL [1957] have made coils cooled by freely boiling hydrogen. They obtained a fieldstrength of about $5 \times 10^6$ A m$^{-1}$, the limit being set by the heat flux where film boiling begins.

TABLE 3.4

Properties of cryogenic fluids at their boiling points and of supercritical helium
at 20 °K

| Fluid | $T$ | $\rho$ | $C_c$ | $\mu$ | $k$ | $W_v$ | $U$ |
|---|---|---|---|---|---|---|---|
| N₂ | 77 | 800 | 1.7 | 160 | 0.14 | 160 | 4.6 |
| (n) H₂ | 20 | 71 | 0.68 | 14 | 0.118 | 32 | 2.9 |
| Ne | 27 | 1200 | 2.22 | 123 | 0.13 | 104 | 6.4 |
| He | 4.2 | 128 | 0.54 | 3.0 | 0.025 | 3 | 2.4 |
| He (50 atm) | | 120 | 0.65 | 3.5 | 0.025 | | 2.4 |

$T$ = boiling point under 1 atm (°K);   $k$ = thermal conductivity
$\rho$ = density (kg m⁻³);                    (W m⁻¹ °K⁻¹);
$C_c$ = specific heat ($10^{-6}$ J m⁻³ °K⁻¹);   $W_v$ = heat of vaporization ($10^{-6}$ J m⁻³)
$\mu$ = viscosity ($10^{-6}$ N s m⁻²);        $U$ = quality number of coolant (see
                                              eq. 3.99) ($10^4$ J s$^{-0.2}$ m$^{-2.6}$ °K⁻¹).

Data are taken from SCOTT [1959], except for the viscosity of neon which value
has been quoted from HUTH [1962].

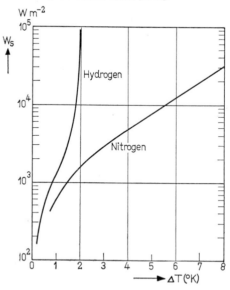

Fig. 3.27. Heat transfer
$W_s$ per unit of metal
surface immersed in a
boiling fluid, as a func-
tion of temperature dif-
ference $\Delta T$ between metal
and fluid. (After WEIL
[1951].)

### § 5.2. *Pulsed cryogenic coils*

The cooling of a coil to a low temperature before applying a pulse has two advantages. The first is that more heat can be dissipated before the coil becomes inadmissibly hot. The second is that, owing to the reduction in resistance, the Joule heat developed by a certain current is less. So pulses of longer duration or higher intensity than with coils at room temperature may be obtained.

Let a coil of inductance $L$ and resistance $R$ be connected to an energy source of constant voltage $V$. The current $i$ is given by

$$V = iR(T) + L\frac{di}{dt}, \tag{3.140}$$

where $R(T)$ is the temperature-dependent resistance of the coil that increases during the pulse due to the Joule heat. The current $i$ is schematically given as a function of time $t$ in Fig. 3.28, together

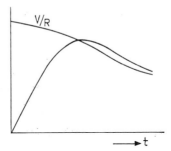

Fig. 3.28. Relation between maximum obtainable current $V/R$ and actual current $i$ as a function of time $t$ (schematic).

with the quantity $V/R(T)$. This quantity determines the value of the current maximum. It is important to keep the variation of $R$ small in order to get a high current maximum.

The temperature rise is given by

$$dT = \frac{R(T)}{C(T)} i^2 \, dt, \tag{3.141}$$

where $C(T)$ is the total heat capacity of the coil body or the specific heat per unit volume $C_v(T)$ times the volume of the coil.

Eq. (3.141) may be rewritten as

$$dT = \frac{\eta(T)}{C_v(T)} \tau^2 \, dt, \qquad (3.142)$$

where $\eta(T)$ is the resistivity of the coil material and $\tau$ the current density per unit of cross-sectional area of the turns (all quantities with allowance for the volume fraction needed for insulation, etc., which is assumed to be zero in our argument). Since $\eta$ and $C_v$ are functions of temperature and $\tau$ is a function of time we may integrate

$$\int_{T_0}^{T_e} \frac{C_v}{\eta} \, dT = \int_0^{t_e} \tau^2 \, dt, \qquad (3.143)$$

where $T_0$ is the temperature of the coil at $t=0$ and $T_e$ is the temperature at $t=t_e$.

The performance of the coil may be expressed in terms of the time integral of the magnetic energy $E_m$

$$\int_0^{t_e} E_m \, dt = \tfrac{1}{2} L \int_0^{t_e} i^2 \, dt. \qquad (3.144)$$

The latter integral is proportional to the integrals of eq. (3.143) which are limited by the temperature $T_e$, this being the highest permissible temperature. In order to obtain a high value of the integral the coil should be made from a metal with a high value of $C_v/\eta$ and operated at a low starting temperature $T_0$.

The value of $C_v$ follows from the theory of DEBYE [1912]. The heat capacity per mole $C_m$ proves to follow the same curve for most metals when plotted as a function of the reduced temperature $\vartheta = T/\theta$, where $\theta$ is a characteristic temperature called the Debye temperature. A plot of $C_m$ as a function of $\vartheta$ is given in Fig. 3.29.

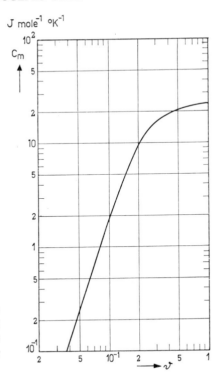

Fig. 3.29. Molar heat capacity $C_m$ as a function of reduced temperature $\vartheta$, with the Debye temperature as unit. (After DEBYE [1912].)

The specific heat per unit volume follows from

$$C_v = C_m \rho / M, \tag{3.145}$$

where $\rho$ is the density and $M$ the molar mass.

The value of the resistivity $\eta$ follows from Fig. 3.24 where $r(T) = \eta(T)/\eta(\theta)$ is plotted as a function of the reduced temperature $\vartheta$. Now the left-hand integral of eq. (3.143) may be rewritten as

$$\int_{T_0}^{T_e} \frac{C_v}{\eta} \, dT = \frac{\rho \theta}{M \eta(\theta)} \int_{\vartheta_0}^{\vartheta_e} \frac{C_m}{r} \, d\vartheta. \tag{3.146}$$

The value of the right-hand integral is given in Fig. 3.30 for $\vartheta_e = 1$

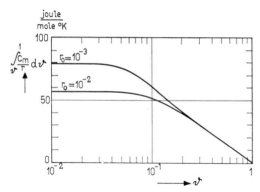

Fig. 3.30. Performance of a pulsed coil as a function of its initial temperature with the residual resistivity as a parameter.

or $T_e = \theta$. We see that cooling below $0.05\theta$ gives no further improvement. The value of $\rho\theta/M\eta(\theta)$ is tabulated in Table 3.5 for various metals. Copper is clearly the best proposition, whereas aluminum

TABLE 3.5

Physical properties of metals

| Element | $\rho$ | $\eta(\theta)$ | $M$ | $\theta$ | $\xi$ |
|---------|--------|----------------|-----|----------|-------|
| Be | 1.85 | 31 | 9.0 | 1160 | 7.7 |
| Na | 0.97 | 2.27 | 23 | 202 | 3.75 |
| Al | 2.70 | 3.82 | 27 | 395 | 10.3 |
| Co | 8.9 | 8.8 | 58.9 | 445 | 7.7 |
| Cu | 8.96 | 1.80 | 63.5 | 330 | 26 |
| Mo | 10.2 | 7.32 | 96 | 425 | 6.2 |
| Ag | 10.5 | 1.16 | 108 | 225 | 17.8 |
| Au | 19.3 | 1.32 | 197 | 175 | 13 |
| Pb | 11.34 | 6.1 | 207 | 95 | 0.86 |

$\rho$    = density in $10^3$ kg m$^{-3}$,

$\eta(\theta)$ = resistivity in $10^{-8}$ $\Omega$m at the Debye temperature,

$M$   = atomic weight,

$\theta$    = Debye temperature in °K,

$\xi$    = $\rho\theta/M\eta(\theta)$ in $10^{11}$ °K mole $\Omega^{-1}$ m$^{-4}$.

is the best one with a saturating magneto-resistance. Making allowance for the magneto-resistance by taking the values of $\eta$ from Fig. 3.26 we get the results given in Fig. 3.31 for copper and for aluminum, both for a mean fieldstrength of $10^7$ A m$^{-1}$. In both figures

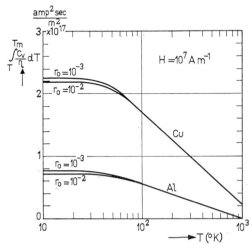

Fig. 3.31.   Performance of pulsed coils made of copper and aluminum of various purity, respectively.

the respective melting points are taken as the upper temperature boundary, although a lower temperature may already soften the metal to an inadmissible extent. An interesting fact is that high purification of copper has not much effect. For aluminum the effect is somewhat greater but also not of importance. Again we see that cooling below 20 °K gives no further improvement. Even cooling to 77 °K already gives us the greatest part of what might be obtained. Although aluminum shows lower magneto-resistance at high fields than copper, the latter is still superior for generating fields up to about several millions oersteds so far as heat-accumulating capacity is concerned (the Biot-Savart forces set a lower limit of course). The other metals mentioned in Table 3.5 are all inferior to copper.

So far we have assumed having an unlimited electrical power at our disposal. If, however, the power (i.e. the amount of energy available per unit time) is limited it is important to keep the resistivity and thus the temperature of the coil as low as possible. This will be illustrated by an example.

Consider a cylindrical coil of inner diameter $= 5$ cm, outer diameter $= 25$ cm and length $= 40$ cm. It is loaded by a uniform current density $\tau$ to generate a fieldstrength of $1.6 \times 10^7$ A m$^{-1}$ at its centre. The required current density follows from Appendix 3 and is found to be $3.4 \times 10^8$ A m$^{-2}$. Before starting the pulse the coil is cooled down to 20 °K. From Figs. 3.26 and 3.31 we derive a relation between the resistivity of the coil material and the performance integral $\int \tau^2 \, dt$ of eq. (3.143). We compare copper with a residual resistivity $r_0 = 10^{-2}$ and aluminum with a residual resistivity $r_0 = 10^{-3}$ as these two materials are readily available in the form of wire or tape. The result is plotted in Fig. 3.32 and may be applied to the coil under consideration, the effective average field causing magneto-resistance being about $10^7$ A m$^{-1}$.

For simplicity we suppose the current pulse to be rectangular,

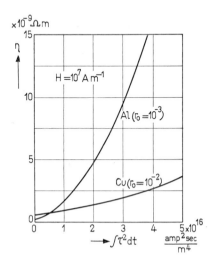

Fig. 3.32. Resistivity of aluminum and copper in a transverse field of $10^7$ A m$^{-1}$ as a function of the performance integral, the initial temperature being 20 °K.

having a value zero before $t=0$ and after $t=t_e$ and being constantly equal to $3.4 \times 10^8$ A m$^{-2}$ between $t=0$ and $t=t_e$. We now see from Fig. 3.32 that for pulses shorter than about 100 ms aluminum is to be preferred owing to its low magneto-resistance. But for longer pulses copper appears to be superior owing to its high $C_v/\eta$ ratio (see also Table 3.5).

Now we shall consider the current density $\tau$. We know from eq. (3.8) that the field produced by a coil with uniform current density is proportional to $\tau \rho_1 F_1$, where $\rho_1$ is the inner radius and $F_1$ is a function of dimensional ratios $\alpha$ and $\beta$ (see Ch. 3, § 1.1). If we now multiply all dimensions by a number $k$, $F_1$ remains constant but $\rho_1$ is multiplied by $k$. So to generate the same central field the current density should have $k^{-1}$ times its original value and the heat developed per unit volume is thus proportional to $k^{-2}$. So increase of the coil volume allows pulses of longer duration or higher intensity. The total power absorbed by the coil is proportional to $k$, the volume being proportional to $k^3$. This prevents us from increasing $k$ indefinitely.

Usually it is advantageous to precool the coil in order to obtain pulses of long duration. Such a pulse should have a flat top, which may be obtained when the variation in $V/R$ as a function of time is small (see Fig. 3.28). Further, the total decrease in $V/R$ during the time required for the current to reach its maximum should be as small as possible since it determines the value of the current maximum. So in both cases we want $\mathrm{d}(V/R)/\mathrm{d}t$ to be as small as possible during the whole pulse. The relative value of the variation is

$$\frac{R}{V} \frac{\mathrm{d}}{\mathrm{d}t} \left( \frac{V}{R} \right) = \frac{1}{R} \frac{\mathrm{d}R}{\mathrm{d}t}. \tag{3.147}$$

Using eq. (3.142) we have per unit volume of the coil

$$\frac{1}{\eta} \frac{\mathrm{d}\eta}{\mathrm{d}t} = \frac{1}{\eta} \frac{\mathrm{d}\eta}{\mathrm{d}T} \frac{\mathrm{d}T}{\mathrm{d}t} = \frac{\mathrm{d}\eta}{\mathrm{d}T} \frac{\tau^2}{C_v}. \tag{3.148}$$

Primarily we could make our design such that $\tau$ has a low value, for instance by increasing the coil volume, as we have already seen. It should be noted, however, that increase of volume of the coil tends to increase the time constant of the system. The time required by the current to reach its maximum increases correspondingly, thus reducing the advantage. The factor $C_v/(d\eta/dT)$ is determined by the choice of the metal. It should be as high as possible, and an expression for it is

$$\frac{C_v}{d\eta/dT} = \frac{\rho\theta}{M\eta(\theta)} \frac{C_m}{dr/d\vartheta}. \tag{3.149}$$

The quantity $\rho\theta/M\eta(\theta)$ is tabulated in Table 3.5 for various metals and in the absence of a magnetic field $C_m/(dr/d\vartheta)$ follows universally from Grüneisen's and Debye's functions. If, however, a field is present (as there always will be in these cases) allowance has to be made for the magneto-resistance. Then the value of $C_m/(dr/d\vartheta)$ becomes dependent on the metal and its purity. The universal curve $(H=0)$ is given in Fig. 3.33 and the curves for aluminum and copper

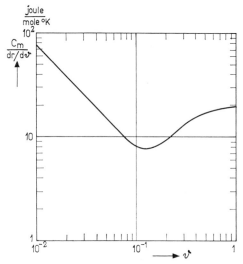

Fig. 3.33. The quantity $C_m/(dr/d\vartheta)$, determining the flatness of the pulse, as a function of reduced temperature.

in a field of $10^7$ A m$^{-1}$ are given in Fig. 3.34. The latter curves are not very accurate and are only meant to show roughly the influence of the magneto-resistance. We see that low temperatures are not favourable for obtaining flat-topped pulses. They can still be

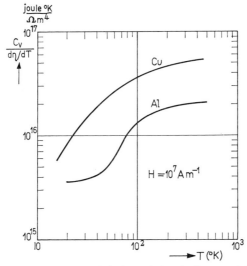

Fig. 3.34. The quantity $C_v/(d\eta/dT)$, determining the flatness of the pulse, as a function of temperature for aluminum and copper in a transverse field of $10^7$ A m$^{-1}$.

obtained by regulating $V$ so that the current is constant for some time (ROELAND and MULLER [1962]). SKELLETT [1962] obtained $8 \times 10^6$ A m$^{-1}$ during about one second in a volume of about 8 l, using liquid-nitrogen cooled copper coils. Using a copper coil in liquid nitrogen ZIJLSTRA [1962] showed that $5.5 \times 10^6$ A m$^{-1}$ in a volume of about 100 cm$^3$ during about one second can be obtained in a relatively cheap and simple way. Details on the performance of coils of various sizes are given in these two articles.

The power required to operate these precooled coils is proportional to the resistance of the coil. For this reason the temperature should be kept as low as possible with the temperature of liquid hydrogen (20.4 °K) as lower useful limit. It should be noted, however, that the refrigerating power is approximately inversely proportional to the absolute temperature. When high fields are required, the use of aluminum might still be recommendable owing to its low magneto-resistance which may compensate its inferiority to copper in other respects.

A typical value of the energy required for these long-time pulses is $10^6$ J, which is conveniently obtained from a motor generator set or from a storage battery. The larger part of this energy is lost as Joule heat.

In conclusion we may state that if the energy supply is unlimited, copper coils cooled by liquid nitrogen are most suitable for the generation of pulsed fields of long duration. If the energy supply is limited and the pulse duration not too long, copper coils cooled by liquid hydrogen might be preferable. If very strong fields of the order of several times $10^7$ A m$^{-1}$ are required the use of high purity aluminum at liquid hydrogen temperature is to be recommended.

### § 5.3. Superconducting coils

The discovery of hard superconductors, such as alloys of niobium with zirconium (MATTHIAS [1953]) and the intermetallic compound $Nb_3Sn$ (MATTHIAS et al. [1954]) opened the possibility of generating magnetic fields of considerable strength without dissipating Joule heat. The critical fieldstrength (beyond which the superconductivity is quenched) appeared to be much higher for these materials than for the soft superconductors discovered by KAMERLINGH ONNES [1911]. The critical field of soft superconductors is only of the order of $10^4$ A m$^{-1}$, but is about $5.5 \times 10^6$ A m$^{-1}$ for Nb-25%Zr alloy at 4.2 °K, and exceeds $1.5 \times 10^7$ A m$^{-1}$ for $Nb_3Sn$ at 4.2 °K (HART et al. [1962]). Critical fields of the same order of magnitude follow from experiments by WERNICK et al. [1962] on the intermetallic compound $V_3Ga$.

The critical field decreases with increasing temperature and becomes zero at the critical temperature, which is about 11 °K for the Nb-25%Zr alloy and 18 °K for Nb$_3$Sn. Besides having a high critical field, hard superconductors may be capable of carrying high currents. Unlike soft superconductors, where the current flows at the surface (due to Meissner-effect), the entire cross-sectional area

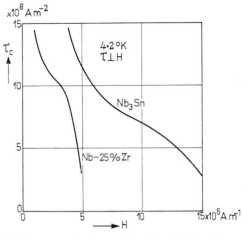

Fig. 3.35.   Critical current density as a function of external transverse field for two superconducting materials at the temperature of liquid helium.

of hard superconductors is used for carrying considerable current densities. It is believed that the current is conducted by super-conducting "filaments" dispersed throughout the wire cross-section. It is therefore possible to plot the critical current density (beyond which the superconductivity is quenched) as a function of the externally applied field strength (KUNZLER [1961]). However, some influence of the wire diameter remains. Typical curves are given in Fig. 3.35 for Nb-25%Zr alloy (quoted from BERLINCOURT [1963]) and for Nb$_3$Sn (quoted from HART et al. [1962]).

Apart from general considerations for the construction of thick solenoids as treated in Ch. 3, §§ 1 and 2 these curves may be used for finding the optimum current distribution in a superconducting solenoid. The critical current density, being field-dependent, is the upper limit for the current density. Our aim is to find the current distribution for which the coil is loaded up to this limit at any point of its body. This may be done by graphical methods, which will be illustrated by the following simple example. Consider a set of long narrow coaxial solenoids numbered sequentially from the outer to the inner one. The thickness of a single solenoid is assumed to be small compared to its diameter. The relation between critical current and transverse fieldstrength is assumed to be given by the curve in Fig. 3.36. We start to feed a current to the outer coil denoted by

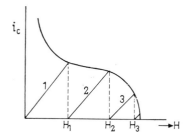

Fig. 3.36. Determination of the optimum current distribution in a layered superconducting coil. The oblique numbered lines correspond with the coil sections.

number 1. The relation between its current density and the (homogeneous) field generated by this is given by the straight line indicated by 1. The current may be increased until the critical current density is reached, but without exceeding it. The inner field is then $H_1$. Now we start to feed the next solenoid denoted by number 2. Since the field $H_1$ is already acting on it we draw the line, giving the relation between current density and the fieldstrength generated by it, through the point $H_1$. The slope of this line, indicated by 2, may be different from the first one, depending on the thickness of the solenoid. Again we may increase the current to just below the limit. Now a field $H_2$ has been produced inside the second solenoid. We then proceed with solenoid number 3, and so on until the inner solenoid is used or until the critical fieldstrength is obtained. To prevent the latter to be the limit we may choose a material with higher critical fieldstrength for the inner windings. So by choosing materials permitting high current density for the outer turns of the solenoid and materials with a high critical field for the inner turns and further applying a suitable current distribution we may thus minimize the volume of the magnet for a given fieldstrength in a given volume (see also GAUSTER and PARKER [1962]).

It should be noted that a superconducting coil working near its critical limits involves a great risk of explosion. As already pointed out in Ch. 3, § 2.3 the energy content of a coil excited to generate some $10^7$ A m$^{-1}$ is considerable. It will be released in less than a second when the superconductivity is quenched. Since the coil is usually immersed in a liquid-helium bath, the vaporizing helium may cause an explosion. The risk is reduced by winding a copper wire together with the superconducting wire when making the coil. The copper wire, forming the secondary winding of a transformer of which the superconducting wire is the primary, is connected to a resistance located outside the helium bath. If the coil is now quenched the greatest part of the energy is transferred from the coil into the resistance and dissipated (see for instance BOOM et al. [1963]). This not only reduces the risk of explosion but also promotes liquid-helium economy. An additional advantage is the low rate at which the energy is dissipated, depending on the inductance-to-resistance ratio of the secondary circuit. This prevents high inductive voltages and damage by arcing occurring.

If a coil is wound from wire having a certain critical-current-to-field relation when measured as a short sample, it sometimes appears that the coil shows quenching of the superconductivity at much lower current densities than expected. This phenomenon is called current degradation and is prominent for Nb-Zr alloy. It is believed to be caused by local transitions to normal conduction during excitation of the coil, which may be mostly of a transient nature but sometimes initiate quenching when the heat developed at the normal spot cannot be lead away quickly enough, the wire itself being a very poor conductor of heat. It is cured by covering the wire with a copper layer capable of leading away the heat developed occasionally at a small spot. Indeed a coil wound of copper-clad wire shows current degradation to a much lesser extent (see for instance DONADIEU [1963]). The copper, not being a superconductor, forms an "insulation" for the supercurrent. However, its resistance is very low, so a tight-wound coil of copper-clad wire will have an unpractically long relaxation time ($L/R$ having a large value). Covering the copper-clad wire with a high-resistive insulating layer will drastically lower the relaxation time, so that changing the field can be done within a convenient time (HULM et al. [1963]). It is recommended to impregnate the coil with some resin, not only to improve its thermal conductivity, but also to prevent the turns from moving under the Biot-Savart forces, since even the small mechanical energy involved in such a movement may heat the turn sufficiently to initiate quenching of the coil; heat capacities are very low at liquid-helium temperature.

The preparation of coils from $Nb_3Sn$ wire calls for special techniques. The intermetallic compound, having $\beta$-tungsten structure is so brittle that it cannot be wound into coils. A common technique is to fill a niobium tube with a mixture of tin and niobium powder, draw this to a small diameter and wind it into a coil. After that the coil is cured at 1000 °C, at which temperature the compound $Nb_3Sn$ is formed (KUNZLER et al. [1961]). The metal tube containing the superconducting core protects the coil against damage due to quenching by taking over the current at the spot where the core accidentally becomes normal. The tube having low resistance thus reduces the rate of current decrease and by this limits the inductive voltage that may damage the coil by arcing. The dielectric insulation, necessary to obtain a low time constant, must withstand the curing temperature of 1000 °C. Electrophoretic covering of the wire by a ceramic powder provides satisfactory results (SALTER et al. [1962]).

Niobium ribbon covered with a thin layer of $Nb_3Sn$ has promising properties. Its main advantage is its flexibility after being cured.

Superconducting solenoids often show some hysteresis in the relation between fieldstrength and current. This is due to flux-trapping in the body of the solenoid by parasitic closed super-currents.

Fields up to $10^7$ A m$^{-1}$ are now readily obtained by various experimenters and coils for these fieldstrengths are commercially sold. If the experiment for which the field is required has to be carried out at liquid-helium temperature, the superconducting coil can be made small and conveniently incorporated in the helium vessel.

§ 5.4. *Power supply for superconducting magnets and flux pumping*

The simplest method of supplying power to a superconducting solenoid is to connect it to a battery or other source of direct current, wait until the current through the coil reaches its required value, then short-circuit it by a superconducting switch and disconnect the battery. The superconducting switch is the closing link of an entirely superconducting circuit in which a persistent current flows. The switch may consist very simply of a short piece of super-conducting material (also immersed in the helium bath) which is in thermal contact with a resistor. When electrical power is fed to the resistor it warms up together with the piece of superconducting material until the critical temperature is passed. Now the switch is normal conductive or "open". Its resistance may be rather high, since superconducting alloys are usually poor electrical conductors when normal. As soon as the electrical power source is disconnected from the resistor, the switch cools down in the helium bath to below its critical temperature and is again superconductive or "closed".

The direct current which is taken from a source outside the helium vessel has to be led into the helium bath containing the solenoid. The leads should conduct the current without heat dissipation, and be a thermal insulator. This combination is only found in soft superconductors that obviously cannot be used here. So we choose a normal conductor, preferably a pure metal that gives the highest ratio of electrical to thermal conductivity. The diameter of the leads should be such that liquid-helium loss due to both Joule heat and heat inleak is minimized. The connection between current leads and superconducting wire should be made by heavy copper clamps or by welding to prevent excessive heat dissipation at the contact. Connections between superconducting wires should also be made by welding, but copper clamps are also suitable. Although in the latter case the connection is not superconductive, its resistance is so low that current decay is hardly noticeable. For instance, a 10 H solenoid closed by a copper-clamped contact, the resistance of which can easily be kept below $10^{-8}$ $\Omega$, has a time constant $L/R$ of $10^9$ s or approximately 30 years!

The whole problem of how to feed electrical power into the helium vessel can be avoided by making use of the property of a superconducting circuit that the magnetic flux enclosed by it is constant. One can transport this flux to a part of the circuit where it is concentrated to give the required fieldstrength. This process is called flux pumping. It will be illustrated by a few examples.

Consider a solenoid closed by two switches $S_1$ and $S_2$ in parallel. The entire circuit, switches included, is supposed to be superconducting. The circuit between the switches forms the secondary winding of a transformer (Fig. 3.37). We start with $S_2$ open and $S_1$ closed and feed a current through the primary winding, generating

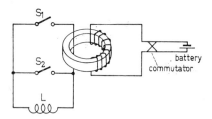

Fig. 3.37. Flux pump after LAQUER [1963].

a magnetic flux $\Phi$ in the core. Now $S_2$ is closed and $S_1$ is opened. By reversing the primary current a persistent current is induced in the coil in order to maintain the flux $\Phi$ enclosed by the circuit. This current is trapped by closing $S_1$. Opening $S_2$ and reversing the primary current gives us the starting position and the cycle can be repeated. This method, which involves no moving parts, was developed by LAQUER [1963]. The disadvantage is that the primary current has still to be fed into the helium vessel. One could wish to do the same thing with permanent magnets. This is possible but requires moving parts. The following example proposed by FELICI [1940] will show this.

Consider the coil to be connected to two parallel wires. The spokes of a rotating cross are sliding along these wires (Fig. 3.38).

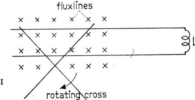

Fig. 3.38.  Flux pump after FELICI [1940].

All conductors, the sliding contacts included, are supposed to be superconductive. The field of a permanent magnet is directed at right angles to the rotating cross. When the cross is rotating clockwise, parts of the magnetic flux are trapped and transferred to the coil. This concept cannot be realized, since superconducting sliding contacts are only possible for very small currents. It may, however, be modified according to Fig. 3.39. The parallel wires, made of a

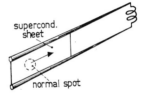

Fig. 3.39.  Flux pump using a moving magnet.

hard superconductor, are connected by a sheet of a soft superconductor. The total inductance of the circuit is denoted by $L$.
Further, we have a permanent magnet having a field strong enough
to quench the superconductivity of the sheet, but not strong enough
to do the same in the wire. The magnet is shaped such that its field,
which is normal to the plane of the diagram (Fig. 3.39), makes a
normal conducting spot, indicated by the dotted line, in the sheet.
The magnetic flux through the spot is denoted by $\Phi$. If we move the
magnet from left to right the flux of the magnet is brought inside
the superconducting circuit without breaking the circuit. By removing the magnet its flux crosses the wire. This induces a supercurrent of strength $\Phi/L$ to maintain the flux enclosed by the circuit,
the wire keeping its superconductivity when it is crossed by the
magnet. Now the magnet may be moved such that the normal spot

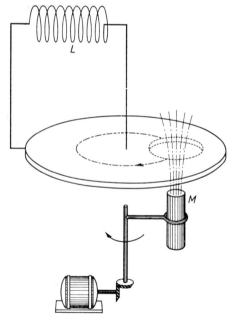

Fig. 3.40.   Flux pump after VOLGER and ADMIRAAL [1962].

again enters at the left edge of the sheet. By repeating the cycle the current is increased by an amount $\Phi/L$ each time. A very elegant realization of this principle has been devised by VOLGER and ADMIRAAL [1962]. It is schematically shown in Fig. 3.40. The coil $L$ is connected to the centre and the periphery of a disk made of a soft superconductor. The magnet M causes the disk to become normal locally. By moving the magnet along a circular path, the flux through the normal spot is pumped into the circuit each time it passes the line connecting the leads of the coil. The whole arrangement is immersed in the helium bath, except for the shaft that drives the magnet. Persistent currents of 1000 A are readily obtained. A survey on flux pumping has been published by VAN SUCHTELEN et al. [1965].

§ 6. BIBLIOGRAPHY

The subjects treated in this chapter have been surveyed by various authors. A great deal of information is accumulated in the proceedings of the International Conference on High Magnetic Fields, held at Cambridge, U.S.A., in 1961 (KOLM et al. [1962]).

The design of water-cooled solenoids has been treated by BITTER ([1936a, b], [1937], [1939], [1962] and [1963]). Cryogenic coils for continuous operation have been discussed by POST and TAYLOR [1960]. A general survey of methods for the generation of high magnetic fields has recently been given by MONTGOMERY [1963].

A survey on the use of superconductors for the generation of magnetic fields was presented by BERLINCOURT [1963] at a Conference on High Magnetic Fields, held at Oxford (Gr. Br.) in 1963. The design of superconducting coils has been treated by KROPSCHOT and ARP [1961] and by GAUSTER and PARKER [1962]. The design of systems for the generation of pulsed fields has been dealt with by CHAMPION [1950] and COTTI [1960].

CHAPTER 4

# IRON-CORE SOLENOIDS

## § 1. THE MAGNETIC CIRCUIT

Consider a ring made of ferromagnetic material of infinitely high permeability $\mu$. Then, since the magnetic permeability is the ratio between the magnetic induction $B$ and the magnetic fieldstrength $H$ in the material ($B$ and $H$ are parallel), the existence of a finite induction does not require a field. In other words the fieldstrength $H$ is zero inside the material.

Let the ring contain an air gap located at one place and be surrounded by a number of turns of copper wire at an other place (Fig. 4.1). The air gap is supposed to have parallel faces with a

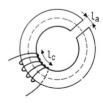

Fig. 4.1.   Soft-iron ring with winding and air gap.

small width-to-area ratio so that to a good approximation the field may be considered as being homogeneous and entirely concentrated within the gap volume. The winding is supposed to have a small diameter-to-length ratio, so that to a good approximation the field generated by the solenoid if no iron were present may be considered as being homogeneous and entirely concentrated within the coil volume. Now consider the line integral of $H$ along the dotted line

124

in Fig. 4.1. According to Maxwell's law

$$\oint H \cdot dl = i, \tag{4.1}$$

where $i$ is the total current through the coil, found by multiplying the current through the wire by the number of turns.

Since the field in the iron is supposed to be zero, the field in the air gap is given by

$$H_1 = i/l_a, \tag{4.2}$$

where $l_a$ is the length of the air gap.

If the iron core were not present, the field $H_2$ in the coil should be

$$H_2 = i/l_c, \tag{4.3}$$

where $l_c$ is the length of the coil.

The presence of the iron makes the field in the coil zero, so in the iron a field

$$H_3 = -H_2 = -i/l_c \tag{4.4}$$

is generated to cancel the field of the coil.

Now we treat the coil with its own field $H_2$ and the iron with its fields $H_1$ and $H_3$ separately. This is permitted because magnetic fields are additive and no separation is made here between fields and their own sources. By doing so we may write for the iron core alone

$$\oint H \cdot dl = 0$$

or

$$H_1 l_a + H_3 l_c = 0. \tag{4.5}$$

In Ch. 1 (eq. (1.6)) a relation is given between magnetic potential and the line integral of the fieldstrength.

In general we may say

$$V_2 - V_1 = -\int_1^2 H \cdot dl, \tag{4.6}$$

where $V_1$ and $V_2$ are the magnetic potentials in the places designatep by 1 and 2, respectively, and the line integral is obtained along any arbitrary path beginning in 1 and ending in 2.

So the coil causes a potential difference

$$\delta V = - H_3 l_{\rm c} = i \tag{4.7}$$

in the iron, so that the two legs of the core that protrude from either side of the coil are at a different potential. This means that the line integral of $H$ along any path from one leg to the other must be equal to $\delta V$.

We have supposed that the field is entirely concentrated in the air gap or in other words, as we see now, that any path outside the air gap is long as compared to a path in the air gap. We observe that this is certainly not true in a real electromagnet, especially not in the case as illustrated in Fig. 4.1. Here large parts of the magnetic circuit are at different potentials so that a considerable part of the magnetic flux through the coil may leak away in the space outside the air gap. Since this flux has also to be generated by the coil, this means a loss in electrical efficiency. Moreover the flux that can be carried by the iron is limited, so that the iron in the coil must have a larger cross-sectional area to carry not only the useful flux in the air gap but also the leakage flux. This means a loss in material efficiency. Therefore a better design is made by placing the coils as close as possible to the air gap (Fig. 4.2). Now the potential difference is almost entirely limited to the air gap, just where we want it. The best design should have the magnetizing coil at the air gap (Fig. 4.3) but this makes the gap inaccessible.

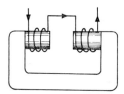

Fig. 4.2.   Recommended design of an electromagnet to reduce stray flux.

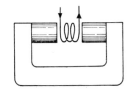

Fig. 4.3.   Ideal design of an electro-magnet having no stray flux.

We have seen that in the part of the magnetic circuit surrounded by a coil a field $H_3$ is generated that is directed opposite to the magnetic flux. This situation can also be obtained in a permanent magnet, without consumption of electrical energy. We consider an ideal magnetic circuit with a permanent magnet of length $l_m$ (Fig. 4.4). The magnet has a cross-sectional area of $S_m$. The length

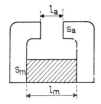

Fig. 4.4.    Permanent-magnet circuit.

of the air gap is $l_a$ and its cross-sectional area is $S_a$. The iron yoke is supposed to be infinitely permeable and leakage flux is supposed to be zero. Now we use the following equations

$$\oint H \cdot dl = 0$$

and

$$\Phi = BS = \text{constant}. \tag{4.8}$$

The latter equation is the continuity condition for the magnetic flux $\Phi$ that follows immediately from Maxwell's law

$$\text{div } B = 0.$$

From eq. (4.7) it follows that

$$H_a l_a = - H_m l_m, \tag{4.9}$$

where $H_a$ and $H_m$ are the fieldstrengths in the air gap and in the permanent magnet, respectively. Both fields are supposed to be homogeneous.

From eq. (4.8) it follows that

$$B_a S_a = B_m S_m, \tag{4.10}$$

where $B_a$ and $B_m$ are the magnetic inductions in the air gap and in the permanent magnet, respectively. Both inductions are supposed to be homogeneous. Considering that in the air gap

$$\mu_0 H_a = B_a,$$            (4.11)

we find by multiplication of eq. (4.9) with eq. (4.10)

$$\mu_0 H_a^2 V_a = -(B_m H_m) V_m,$$            (4.12)

where $V_a$ and $V_m$ are the volumes of the air gap and the permanent

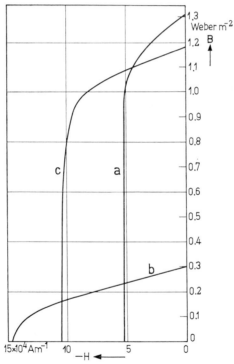

Fig. 4.5. Demagnetization curves (second quadrant of $B$ versus $H$ hysteresis loop) of various commercial permanent-magnet materials: a) "Ticonal" $G$ or Alnico 5. b) Ferroxdure III. (After STUIJTS *et al.* [1954/55].) c) "Ticonal" XX. (After LUTEIJN and DE VOS [1956].)

magnet, respectively. The left-hand member of eq. (4.12) is proportional to a magnetic energy. Hence the product $(-B_m H_m)$ is often called energy product. It is a function of $H_m$ and attains a maximum value at a certain field that is different for various permanent-magnet materials. The highest value of $(BH)_{max}$ so far reported is $10^5$ J m$^{-3}$ ($=12 \times 10^6$ G Oe) (LUTEIJN and DE VOS [1956]). The relation between $B$ and $-H$ is called the demagnetization curve. A few are given in Fig. 4.5 for commercially available materials. The relatively low saturation-magnetization of these materials as compared to iron leads to either large constructions or limits the fieldstrength in the air gap.

However, there are advantages. The first is the absence of energy dissipation, which allows incorporation of small magnet systems inside Dewar vessels, for instance. The second is that the magnet material can be used at elevated temperatures; especially "Ticonal", which retains its permanent-magnet properties up to 600 °C, at which temperature structural changes begin to take place.

An electromagnet with cylindrical poles covered by coils im-

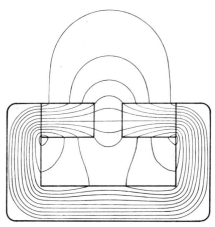

Fig. 4.6.    Schematic view of the lines of force of the electromagnet shown in
Fig. 4.2.

mediately facing the air gap was first constructed by RUHMKORFF [1846] although this type of magnet is usually called a Weiss-type magnet nowadays. It will be clear from the foregoing that even in this design the poles are at different potentials over a certain length. This results in a stray flux going out from the cylindrical surfaces, this flux having to enter through the far ends of the poles (see Fig. 4.6). So there the flux density is highest and core saturation will start. But as saturation is approached the magnetic resistivity is rapidly increasing and further increase of the excitating current will give no further increase of the field in the air gap. DREYFUS [1935] showed that conical poles with an apex angle of 90° are required to ensure that saturation starts at the pole tips. He applied this idea when he constructed the magnet at Uppsala University.

## § 2. UNIFORMLY MAGNETIZED CYLINDRICAL POLES

A widely used type of magnet has cylindrical poles with coils immediately facing the air gap. The poles of such a magnet may to a good approximation be considered as being magnetized uniformly with magnetic charges occurring on the pole faces with a uniform density $I$ and $-I$ respectively. To calculate the field between the pole faces we use eq. (1.4). The contribution $dV$ of a positively charged zone lying between the circles with radii $\rho$ and $\rho + d\rho$, respectively, to the magnetic potential $V$ at a point P on the axis is

$$dV = \frac{I}{2\mu_0} \frac{\rho \, d\rho}{(z^2 + \rho^2)^{\frac{1}{2}}}, \qquad (4.13)$$

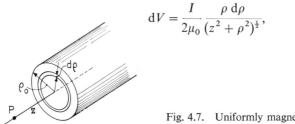

Fig. 4.7.   Uniformly magnetized cylinder.

where $z$ is the distance between P and the pole face (Fig. 4.7). This contribution integrated from $\rho = 0$ to $\rho = \rho_0$ ($\rho_0$ being the radius of the cylindrical pole) gives the total magnetic potential of one pole face

$$V = \int_0^{\rho_0} dV = \frac{I}{2\mu_0} \left[ (z^2 + \rho_0^2)^{\frac{1}{2}} - z \right].  \tag{4.14}$$

By differentiation with respect to $z$ and using the reduction $z/\rho_0 = \alpha$, for the $z$-component of the field and its derivatives we find

$$H_z(0) = \frac{I}{2\mu_0} \left[ 1 - \frac{\alpha}{(\alpha^2 + 1)^{\frac{1}{2}}} \right] = \frac{I}{\mu_0} L_0,  \tag{4.15}$$

$$H_z^{(1)}(0) = -\frac{I}{2\mu_0\rho_0} \frac{1}{(\alpha^2 + 1)^{\frac{3}{2}}} = \frac{I}{\mu_0} \frac{1}{\rho_0} L_1,  \tag{4.16}$$

$$H_z^{(2)}(0) = \frac{I}{2\mu_0\rho_0^2} \frac{3\alpha}{(\alpha^2 + 1)^{\frac{5}{2}}} = \frac{I}{\mu_0} \frac{1}{\rho_0^2} L_2,  \tag{4.17}$$

$$H_z^{(3)}(0) = -\frac{I}{2\mu_0\rho_0^3} \frac{12\alpha^2 - 3}{(\alpha^2 + 1)^{\frac{7}{2}}} = \frac{I}{\mu_0} \frac{1}{\rho_0^3} L_3,  \tag{4.18}$$

$$H_z^{(4)}(0) = \frac{I}{2\mu_0\rho_0^4} \frac{60\alpha^3 - 45\alpha}{(\alpha^2 + 1)^{\frac{9}{2}}} = \frac{I}{\mu_0} \frac{1}{\rho_0^4} L_4.  \tag{4.19}$$

Here $H_z^n(0)$ is the $n^{\text{th}}$ derivative of the $z$-component of $\boldsymbol{H}$ at the point P. The values of $L$ are given in Fig. 4.8. They can be applied to expand the field around point P by using eq. (2.79)

$$\begin{aligned} H_z = H_z(0) + H_z^{(1)}(0)\, rP_1 + \tfrac{1}{2}H_z^{(2)}(0)\, r^2P_2 + \\ + \tfrac{1}{6}H_z^{(3)}(0)\, r^3P_3 + \tfrac{1}{24}H_z^{(4)}(0)\, r^4P_4 + \cdots, \end{aligned}  \tag{4.20}$$

where $P_l$ is the Legendre polynomial of degree $l$ (see Appendix 2) and $r$ the length of the radius vector from point P to the point where $H_z$ is to be determined. If point P is chosen to lie at the centre between two oppositely charged pole faces (at a distance $2z$) the terms with odd powers of $r$ vanish and those with even powers of $r$ are doubled. So we find about the centre between two circular pole faces charged uniformly to a density $+I$ and $-I$ respectively:

$$H_z = \frac{I}{\mu_0}\left[\left\{1 - \frac{\alpha}{(\alpha^2+1)^{\frac{1}{2}}}\right\} + \frac{3\alpha}{2(\alpha^2+1)^{\frac{5}{2}}}\left(\frac{r}{\rho_0}\right)^2 P_2 +\right.$$
$$\left. + \frac{60\alpha^3 - 45\alpha}{24(\alpha^2+1)^{\frac{9}{2}}}\left(\frac{r}{\rho_0}\right)^4 P_4 + \cdots\right] \qquad (4.21)$$

or

$$H_z = \frac{2I}{\mu_0}\left[L_0 + \tfrac{1}{2}L_2\left(\frac{r}{\rho_0}\right)^2 P_2 + \tfrac{1}{24}L_4\left(\frac{r}{\rho_0}\right)^4 P_4 + \cdots\right], \qquad (4.22)$$

where the values of $L_0$, $L_2$ and $L_4$ may be found from Fig. 4.8. Reducing $\alpha$, which means large-area pole faces at a small distance, rapidly reduces the terms dependent on coordinates and results ultimately in a homogeneous fieldstrength

$$H_z = I/\mu_0. \qquad (4.23)$$

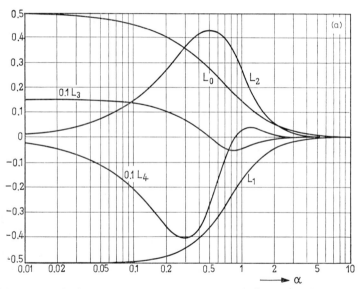

Fig. 4.8a. The functions $L_0, \ldots, L_4$ (eqs. (4.15)–(4.19)) plotted linearly as functions of the reduced distance $\alpha$ from the pole face, with the pole radius as a unit.

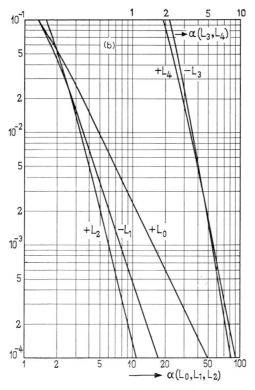

Fig. 4.8b. The functions $L_0,\ldots,L_4$ (eqs. (4.15)–(4.19)) plotted logarithmically as functions of the reduced distance $\alpha$ from the pole face, with the pole radius as a unit.

The values of $H_z$ as calculated in this section are only due to the magnetized iron poles. Especially in modern designs where the magnetizing coils are close to the air gap, these coils may contribute appreciably to the field in the air gap. They thus give a further increase of the field in a linear relation with the magnetizing current when the poles are saturated. This is schematically illustrated by Fig. 4.9 where the linear extrapolation of the upper part of the curve to meet the vertical axis gives the contribution of the saturated iron poles to the field in the air gap and the remainder the contribution of the coils.

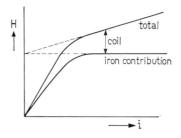

Fig. 4.9. The fieldstrength $H$ in the air gap of an electromagnet considered as separate contributions from the iron core and from the magnetizing coils, as a function of the magnetizing current.

## § 3. UNIFORMLY MAGNETIZED CONICAL POLES

We see from eq. (4.21) that the maximum field that can be obtained with uniformly magnetized cylindrical poles equals the saturation magnetization of the material from which the poles are made, no matter how big the magnet is made.

The reason is that part of the iron has a negative contribution to the field at the centre of the air gap. Increasing the size of the magnet not only increases the positively but also the negatively contributing part. This can be overcome by cutting away the negatively contributing part. We thus obtain a higher field at the centre of the air gap, but at the expense of the homogeneity of the field. To determine which part of the poles has to be removed we consider the field in the centre of the air gap as generated by a uniform distribution of parallel dipoles throughout the magnetized material.

Consider an elementary ring of the pole bounded by the radii $\rho$ and $\rho + d\rho$ and by the axial coordinates $z$ and $z + dz$. The ring is magnetized in the positive $z$-direction with a magnetic moment per unit volume of $I$ (Fig. 4.10). The magnetic moment of the ring is then

$$dm = 2\pi I \rho \, d\rho \, dz, \qquad (4.24)$$

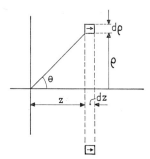

Fig. 4.10. Ring-shaped element of
an axially magnetized cylinder.

and its contribution to the magnetic potential at the origin follows
by eq. (1.18):

$$dV_1 = \frac{I}{2\mu_0} \frac{z}{(z^2 + \rho^2)^{\frac{3}{2}}} \rho \, d\rho \, dz. \qquad (4.25)$$

The contribution $dH_z$ to the axial component of the field at the
origin is then

$$dH_z = -\frac{\partial}{\partial z} dV_1 = -\frac{I}{2\mu_0} \frac{\rho^2 - 2z^2}{(\rho^2 + z^2)^{\frac{5}{2}}} \rho \, d\rho \, dz. \qquad (4.26)$$

This contribution is positive if $\rho^2 < 2z^2$ or

$$\tan \theta < 2^{\frac{1}{2}},$$
$$\theta < 54°44', \qquad (4.27)$$

where $\theta$ is the polar angle of the magnetized ring with respect to the
origin.

So if we cut away all iron for which $\theta > 54°44'$ we have the
maximum field obtainable with uniformly magnetized poles. If we
could fill the remaining space with diamagnetic material (which is
oppositely magnetized under the same magnetizing force) we could
produce even stronger fields. Except for superconductors we do not
know of materials with an appreciable diamagnetic susceptibility in
static fields. But the flux concentrator as it is used to reinforce a
pulsed field (see Ch. 3, § 4.3) may be considered as a body that
owing to its eddy currents acts more or less as a diamagnetic.

In order to calculate the field at the apex of a truncated conical pole we consider a ring of the conical surface bounded by the radii $\rho$ and $\rho + d\rho$, the apex of the cone lying at the origin of the coordinate system (Fig. 4.11). The radius of the pole face is $\rho_1$ and the outer

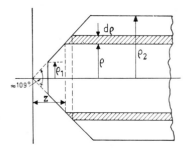

Fig. 4.11. Uniformly magnetized cone.

radius of the pole is $\rho_2$. The pole body extends to infinity to the right. The apex angle is about $109°$ so that $\tan \theta = 2^{\frac{1}{2}}$ in agreement with the condition for maximum field. The magnetic charge of the ring is

$$dq = 2\pi I \rho \, d\rho \tag{4.28}$$

and its potential at the origin is

$$dV = \frac{I}{2\mu_0} \frac{\rho \, d\rho}{(z^2 + \rho^2)^{\frac{1}{2}}}, \tag{4.29}$$

where $z$ is the distance between the apex of the cone and the plane of the ring at radius $\rho$.

The contribution of the ring to the axial field $H_z$ at the origin is

$$dH_z = -\frac{\partial}{\partial z} dV = \frac{I}{2\mu_0} \frac{z\rho \, d\rho}{(z^2 + \rho^2)^{\frac{3}{2}}}. \tag{4.30}$$

Since $\tan \theta = 2^{\frac{1}{2}}$ we may substitute

$$z^2 = \tfrac{1}{2}\rho^2 \tag{4.31}$$

to find

$$dH_z = \frac{1}{3\sqrt{3}} \frac{I}{\mu_0} \frac{d\rho}{\rho}. \tag{4.32}$$

Integration of eq. (4.32) gives the total field due to the conical part of a uniformly magnetized pole

$$H_z = \frac{I}{3\mu_0\sqrt{3}} \int_{\rho_1}^{\rho_2} \frac{d\rho}{\rho} = \frac{I}{\mu_0} \frac{\ln \alpha}{3\sqrt{3}}, \tag{4.33}$$

where $\alpha = \rho_2/\rho_1$.

When $\rho_1$ is different from zero there is also a contribution from the flat face of the truncated pole, that has been calculated in § 2 of this chapter. We see that $H_z$ rises to infinity when $\alpha$ does so.

A practical limit is set by the weight of the magnet. A magnet weighing several thousands of kilogrammes equipped with conical poles and pole-pieces can generate a field of the order of $4 \times 10^6$ A m$^{-1}$ in a pole gap of 1 cm$^3$. If the gap length and the pole face diameter are increased the field decreases rapidly. It will be obvious that the increase of the fieldstrength by using conical pole-pieces is obtained at the expense of field homogeneity. In general we may say that for resonance experiments where a homogeneous field is required large pole faces at a small distance are to be recommended (see Ch. 4, § 2). For other experiments where a large fieldstrength is more important than field homogeneity a magnet with conical poles may be useful.

## § 4. OPTIMUM DIPOLE DISTRIBUTION

So far we have only considered uniformly magnetized poles. If we drop the condition of uniform magnetization the efficiency of the electromagnet can be increased by orienting the local magnetization to produce a maximum field in the air gap. Consider a volume element $dv$ with a magnetic moment $I\,dv$. The modulus of the magnetization $I$ is supposed to be independent of coordinates. The system has rotational symmetry and the polar angle between the magnetization $I$ and the positive $z$-axis is $\theta_0$ (Fig. 4.12). The volume element is located at $z = z_0$ and $\rho = \rho_0$ or at the end of the radius vector $r$ with a polar angle $\theta$.

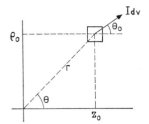

Fig. 4.12. Volume element of a magnetized system with rotational symmetry about the $z$-axis.

Eq. (1.18) applied to this case gives the magnetic potential at the origin due to the volume element

$$V_1 = - \frac{I}{4\pi\mu_0} \, dv \cdot \mathrm{grad} \, \frac{1}{r} = \frac{I \cdot r}{4\pi\mu_0 r^3} \, dv. \qquad (4.34)$$

The axial component $H_z$ of the field $H$ is then

$$H_z = \frac{I \, dv}{4\pi\mu_0 r^3} \left[ 3 \sin\theta \cos\theta \sin\theta_0 + \cos\theta_0 (3\cos^2\theta - 1) \right], \qquad (4.35)$$

which is maximum if

$$\frac{\partial H_z}{\partial \theta_0} = 0$$

or

$$\tan\theta_0 = \frac{3 \sin\theta \cos\theta}{3 \cos^2\theta - 1}. \qquad (4.36)$$

This equation gives the condition for the magnetization direction at any point in order to produce the maximum axial field at the centre of the system.

Straight lines going through the origin are isoclinal lines for the magnetization.

For comparison we calculate the field direction at some arbitrary point due to a dipole moment $Q_{1z}$ pointing in the positive $z$-direction and located at the origin (Fig. 4.13).

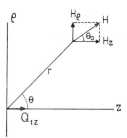

Fig. 4.13. Field due to dipole at the origin.

The potential at any point due to this dipole is

$$V = Q_{1z}z/4\pi\mu_0 r^3$$

and the field components at this point

$$H_z = \frac{Q_{1z}}{4\pi\mu_0 r^5}(3\cos^2\theta - 1)$$

and

$$H_\rho = \frac{Q_{1z}}{4\pi\mu_0 r^5}3\sin\theta\cos\theta,$$

where $H_z$ is the axial and $H_\rho$ the radial field component. Owing to the rotational symmetry there is no tangential field component.

The direction of the field $\boldsymbol{H}$ is now given by

$$\tan\theta_0 = \frac{H_\rho}{H_z} = \frac{3\sin\theta\cos\theta}{3\cos^2\theta - 1}, \qquad (4.37)$$

where $\theta_0$ is the polar angle of $\boldsymbol{H}$ with respect to the $z$-axis.

If we compare this result with eq. (4.36) we see that the two expressions have the same appearance. The angular distribution of the magnetization for maximum field with a certain orientation at a certain point follows the same rule as the angular distribution of the field around a dipole at the same point and with the same orientation. If we substitute the condition of eq. (4.36) into eq. (4.35) we find

$$H_z = \frac{I (3 \cos^2\theta + 1)^{\frac{1}{2}}}{4\pi\mu_0 r^3} \, dv. \tag{4.38}$$

This expression has to be integrated excluding the centre where the function that describes the direction of the magnetization has a singularity. Moreover, the field is infinite at the centre of an optimally magnetized solid body. MAMMEL and MORGAN [1962] have treated this problem for a set of coaxial disks and for hollow cylinders (Fig. 4.14). They integrated eq. (4.38) by using a numerical

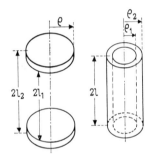

Fig. 4.14. Disks and cylinders with optimum magnetization distribution.

method resulting in

$$H_z = \frac{I}{\mu_0} \{S(\beta) - S(\alpha)\}, \tag{4.39}$$

where $H_z$ is the field at the centre of a hollow cylinder with inner radius $\rho_1$, outer radius $\rho_2$ and length $2l$, and where $\alpha = l/\rho_1$ and $\beta = = l/\rho_2$. The function $S(x)$ is given in Fig. 4.15. For a set of circular disks of radius $\rho$ and a separation $2l_1$ between the inner surfaces and $2l_2$ between the outer surfaces they found at the centre between the disks an axial fieldstrength

$$H_z = \frac{I}{\mu_0} \{T(\delta) - T(\gamma)\}, \tag{4.40}$$

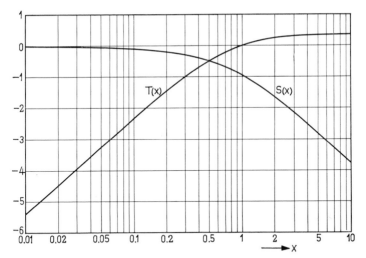

Fig. 4.15. $S$ and $T$ as functions of $x$ for use in eqs. (4.39) and (4.40). (After MAMMEL and MORGAN [1962].)

where $\gamma = l_1/\rho$ and $\delta = l_2/\rho$. The function $T(x)$ is also given in Fig. 4.15.

Since optimum magnetization can only be approximated in practice, the fields as given by eqs. (4.39) and (4.40) should be considered as upper bounds.

## § 5. IRON-CLAD SOLENOIDS

In order to obtain the optimum dipole distribution as treated in the previous section the exciting field that magnetizes the iron should have the form of a field around a dipole. If this field is strong enough the magnetization of the iron will have the same form. This idea, first proposed by BITTER [1936a], was realized by CIOFFI [1962] who provided a high-power solenoid with an external magnetic circuit (Fig. 4.16). The magnetic field in the iron due to the short solenoid resembles approximately the field of a dipole. The deviation from optimum magnetization will be greater the

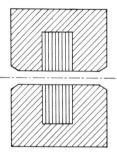

Fig. 4.16.   Iron-clad solenoid.

longer is the solenoid. To calculate the contribution of the iron exactly requires elaborate computation that goes beyond the scope of this book.

A few general remarks can, however, be made here. We shall see where it is advantageous to have magnetizing windings and where magnetized iron. We assume uniform current density in the windings and optimum magnetization of the iron. Consider a ring between the axial planes $z$ and $z + dz$ and the radii $\rho$ and $\rho + d\rho$ (Fig. 4.17). If the ring is filled by windings with current density $\tau$

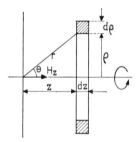

Fig. 4.17.   Element of an electromagnet with rotational symmetry. The element may either consist of copper winding or of iron.

its contribution to the axial field at the origin is found from eq. (2.89):

$$H_z = \frac{\tau \sin^2 \theta}{2r} \, d\rho \, dz, \qquad (4.41)$$

and if filled with iron with optimally oriented magnetization $I$

(eq. (4.38)):

$$H_z = \frac{I \sin \theta \, (3 \cos^2\theta + 1)^{\frac{1}{2}}}{2\mu_0 r^2} \, d\rho \, dz .$$ (4.42)

Since the former contribution decreases proportionally to $r^{-1}$ and the latter to $r^{-2}$ the iron should come as close as possible to the origin where the centre of the system is located. This is easily seen by combining eqs. (4.41) and (4.42) considering that the use of the iron is required if

$$\frac{I \sin \theta \, (3 \cos^2\theta + 1)^{\frac{1}{2}}}{2\mu_0 r^2} > \frac{\tau \sin^2\theta}{2r}$$ (4.43)

or

$$\frac{r \sin \theta}{(3 \cos^2\theta + 1)^{\frac{1}{2}}} < \frac{I}{\mu_0\tau},$$ (4.44)

which gives a maximum radius for the iron. This condition, however, is incompatible with the requirement that the iron should be outside the solenoid. The conclusion is therefore to keep the solenoid as small as possible with a great power density, in order to have the iron as close as possible near the centre. A recommendable construction is given in Fig. 4.18, where the tapered poles are still

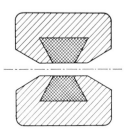

Fig. 4.18. Recommended design of an iron-clad solenoid (schematically).

subjected to a diverging field that magnetizes them in the desired way. Thereby they closely approach the centre of the system thus contributing appreciably to the axial field. Although optimum magnetization can only be approximated to, a gain of 1.5 to $2.5 \times 10^6$ A m$^{-1}$ is readily obtained in practice. A survey of the efficiency of several commercial electromagnets is given by DE KLERK and GORTER [1962].

## § 6. FERROMAGNETIC MATERIALS OF HIGH
## SATURATION-MAGNETIZATION

In the previous sections of this chapter we have seen that the field obtained by using magnetized ferromagnetic material is proportional to the magnetization $I$. Hence it is limited by the saturation-magnetization $I_s$, so the pole-pieces should be made of a material of which $I_s$ is as high as possible.

Iron pole-pieces are widely used owing to the high saturation-magnetization, the low fieldstrength required to magnetize it and the low price. An alloy of 50% iron and 50% cobalt (by weight) has a slightly higher saturation-magnetization. It has to be made by vacuum melting starting from rather pure elements for better machinability; for the same purpose a few percent vanadium is often added, all this making the alloy rather expensive. The high Curie point makes it suitable for high-temperature applications. Pure cobalt has an even higher Curie point.

The development of magnets to be operated at low temperatures (superconducting coils, for instance) makes it possible to use ferromagnetic materials with a low Curie point. Some rare-earth metals, though being very expensive, offer interesting possibilities. Their atomic moment is high, leading to high saturation-magnetization. However, they are usually not easily magnetizable, due to high crystalline anisotropy and weak antiferromagnetism. So they consume a great part of the available magnetomotive force which reduces the gain that could be obtained. This point is of greater importance for the rest of the ferromagnetic circuit. The magnet yoke should be made of material of high permeability that persists even when the magnetization approaches saturation. Low-carbon steel (e.g. case-hardening quality) annealed at 800 °C and cooled down slowly is a suitable material for yoke construction. The magnetomotive force required for magnetizing the iron can also be reduced by increasing the cross-sectional area of the yoke. This reduces the required magnetization per unit area, thus appreciably reducing the magnetomotive force. The relevant properties of various ferromagnetic materials are given in Table 4.1.

TABLE 4.1

Magnetic properties of various ferromagnetic materials

| Material | Saturation-magnetization | | Curie point | Density | Price (1965) |
|---|---|---|---|---|---|
| | 0°K | room temp. | | | |
| | Wb m⁻² | Wb m⁻² | °K | 10³ kg m⁻³ | $ kg⁻¹ |
| Fe[1]) | 2.20 | 2.16 | 1043 | 7.9 | 0.2 |
| Permendur[2]) | | 2.45 | 980 | 8.3 | 20 |
| V-Permendur[3]) | | 2.38 | 980 | 8.2 | 20 |
| Co | 1.82 | 1.76 | 1400 | 8.9 | 4 |
| Gd[4]) | 2.51 | | 290 | 7.9 | 550 |
| Dy[5]) | 3.77 | | 85 | 8.6 | 550 |
| Ho[6]) | 3.33 | | 20 | 8.8 | 600 |
| Tb[7]) | 3.33 | | 218 | 8.3 | 2800 |

1) Low-carbon steel, case-hardening quality
2) 50%Fe, 50%Co, by weight. The Curie point is not a magnetic, but a crystallographic transition point
3) 49%Fe, 49%Co, 2%V, by weight. For Curie point see [2])
4) Quoted from ELLIOTT et al. [1953]
5) Quoted from BEHRENDT et al. [1958]
6) Quoted from RHODES et al. [1958]
7) Quoted from THOBURN et al. [1958]

# APPENDIX 1

## COMPARISON OF UNIT SYSTEMS

### (see also Ch. 1, § 2)

TABLE A.1

|  | emcgs | Gauss | mksA |
|---|---|---|---|
| Force between two charges (Coulomb) | $F = \dfrac{QQ'}{r^2}$ | $F = \dfrac{QQ'}{r^2}$ | $F = \dfrac{1}{4\pi\mu_0} \dfrac{QQ'}{r^2}$ |
| Potential due to a single charge | $V = \dfrac{Q}{r}$ | $V = \dfrac{Q}{r}$ | $V = \dfrac{1}{4\pi\mu_0} \dfrac{Q}{r}$ |
| Force on a charge in a field | $F = QH$ | $F = QH$ | $F = QH$ |
| Field inside a long current sheet[1] | $H = \dfrac{4\pi i}{l}$ | $H = \dfrac{4\pi\,i}{c\;l}$ | $H = \dfrac{i}{l}$ |
| Force on a current in a field[2] | $F = B_n i l$ | $F = \dfrac{1}{c} B_n i l$ | $F = B_n i l$ |
| Induction in matter | $B = \mu_0 H + 4\pi I$ | $B = \mu_0 H + 4\pi I$ | $B = \mu_0 H + I$ |
| Energy of magnetic field | $W = \dfrac{1}{8\pi} HB$ | $W = \dfrac{1}{8\pi} HB$ | $W = \tfrac{1}{2}HB$ |

[1]) In this formula $i$ is the total strength of the current sheet and $l$ is its length, which is large compared to its diameter.

[2]) In this formula $l$ is the length of the wire through which the current $i$ flows. $B_n$ is the component of the induction of the field perpendicular to the wire.

146

TABLE A.2

|  | emcgs | Gauss | mksA |
|---|---|---|---|
| length | $cm = 10^{-2}m$ | $cm = 10^{-2}m$ | m |
| mass | $g = 10^{-3}kg$ | $g = 10^{-3}kg$ | kg |
| time | s | s | s |
| force | $dyne = 10^{-5}N$ | $dyne = 10^{-5}N$ | N |
| energy | $erg = 10^{-7}J$ | $erg = 10^{-7}J$ | J |
| voltage | $emu = 10^{-8}V$ | $gu = c \times 10^{-6}V$ | V |
| current | $emu = 10A$ | $gu = \dfrac{10^{-1}}{c}A$ | A |
| resistance | $emu = 10^{-9}\Omega$ | $gu = c^2 \times 10^{-5}\Omega$ | $\Omega$ |
| capacitance | $emu = 10^9 F$ | $cm = \dfrac{10^5}{c}F$ | F |
| inductance | $cm = 10^{-9}H$ | $cm = 10^{-9}H$ | H |
| $\varepsilon_0$ | $c^{-2}$ | 1 | $\dfrac{10^7}{4\pi c^2}\dfrac{F}{m}$ |
| $\mu_0$ | 1 | 1 | $4\pi \times 10^{-7}\dfrac{H}{m}$ |
| magn. charge | \multicolumn{2}{c}{$\dfrac{erg}{Oe\ cm} = 4\pi \times 10^{-8}$ V s} | V s |
| magnetic fieldstrength | \multicolumn{2}{c}{$Oe = \dfrac{10^3}{4\pi}\dfrac{A}{m}$} | $\dfrac{A}{m}$ |
| magnetic moment | \multicolumn{2}{c}{$\dfrac{erg}{Oe} = 4\pi \times 10^{-10}$ V s m} | V s m |
| mass magnetization | \multicolumn{2}{c}{$\dfrac{erg}{Oe\ g} = 4\pi \times 10^{-7}\dfrac{V\ s\ m}{kg}$} | $\dfrac{V\ s\ m}{kg}$ |
| volume magnetization | \multicolumn{2}{c}{$\dfrac{erg}{Oe\ cm^3} = 4\pi \times 10^{-4}\dfrac{V\ s}{m^2}$} | $\dfrac{V\ s}{m^2}$ |
| magnetic induction | \multicolumn{2}{c}{$G = 10^{-4}\dfrac{V\ s}{m^2}$} | $\dfrac{V\ s}{m^2}$ |

The "V s" has been given the name "weber" (Wb). The "V s m$^{-2}$" is also called "tesla". The "G" and the "Oe" have the same dimension. The velocity of light is $c = 2.998 \times 10^8$ m s$^{-1}$.

## ASSOCIATED LEGENDRE POLYNOMIALS IN SPHERICAL
## AND CARTESIAN COORDINATES

$$P_0 = 1 \qquad\qquad\qquad\qquad\qquad = 1$$

$$P_1^0 = \cos\theta \qquad\qquad\qquad\qquad = z/r$$

$$P_1^1 = \sin\theta \qquad\qquad\qquad\qquad = (r^2 - z^2)^{\frac{1}{2}}/r$$

$$P_2^0 = \tfrac{1}{2}(3\cos^2\theta - 1) \qquad\qquad = \tfrac{1}{2}(3z^2 - r^2)/r^2$$

$$P_2^1 = 3\sin\theta\cos\theta \qquad\qquad\quad = 3(r^2 - z^2)^{\frac{1}{2}}z/r^2$$

$$P_2^2 = 3\sin^2\theta \qquad\qquad\qquad\quad = 3(r^2 - z^2)/r^2$$

$$P_3^0 = \tfrac{1}{2}(5\cos^3\theta - 3\cos\theta) \qquad = \tfrac{1}{2}(5z^3 - 3rz^2)/r^3$$

$$P_3^1 = \tfrac{3}{2}\sin\theta(5\cos^2\theta - 1) \qquad = \tfrac{3}{2}(r^2 - z^2)^{\frac{1}{2}}(5z^2 - 1)/r^3$$

$$P_3^2 = 15\sin^2\theta\cos\theta \qquad\qquad = 15(r^2 - z^2)z/r^3$$

$$P_3^3 = 15\sin^3\theta \qquad\qquad\qquad = 15(r^2 - z^2)^{\frac{3}{2}}/r^3$$

$$P_4^0 = \tfrac{1}{8}(35\cos^4\theta - 30\cos^2\theta + 3) = \tfrac{1}{8}(35z^4 - 30r^2z^2 + 3r^4)/r^4$$

$$P_4^1 = \tfrac{5}{2}\sin\theta(7\cos^3\theta - 3\cos\theta) \quad = \tfrac{5}{2}(r^2 - z^2)^{\frac{1}{2}}(7z^3 - 3r^2z)/r^4$$

$$P_4^2 = \tfrac{15}{2}\sin^2\theta(7\cos^2\theta - 1) \qquad = \tfrac{15}{2}(r^2 - z^2)(7z^2 - r^2)/r^4$$

$$P_4^3 = 105\sin^3\theta\cos\theta \qquad\qquad = 105(r^2 - z^2)^{\frac{3}{2}}z/r^4$$

$$P_4^4 = 105\sin^4\theta \qquad\qquad\qquad = 105(r^2 - z^2)^2/r^4$$

## TABLES FOR $F_1$, $F_2$, $F_3$ AND $F_4$:

### (see also Ch. 3, § 1.1)

$$F_1 = \tfrac{1}{2}\beta \ln \frac{\alpha + (\alpha^2 + \beta^2)^{\frac{1}{2}}}{1 + (1 + \beta^2)^{\frac{1}{2}}} = \tfrac{1}{2}\beta \left( \operatorname{arcsinh} \frac{\alpha}{\beta} - \operatorname{arcsinh} \frac{1}{\beta} \right);$$

$$F_2 = \tfrac{1}{2} \left[ \frac{\alpha}{(\alpha^2 + \beta^2)^{\frac{1}{2}}} - \frac{1}{(1 + \beta^2)^{\frac{1}{2}}} - \ln \frac{\alpha + (\alpha^2 + \beta^2)^{\frac{1}{2}}}{\alpha \{1 + (1 + \beta^2)^{\frac{1}{2}}\}} \right] =$$

$$= \tfrac{1}{2} \left[ \frac{\alpha}{(\alpha^2 + \beta^2)^{\frac{1}{2}}} - \frac{1}{(1 + \beta^2)^{\frac{1}{2}}} - \operatorname{arcsinh} \frac{\alpha}{\beta} + \right.$$

$$\left. + \operatorname{arcsinh} \frac{1}{\beta} + \ln \alpha \right];$$

$$F_3 = - \frac{1}{2\beta} \left\{ \frac{\alpha^3}{(\alpha^2 + \beta^2)^{\frac{3}{2}}} - \frac{1}{(1 + \beta^2)^{\frac{3}{2}}} \right\};$$

$$F_4 = - \tfrac{1}{2} \left\{ \frac{\alpha^3 (\alpha^2 + 4\beta^2)}{\beta^2 (\alpha^2 + \beta^2)^{\frac{5}{2}}} - \frac{1 + 4\beta^2}{\beta^2 (1 + \beta^2)^{\frac{5}{2}}} - \frac{3}{2\alpha^2} + \tfrac{3}{2} \right\}.$$

For a coil extending from $-\beta$ to $0$:

$$F_1 = \quad F_1(\alpha, \beta); \qquad F_3 = \quad F_3(\alpha, \beta);$$

$$F_2 = - F_2(\alpha, \beta); \qquad F_4 = - F_4(\alpha, \beta).$$

*Example of the use of the tables*

Consider a cylindrical coil with external diameter of 50 cm, internal diameter of 8 cm and length of 160 cm. The axial fieldstrength is required at point A at a distance of 8 cm from the centre (see Fig.).

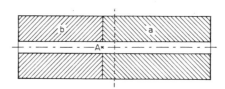

We calculate separately the field $H_a$ due to the part of the coil lying to the right of point A and the field $H_b$ due to the part lying to the left of point A. These two fields are added to give the total field $H$ at A.

The dimensional ratios of the two coils are:

$$\alpha = 6.25$$
$$\beta_a = 11$$
$$\beta_b = -9$$
with
$$\rho_1 = 0.04 \text{ m}.$$

Using the first of eqs. (3.8) we have

$$H_a = \tau\rho_1 F_1(\alpha, \beta_a)$$
$$H_b = \tau\rho_1 F_1(\alpha, \beta_b) = \tau\rho_1 F_1(\alpha, -\beta_b).$$

We see that $\alpha$ is not an integer. To avoid interpolation in the tables we scale the coil up by a factor $s$ until all dimensional ratios are integers. This means that we obtain the field of a coil with $s$ times the original internal radius. To calculate the correct value of the fieldstrength we must scale down again by substituting in eqs. (3.8)

$$\rho_1' \rightarrow \frac{1}{s}\rho_1.$$

We thus have with $s = 4$:

external reduced radius  $\alpha'_2 = $    25
internal reduced radius  $\alpha'_1 = $     4
$\qquad\qquad\qquad\quad \beta'_a = $    44
$\qquad\qquad\qquad\quad \beta'_b = -36$
$\qquad\qquad\qquad\quad \rho'_1 = $    0.01 m

and, using the table for $F_1$:

$$H_a = \tau\rho'_1 \{F_1(\alpha'_2, \beta'_a) - F_1(\alpha'_1, \beta'_a)\} =$$
$$= 0.01\tau(11.4097 - 1.4973) = 0.099\,124\,\tau$$

Similarly we find

$$H_b = \tau\rho'_1 \{F_1(\alpha'_2, \beta'_b) - F_1(\alpha'_1, \beta'_b)\} =$$
$$= 0.01\tau(11.1660 - 1.4960) = 0.096\,700\,\tau$$

The total field at A is

$$H = 0.195\,82\,\tau\,A\,m^{-1},$$

where $\tau$ is the current density in $A\,m^{-2}$.

| $F_1$ | $\beta=1$ | 2 | 3 | 4 | 5 | 6 | 7 | 8 | 9 | 10 |
|---|---|---|---|---|---|---|---|---|---|---|
| $\alpha=1$ | 0.0000 | 0.0000 | 0.0000 | 0.0000 | 0.0000 | 0.0000 | 0.0000 | 0.0000 | 0.0000 | 0.0000 |
|  | 0.2811 | 0.4002 | 0.4465 | 0.4675 | 0.4784 | 0.4846 | 0.4886 | 0.4912 | 0.4930 | 0.4943 |
|  | 0.4685 | 0.7136 | 0.8309 | 0.8914 | 0.9253 | 0.9459 | 0.9592 | 0.9682 | 0.9745 | 0.9792 |
|  | 0.6067 | 0.9624 | 1.1567 | 1.2678 | 1.3349 | 1.3777 | 1.4063 | 1.4261 | 1.4404 | 1.4510 |
|  | 0.7155 | 1.1660 | 1.4345 | 1.6003 | 1.7067 | 1.7777 | 1.8268 | 1.8619 | 1.8876 | 1.9069 |
| 5 | 0.8052 | 1.3372 | 1.6743 | 1.8946 | 2.0432 | 2.1464 | 2.2200 | 2.2739 | 2.3142 | 2.3450 |
|  | 0.8814 | 1.4845 | 1.8841 | 2.1569 | 2.3482 | 2.4857 | 2.5865 | 2.6620 | 2.7195 | 2.7642 |
|  | 0.9475 | 1.6135 | 2.0699 | 2.3923 | 2.6257 | 2.7981 | 2.9277 | 3.0268 | 3.1037 | 3.1642 |
|  | 1.0060 | 1.7281 | 2.2365 | 2.6054 | 2.8794 | 3.0866 | 3.2457 | 3.3695 | 3.4672 | 3.5452 |
|  | 1.0584 | 1.8312 | 2.3872 | 2.7995 | 3.1124 | 3.3537 | 3.5424 | 3.6917 | 3.8111 | 3.9077 |
| 10 | 1.1059 | 1.9248 | 2.5246 | 2.9776 | 3.3274 | 3.6018 | 3.8198 | 3.9948 | 4.1366 | 4.2526 |
|  | 1.1492 | 2.0106 | 2.6509 | 3.1420 | 3.5269 | 3.8332 | 4.0798 | 4.2803 | 4.4448 | 4.5807 |
|  | 1.1891 | 2.0896 | 2.7676 | 3.2944 | 3.7126 | 4.0496 | 4.3242 | 4.5499 | 4.7370 | 4.8931 |
|  | 1.2261 | 2.1629 | 2.8761 | 3.4365 | 3.8863 | 4.2528 | 4.5544 | 4.8049 | 5.0144 | 5.1907 |
|  | 1.2605 | 2.2313 | 2.9775 | 3.5695 | 4.0494 | 4.4440 | 4.7718 | 5.0465 | 5.2781 | 5.4746 |
| 15 | 1.2927 | 2.2953 | 3.0725 | 3.6945 | 4.2029 | 4.6245 | 4.9777 | 5.2758 | 5.5292 | 5.7457 |
|  | 1.3229 | 2.3554 | 3.1620 | 3.8123 | 4.3480 | 4.7954 | 5.1730 | 5.4940 | 5.7687 | 6.0049 |
|  | 1.3515 | 2.4122 | 3.2465 | 3.9238 | 4.4854 | 4.9576 | 5.3587 | 5.7019 | 5.9974 | 6.2530 |
|  | 1.3785 | 2.4660 | 3.3265 | 4.0295 | 4.6158 | 5.1119 | 5.5357 | 5.9004 | 6.2161 | 6.4908 |
|  | 1.4041 | 2.5170 | 3.4026 | 4.1299 | 4.7401 | 5.2590 | 5.7047 | 6.0902 | 6.4257 | 6.7190 |
| 20 | 1.4284 | 2.5656 | 3.4750 | 4.2257 | 4.8586 | 5.3994 | 5.8662 | 6.2720 | 6.6267 | 6.9382 |
|  | 1.4517 | 2.6119 | 3.5441 | 4.3172 | 4.9718 | 5.5339 | 6.0211 | 6.4464 | 6.8198 | 7.1491 |
|  | 1.4739 | 2.6562 | 3.6102 | 4.4047 | 5.0803 | 5.6627 | 6.1696 | 6.6139 | 7.0055 | 7.3522 |
|  | 1.4951 | 2.6986 | 3.6735 | 4.4886 | 5.1844 | 5.7864 | 6.3124 | 6.7751 | 7.1844 | 7.5480 |
|  | 1.5155 | 2.7393 | 3.7343 | 4.5692 | 5.2844 | 5.9054 | 6.4497 | 6.9303 | 7.3568 | 7.7370 |
| 25 | 1.5351 | 2.7784 | 3.7927 | 4.6467 | 5.3806 | 6.0199 | 6.5821 | 7.0800 | 7.5232 | 7.9195 |
|  | 1.5540 | 2.8160 | 3.8490 | 4.7213 | 5.4733 | 6.1303 | 6.7098 | 7.2245 | 7.6840 | 8.0961 |
|  | 1.5721 | 2.8523 | 3.9032 | 4.7933 | 5.5628 | 6.2368 | 6.8332 | 7.3642 | 7.8396 | 8.2670 |
|  | 1.5897 | 2.8873 | 3.9556 | 4.8628 | 5.6492 | 6.3399 | 6.9525 | 7.4993 | 7.9901 | 8.4325 |
|  | 1.6066 | 2.9211 | 4.0062 | 4.9300 | 5.7327 | 6.4396 | 7.0679 | 7.6302 | 8.1361 | 8.5931 |
| 30 |  |  |  |  |  |  |  |  |  |  |

| $F_1$ $\alpha = 1$ | $\beta=11$ | 12 | 13 | 14 | 15 | 16 | 17 | 18 | 19 | 20 |
|---|---|---|---|---|---|---|---|---|---|---|
| 5 | 0.0000 | 0.0000 | 0.0000 | 0.0000 | 0.0000 | 0.0000 | 0.0000 | 0.0000 | 0.0000 | 0.0000 |
|  | 0.4953 | 0.4960 | 0.4966 | 0.4971 | 0.4974 | 0.4977 | 0.4980 | 0.4982 | 0.4984 | 0.4985 |
|  | 0.9827 | 0.9854 | 0.9875 | 0.9892 | 0.9905 | 0.9917 | 0.9926 | 0.9934 | 0.9941 | 0.9946 |
|  | 1.4590 | 1.4653 | 1.4702 | 1.4742 | 1.4774 | 1.4801 | 1.4823 | 1.4842 | 1.4857 | 1.4871 |
|  | 1.9217 | 1.9334 | 1.9426 | 1.9501 | 1.9562 | 1.9613 | 1.9656 | 1.9692 | 1.9722 | 1.9749 |
| 10 | 2.3689 | 2.3878 | 2.4031 | 2.4154 | 2.4256 | 2.4341 | 2.4413 | 2.4473 | 2.4525 | 2.4569 |
|  | 2.7993 | 2.8275 | 2.8502 | 2.8689 | 2.8844 | 2.8873 | 2.9082 | 2.9176 | 2.9255 | 2.9324 |
|  | 3.2124 | 3.2514 | 3.2833 | 3.3096 | 3.3316 | 3.3500 | 3.3657 | 3.3791 | 3.3906 | 3.4006 |
|  | 3.6081 | 3.6595 | 3.7018 | 3.7370 | 3.7666 | 3.7916 | 3.8129 | 3.8312 | 3.8470 | 3.8607 |
|  | 3.9865 | 4.0515 | 4.1055 | 4.1507 | 4.1890 | 4.2215 | 4.2493 | 4.2733 | 4.2942 | 4.3123 |
| 15 | 4.3482 | 4.4278 | 4.4945 | 4.5507 | 4.5986 | 4.6395 | 4.6747 | 4.7052 | 4.7318 | 4.7550 |
|  | 4.6939 | 4.7888 | 4.8690 | 4.9371 | 4.9954 | 5.0455 | 5.0889 | 5.1266 | 5.1595 | 5.1885 |
|  | 5.0242 | 5.1351 | 5.2294 | 5.3101 | 5.3795 | 5.4395 | 5.4917 | 5.5372 | 5.5772 | 5.6125 |
|  | 5.3401 | 5.4673 | 5.5763 | 5.6700 | 5.7512 | 5.8217 | 5.8832 | 5.9372 | 5.9848 | 6.0269 |
|  | 5.6423 | 5.7861 | 5.9101 | 6.0174 | 6.1107 | 6.1922 | 6.2637 | 6.3266 | 6.3823 | 6.4317 |
| 20 | 5.9317 | 6.0923 | 6.2314 | 6.3525 | 6.4584 | 6.5513 | 6.6332 | 6.7055 | 6.7697 | 6.8269 |
|  | 6.2091 | 6.3864 | 6.5409 | 6.6760 | 6.7948 | 6.8994 | 6.9920 | 7.0741 | 7.1473 | 7.2126 |
|  | 6.4752 | 6.6692 | 6.8390 | 6.9884 | 7.1202 | 7.2368 | 7.3404 | 7.4326 | 7.5150 | 7.5889 |
|  | 6.7308 | 6.9413 | 7.1265 | 7.2901 | 7.4351 | 7.5639 | 7.6787 | 7.7813 | 7.8733 | 7.9559 |
|  | 6.9765 | 7.2034 | 7.4039 | 7.5818 | 7.7400 | 7.8811 | 8.0073 | 8.1205 | 8.2222 | 8.3139 |
| 25 | 7.2129 | 7.4560 | 7.6717 | 7.8638 | 8.0352 | 8.1887 | 8.3265 | 8.4504 | 8.5621 | 8.6631 |
|  | 7.4407 | 7.6997 | 7.9304 | 8.1366 | 8.3213 | 8.4872 | 8.6366 | 8.7714 | 8.8932 | 9.0037 |
|  | 7.6603 | 7.9350 | 8.1806 | 8.4006 | 8.5977 | 8.7770 | 8.9380 | 9.0837 | 9.2158 | 9.3359 |
|  | 7.8723 | 8.1624 | 8.4226 | 8.6567 | 8.8677 | 9.0584 | 9.2311 | 9.3878 | 9.5302 | 9.6599 |
|  | 8.0771 | 8.3823 | 8.6570 | 8.9048 | 9.1288 | 9.3318 | 9.5162 | 9.6838 | 9.8366 | 9.9761 |
| 30 | 8.2752 | 8.5953 | 8.8841 | 9.1454 | 9.3824 | 9.5976 | 9.7935 | 9.9722 | 10.1354 | 10.2847 |
|  | 8.4669 | 8.8015 | 9.1043 | 9.3790 | 9.6287 | 9.8560 | 10.0635 | 10.2531 | 10.4267 | 10.5859 |
|  | 8.6526 | 9.0015 | 9.3181 | 9.6059 | 9.8681 | 10.1075 | 10.3264 | 10.5270 | 10.7110 | 10.8800 |
|  | 8.8326 | 9.1956 | 9.5256 | 9.8263 | 10.1010 | 10.3523 | 10.5826 | 10.7940 | 10.9883 | 11.1673 |
|  | 9.0073 | 9.3840 | 9.7272 | 10.0407 | 10.3276 | 10.5907 | 10.8322 | 11.0544 | 11.2591 | 11.4478 |

| $F_1$ | $\beta=21$ | 22 | 23 | 24 | 25 | 26 | 27 | 28 | 29 | 30 |
|---|---|---|---|---|---|---|---|---|---|---|
| $\alpha=1$ | 0.0000 | 0.0000 | 0.0000 | 0.0000 | 0.0000 | 0.0000 | 0.0000 | 0.0000 | 0.0000 | 0.0000 |
| | 0.4987 | 0.4988 | 0.4989 | 0.4990 | 0.4991 | 0.4991 | 0.4992 | 0.4993 | 0.4993 | 0.4994 |
| | 0.9951 | 0.9956 | 0.9959 | 0.9963 | 0.9966 | 0.9970 | 0.9973 | 0.9974 | 0.9974 | 0.9976 |
| | 1.4883 | 1.4893 | 1.4902 | 1.4910 | 1.4917 | 1.4923 | 1.4929 | 1.4934 | 1.4938 | 1.4942 |
| 5 | 1.9772 | 1.9791 | 1.9809 | 1.9824 | 1.9838 | 1.9850 | 1.9860 | 1.9870 | 1.9879 | 1.9887 |
| | 2.4608 | 2.4642 | 2.4671 | 2.4697 | 2.4721 | 2.4741 | 2.4760 | 2.4776 | 2.4791 | 2.4804 |
| | 2.9384 | 2.9437 | 2.9483 | 2.9523 | 2.9559 | 2.9592 | 2.9620 | 2.9646 | 2.9670 | 2.9691 |
| | 3.4043 | 3.4162 | 3.4236 | 3.4295 | 3.4348 | 3.4396 | 3.4438 | 3.4476 | 3.4510 | 3.4541 |
| | 3.8727 | 3.8833 | 3.8926 | 3.9008 | 3.9082 | 3.9148 | 3.9207 | 3.9260 | 3.9308 | 3.9352 |
| 10 | 4.3282 | 4.3423 | 4.3547 | 4.3657 | 4.3756 | 4.3844 | 4.3923 | 4.3995 | 4.4060 | 4.4118 |
| | 4.7754 | 4.7935 | 4.8095 | 4.8236 | 4.8366 | 4.8480 | 4.8583 | 4.8676 | 4.8761 | 4.8838 |
| | 5.2140 | 5.2366 | 5.2567 | 5.2747 | 5.2908 | 5.3053 | 5.3183 | 5.3301 | 5.3409 | 5.3506 |
| | 5.6436 | 5.6713 | 5.6960 | 5.7181 | 5.7380 | 5.7559 | 5.7720 | 5.7867 | 5.8000 | 5.8122 |
| | 6.0642 | 6.0975 | 6.1272 | 6.1539 | 6.1779 | 6.1996 | 6.2192 | 6.2371 | 6.2533 | 6.2681 |
| 15 | 6.4757 | 6.5150 | 6.5502 | 6.5819 | 6.6104 | 6.6363 | 6.6597 | 6.6811 | 6.7005 | 6.7183 |
| | 6.8779 | 6.9237 | 6.9648 | 7.0019 | 7.0354 | 7.0658 | 7.0934 | 7.1185 | 7.1415 | 7.1625 |
| | 7.2711 | 7.3237 | 7.3711 | 7.4139 | 7.4527 | 7.4879 | 7.5200 | 7.5493 | 7.5760 | 7.6006 |
| | 7.6552 | 7.7150 | 7.7690 | 7.8179 | 7.8623 | 7.9027 | 7.9396 | 7.9733 | 8.0041 | 8.0325 |
| | 8.0304 | 8.0977 | 8.1586 | 8.2139 | 8.2642 | 8.3101 | 8.3520 | 8.3904 | 8.4257 | 8.4580 |
| 20 | 8.3968 | 8.4719 | 8.5400 | 8.6020 | 8.6585 | 8.7101 | 8.7574 | 8.8007 | 8.8406 | 8.8773 |
| | 8.7546 | 8.8377 | 8.9133 | 8.9822 | 9.0451 | 9.1028 | 9.1556 | 9.2042 | 9.2489 | 9.2901 |
| | 9.1040 | 9.1953 | 9.2785 | 9.3546 | 9.4242 | 9.4881 | 9.5467 | 9.6007 | 9.6505 | 9.6965 |
| | 9.4452 | 9.5448 | 9.6360 | 9.7194 | 9.7959 | 9.8662 | 9.9309 | 9.9905 | 10.0456 | 10.0965 |
| | 9.7783 | 9.8866 | 9.9857 | 10.0766 | 10.1602 | 10.2371 | 10.3080 | 10.3735 | 10.4340 | 10.4901 |
| 25 | 10.1037 | 10.2206 | 10.3279 | 10.4265 | 10.5173 | 10.6010 | 10.6783 | 10.7498 | 10.8160 | 10.8774 |
| | 10.4216 | 10.5473 | 10.6628 | 10.7692 | 10.8673 | 10.9580 | 11.0418 | 11.1195 | 11.1915 | 11.2584 |
| | 10.7322 | 10.8667 | 10.9906 | 11.1049 | 11.2105 | 11.3082 | 11.3987 | 11.4826 | 11.5606 | 11.6331 |
| | 11.0356 | 11.1790 | 11.3113 | 11.4336 | 11.5468 | 11.6517 | 11.7490 | 11.8393 | 11.9234 | 12.0017 |
| | 11.3322 | 11.4845 | 11.6254 | 11.7557 | 11.8765 | 11.9887 | 12.0928 | 12.1898 | 12.2800 | 12.3642 |
| 30 | 11.6222 | 11.7835 | 11.9328 | 12.0713 | 12.1998 | 12.3193 | 12.4304 | 12.5340 | 12.6305 | 12.7207 |

| $F_1$ $\alpha$ | $\beta=31$ | 32 | 33 | 34 | 35 | 36 | 37 | 38 | 39 | 40 |
|---|---|---|---|---|---|---|---|---|---|---|
| 1 | 0.0000 | 0.0000 | 0.0000 | 0.0000 | 0.0000 | 0.0000 | 0.0000 | 0.0000 | 0.0000 | 0.0000 |
|  | 0.4994 | 0.4994 | 0.4995 | 0.4995 | 0.4995 | 0.4996 | 0.4996 | 0.4996 | 0.4996 | 0.4996 |
|  | 0.9978 | 0.9979 | 0.9980 | 0.9981 | 0.9982 | 0.9983 | 0.9984 | 0.9985 | 0.9986 | 0.9986 |
|  | 1.4946 | 1.4949 | 1.4952 | 1.4955 | 1.4957 | 1.4960 | 1.4962 | 1.4964 | 1.4966 | 1.4967 |
| 5 | 1.9894 | 1.9900 | 1.9906 | 1.9911 | 1.9916 | 1.9921 | 1.9925 | 1.9929 | 1.9933 | 1.9936 |
|  | 2.4817 | 2.4828 | 2.4838 | 2.4847 | 2.4856 | 2.4863 | 2.4871 | 2.4877 | 2.4883 | 2.4889 |
|  | 2.9710 | 2.9728 | 2.9743 | 2.9758 | 2.9771 | 2.9784 | 2.9795 | 2.9806 | 2.9815 | 2.9824 |
|  | 3.4570 | 3.4595 | 3.4619 | 3.4641 | 3.4660 | 3.4679 | 3.4695 | 3.4711 | 3.4725 | 3.4739 |
|  | 3.9392 | 3.9428 | 3.9461 | 3.9491 | 3.9519 | 3.9545 | 3.9568 | 3.9590 | 3.9610 | 3.9629 |
| 10 | 4.4172 | 4.4221 | 4.4266 | 4.4307 | 4.4344 | 4.4379 | 4.4411 | 4.4441 | 4.4468 | 4.4494 |
|  | 4.8908 | 4.8971 | 4.9030 | 4.9084 | 4.9133 | 4.9179 | 4.9221 | 4.9260 | 4.9296 | 4.9330 |
|  | 5.3595 | 5.3675 | 5.3751 | 5.3820 | 5.3883 | 5.3942 | 5.3996 | 5.4046 | 5.4092 | 5.4135 |
|  | 5.8232 | 5.8334 | 5.8427 | 5.8513 | 5.8592 | 5.8665 | 5.8733 | 5.8795 | 5.8853 | 5.8907 |
|  | 6.2816 | 6.2941 | 6.3055 | 6.3160 | 6.3257 | 6.3347 | 6.3430 | 6.3507 | 6.3578 | 6.3645 |
| 15 | 6.7345 | 6.7495 | 6.7632 | 6.7759 | 6.7876 | 6.7984 | 6.8085 | 6.8178 | 6.8265 | 6.8345 |
|  | 7.1818 | 7.1995 | 7.2158 | 7.2309 | 7.2448 | 7.2577 | 7.2696 | 7.2808 | 7.2911 | 7.3008 |
|  | 7.6231 | 7.6439 | 7.6630 | 7.6807 | 7.6970 | 7.7122 | 7.7263 | 7.7394 | 7.7516 | 7.7630 |
|  | 8.0585 | 8.0825 | 8.1047 | 8.1252 | 8.1442 | 8.1616 | 8.1783 | 8.1935 | 8.2078 | 8.2210 |
|  | 8.4879 | 8.5154 | 8.5409 | 8.5644 | 8.5863 | 8.6066 | 8.6255 | 8.6431 | 8.6595 | 8.6749 |
| 20 | 8.9111 | 8.9424 | 8.9713 | 8.9982 | 9.0231 | 9.0462 | 9.0678 | 9.0879 | 9.1067 | 9.1243 |
|  | 9.3282 | 9.3634 | 9.3960 | 9.4263 | 9.4545 | 9.4807 | 9.5052 | 9.5280 | 9.5493 | 9.5693 |
|  | 9.7390 | 9.7784 | 9.8150 | 9.8489 | 9.8811 | 9.9140 | 9.9375 | 9.9631 | 9.9872 | 10.0097 |
|  | 10.1437 | 10.1874 | 10.2281 | 10.2659 | 10.3011 | 10.3340 | 10.3647 | 10.3934 | 10.4203 | 10.4454 |
|  | 10.5421 | 10.5904 | 10.6354 | 10.6772 | 10.7162 | 10.7527 | 10.7867 | 10.8186 | 10.8485 | 10.8766 |
| 25 | 10.9344 | 10.9874 | 11.0368 | 11.0829 | 11.1259 | 11.1660 | 11.2036 | 11.2389 | 11.2719 | 11.3029 |
|  | 11.3206 | 11.3785 | 11.4325 | 11.4829 | 11.5300 | 11.5740 | 11.6153 | 11.6540 | 11.6904 | 11.7245 |
|  | 11.7006 | 11.7636 | 11.8223 | 11.8772 | 11.9286 | 11.9767 | 12.0218 | 12.0642 | 12.1039 | 12.1414 |
|  | 12.0747 | 12.1428 | 12.2064 | 12.2660 | 12.3218 | 12.3740 | 12.4231 | 12.4692 | 12.5126 | 12.5534 |
|  | 12.4427 | 12.5162 | 12.5849 | 12.6492 | 12.7095 | 12.7661 | 12.8192 | 12.8692 | 12.9163 | 12.9606 |
| 30 | 12.8050 | 12.8838 | 12.9576 | 13.0268 | 13.0918 | 13.1528 | 13.2102 | 13.2642 | 13.3150 | 13.3630 |

| $F_1$ $\alpha$ | $\beta=41$ | 42 | 43 | 44 | 45 | 46 | 47 | 48 | 49 | 50 |
|---|---|---|---|---|---|---|---|---|---|---|
| 1 | 0.0000 | 0.0000 | 0.0000 | 0.0000 | 0.0000 | 0.0000 | 0.0000 | 0.0000 | 0.0000 | 0.0000 |
|  | 0.4997 | 0.4997 | 0.4997 | 0.4997 | 0.4997 | 0.4997 | 0.4997 | 0.4997 | 0.4998 | 0.4998 |
|  | 0.9987 | 0.9988 | 0.9988 | 0.9989 | 0.9989 | 0.9990 | 0.9990 | 0.9991 | 0.9991 | 0.9991 |
|  | 1.4969 | 1.4970 | 1.4972 | 1.4973 | 1.4974 | 1.4975 | 1.4976 | 1.4977 | 1.4978 | 1.4979 |
| 5 | 1.9939 | 1.9942 | 1.9944 | 1.9947 | 1.9949 | 1.9951 | 1.9953 | 1.9955 | 1.9957 | 1.9959 |
|  | 2.4894 | 2.4899 | 2.4904 | 2.4908 | 2.4912 | 2.4916 | 2.4919 | 2.4923 | 2.4926 | 2.4929 |
|  | 2.9833 | 2.9840 | 2.9848 | 2.9854 | 2.9861 | 2.9867 | 2.9872 | 2.9877 | 2.9882 | 2.9887 |
|  | 3.4751 | 3.4762 | 3.4773 | 3.4783 | 3.4793 | 3.4801 | 3.4810 | 3.4817 | 3.4825 | 3.4832 |
|  | 3.9647 | 3.9663 | 3.9678 | 3.9692 | 3.9706 | 3.9718 | 3.9730 | 3.9741 | 3.9751 | 3.9761 |
| 10 | 4.4518 | 4.4540 | 4.4560 | 4.4580 | 4.4598 | 4.4615 | 4.4631 | 4.4646 | 4.4660 | 4.4673 |
|  | 4.9361 | 4.9390 | 4.9418 | 4.9443 | 4.9467 | 4.9489 | 4.9510 | 4.9530 | 4.9549 | 4.9566 |
|  | 5.4175 | 5.4213 | 5.4248 | 5.4280 | 5.4311 | 5.4340 | 5.4367 | 5.4392 | 5.4416 | 5.4439 |
|  | 5.8958 | 5.9005 | 5.9049 | 5.9090 | 5.9129 | 5.9165 | 5.9199 | 5.9231 | 5.9261 | 5.9289 |
|  | 6.3707 | 6.3765 | 6.3819 | 6.3870 | 6.3918 | 6.3962 | 6.4004 | 6.4044 | 6.4081 | 6.4117 |
| 15 | 6.8421 | 6.8491 | 6.8557 | 6.8619 | 6.8677 | 6.8731 | 6.8782 | 6.8830 | 6.8876 | 6.8919 |
|  | 7.3098 | 7.3182 | 7.3261 | 7.3335 | 7.3404 | 7.3469 | 7.3531 | 7.3588 | 7.3643 | 7.3694 |
|  | 7.7736 | 7.7836 | 7.7929 | 7.8016 | 7.8098 | 7.8176 | 7.8248 | 7.8317 | 7.8381 | 7.8442 |
|  | 8.2335 | 8.2451 | 8.2560 | 8.2662 | 8.2758 | 8.2849 | 8.2934 | 8.3014 | 8.3090 | 8.3162 |
|  | 8.6892 | 8.7027 | 8.7153 | 8.7271 | 8.7383 | 8.7488 | 8.7586 | 8.7680 | 8.7768 | 8.7851 |
| 20 | 9.1407 | 9.1562 | 9.1706 | 9.1843 | 9.1971 | 9.2091 | 9.2205 | 9.2312 | 9.2413 | 9.2509 |
|  | 9.5880 | 9.6055 | 9.6220 | 9.6375 | 9.6521 | 9.6658 | 9.6788 | 9.6910 | 9.7026 | 9.7135 |
|  | 10.0308 | 10.0506 | 10.0692 | 10.0867 | 10.1032 | 10.1188 | 10.1335 | 10.1473 | 10.1604 | 10.1729 |
|  | 10.4691 | 10.4913 | 10.5122 | 10.5310 | 10.5504 | 10.5679 | 10.5844 | 10.6001 | 10.6148 | 10.6288 |
|  | 10.9029 | 10.9276 | 10.9509 | 10.9729 | 10.9936 | 11.0132 | 11.0316 | 11.0491 | 11.0657 | 11.0813 |
| 25 | 11.3321 | 11.3595 | 11.3854 | 11.4097 | 11.4327 | 11.4545 | 11.4750 | 11.4945 | 11.5129 | 11.5303 |
|  | 11.7567 | 11.7869 | 11.8154 | 11.8423 | 11.8678 | 11.8918 | 11.9145 | 11.9360 | 11.9564 | 11.9757 |
|  | 12.1766 | 12.2098 | 12.2411 | 12.2707 | 12.2986 | 12.3250 | 12.3500 | 12.3737 | 12.3962 | 12.4175 |
|  | 12.5918 | 12.6281 | 12.6623 | 12.6947 | 12.7252 | 12.7542 | 12.7816 | 12.8076 | 12.8322 | 12.8556 |
|  | 13.0024 | 13.0418 | 13.0791 | 13.1143 | 13.1476 | 13.1792 | 13.2091 | 13.2375 | 13.2644 | 13.2900 |
| 30 | 13.4082 | 13.4510 | 13.4914 | 13.5296 | 13.5658 | 13.6001 | 13.6326 | 13.6635 | 13.6928 | 13.7207 |

$10F_2$

| $\alpha$ | $\beta=1$ | 2 | 3 | 4 | 5 | 6 | 7 | 8 | 9 | 10 |
|---|---|---|---|---|---|---|---|---|---|---|
| 1 | 0.0000 | 0.0000 | 0.0000 | 0.0000 | 0.0000 | 0.0000 | 0.0000 | 0.0000 | 0.0000 | 0.0000 |
|  | 1.5910 | 2.7644 | 3.1696 | 3.3204 | 3.3854 | 3.4172 | 3.4343 | 3.4443 | 3.4505 | 3.4545 |
|  | 2.0156 | 3.8495 | 4.6778 | 5.0520 | 5.2343 | 5.3306 | 5.3853 | 5.4183 | 5.4392 | 5.4531 |
|  | 2.1800 | 4.3554 | 5.4945 | 6.0848 | 6.4045 | 6.5868 | 6.6961 | 6.7647 | 6.8095 | 6.8399 |
| 5 | 2.2592 | 4.6234 | 5.9718 | 6.7382 | 7.1887 | 7.4632 | 7.6365 | 7.7497 | 7.8260 | 7.8789 |
|  | 2.3032 | 4.7800 | 6.2689 | 7.1699 | 7.7329 | 8.0950 | 8.3342 | 8.4963 | 8.6088 | 8.6888 |
|  | 2.3300 | 4.8786 | 6.4639 | 7.4659 | 8.1212 | 8.5611 | 8.8630 | 9.0744 | 9.2254 | 9.3352 |
|  | 2.3476 | 4.9443 | 6.5979 | 7.6758 | 8.4052 | 8.9117 | 9.2705 | 9.5291 | 9.7184 | 9.8590 |
|  | 2.3597 | 4.9903 | 6.6934 | 7.8290 | 8.6176 | 9.1801 | 9.5891 | 9.8911 | 10.1171 | 10.2883 |
| 10 | 2.3683 | 5.0236 | 6.7637 | 7.9438 | 8.7798 | 9.3889 | 9.8415 | 10.1825 | 10.4427 | 10.6432 |
|  | 2.3748 | 5.0485 | 6.8168 | 8.0317 | 8.9059 | 9.5539 | 10.0438 | 10.4195 | 10.7109 | 10.9391 |
|  | 2.3797 | 5.0676 | 6.8578 | 8.1004 | 9.0056 | 9.6860 | 10.2080 | 10.6142 | 10.9337 | 11.1874 |
|  | 2.3835 | 5.0825 | 6.8901 | 8.1549 | 9.0854 | 9.7932 | 10.3426 | 10.7755 | 11.1202 | 11.3973 |
|  | 2.3865 | 5.0944 | 6.9160 | 8.1990 | 9.1507 | 9.8811 | 10.4540 | 10.9102 | 11.2775 | 11.5757 |
| 15 | 2.3890 | 5.1041 | 6.9371 | 8.2350 | 9.2043 | 9.9540 | 10.5472 | 11.0238 | 11.4110 | 11.7283 |
|  | 2.3910 | 5.1120 | 6.9544 | 8.2647 | 9.2489 | 10.0151 | 10.6257 | 11.1201 | 11.5251 | 11.8597 |
|  | 2.3927 | 5.1185 | 6.9689 | 8.2897 | 9.2864 | 10.0666 | 10.6924 | 11.2025 | 11.6232 | 11.9733 |
|  | 2.3940 | 5.1240 | 6.9810 | 8.3107 | 9.3181 | 10.1106 | 10.7495 | 11.2733 | 11.7081 | 12.0721 |
|  | 2.3952 | 5.1287 | 6.9914 | 8.3286 | 9.3453 | 10.1483 | 10.7987 | 11.3347 | 11.7819 | 12.1584 |
| 20 | 2.3962 | 5.1327 | 7.0002 | 8.3440 | 9.3687 | 10.1808 | 10.8413 | 11.3881 | 11.8464 | 12.2343 |
|  | 2.3971 | 5.1362 | 7.0079 | 8.3573 | 9.3890 | 10.2092 | 10.8786 | 11.4349 | 11.9032 | 12.3012 |
|  | 2.3979 | 5.1392 | 7.0145 | 8.3689 | 9.4066 | 10.2339 | 10.9112 | 11.4760 | 11.9532 | 12.3604 |
|  | 2.3985 | 5.1418 | 7.0203 | 8.3791 | 9.4222 | 10.2557 | 10.9400 | 11.5124 | 11.9976 | 12.4131 |
|  | 2.3991 | 5.1441 | 7.0254 | 8.3880 | 9.4358 | 10.2749 | 10.9655 | 11.5447 | 12.0371 | 12.4601 |
| 25 | 2.3996 | 5.1461 | 7.0299 | 8.3959 | 9.4480 | 10.2920 | 10.9882 | 11.5735 | 12.0724 | 12.5023 |
|  | 2.4001 | 5.1479 | 7.0339 | 8.4029 | 9.4588 | 10.3073 | 11.0084 | 11.5992 | 12.1041 | 12.5401 |
|  | 2.4005 | 5.1495 | 7.0375 | 8.4092 | 9.4684 | 10.3209 | 11.0266 | 11.6224 | 12.1326 | 12.5743 |
|  | 2.4008 | 5.1509 | 7.0407 | 8.4148 | 9.4771 | 10.3332 | 11.0429 | 11.6433 | 12.1584 | 12.6052 |
|  | 2.4011 | 5.1522 | 7.0436 | 8.4199 | 9.4849 | 10.3442 | 11.0577 | 11.6621 | 12.1817 | 12.6333 |
| 30 | 2.4014 | 5.1534 | 7.0462 | 8.4245 | 9.4919 | 10.3542 | 11.0711 | 11.6792 | 12.2029 | 12.6588 |

$10F_2$

| $\alpha$ | $\beta=11$ | 12 | 13 | 14 | 15 | 16 | 17 | 18 | 19 | 20 |
|---|---|---|---|---|---|---|---|---|---|---|
| 1 | 0.0000 | 0.0000 | 0.0000 | 0.0000 | 0.0000 | 0.0000 | 0.0000 | 0.0000 | 0.0000 | 0.0000 |
|  | 3.4573 | 3.4592 | 3.4605 | 3.4616 | 3.4623 | 3.4629 | 3.4634 | 3.4638 | 3.4641 | 3.4643 |
|  | 5.4626 | 5.4694 | 5.4743 | 5.4779 | 5.4807 | 5.4828 | 5.4845 | 5.4858 | 5.4869 | 5.4878 |
|  | 6.8611 | 6.8763 | 6.8875 | 6.8959 | 6.9023 | 6.9072 | 6.9111 | 6.9142 | 6.9168 | 6.9188 |
|  | 7.9165 | 7.9439 | 7.9643 | 7.9797 | 7.9916 | 8.0008 | 8.0082 | 8.0141 | 8.0188 | 8.0227 |
| 5 | 8.7468 | 8.7898 | 8.8221 | 8.8468 | 8.8661 | 8.8812 | 8.8933 | 8.9030 | 8.9109 | 8.9174 |
|  | 9.4164 | 9.4775 | 9.5241 | 9.5602 | 9.5885 | 9.6109 | 9.6290 | 9.6436 | 9.6555 | 9.6654 |
|  | 9.9650 | 10.0459 | 10.1086 | 10.1577 | 10.1965 | 10.2276 | 10.2528 | 10.2733 | 10.2902 | 10.3042 |
|  | 10.4195 | 10.5213 | 10.6012 | 10.6644 | 10.7150 | 10.7558 | 10.7891 | 10.8164 | 10.8390 | 10.8579 |
|  | 10.7995 | 10.9224 | 11.0199 | 11.0981 | 11.1612 | 11.2126 | 11.2548 | 11.2897 | 11.3188 | 11.3431 |
| 10 | 11.1194 | 11.2630 | 11.3784 | 11.4718 | 11.5480 | 11.6105 | 11.6623 | 11.7054 | 11.7415 | 11.7719 |
|  | 11.3905 | 11.5542 | 11.6871 | 11.7957 | 11.8852 | 11.9592 | 12.0209 | 12.0726 | 12.1162 | 12.1531 |
|  | 11.6215 | 11.8043 | 11.9542 | 12.0778 | 12.1805 | 12.2661 | 12.3380 | 12.3986 | 12.4500 | 12.4938 |
|  | 11.8196 | 12.0202 | 12.1863 | 12.3246 | 12.4402 | 12.5374 | 12.6195 | 12.6892 | 12.7486 | 12.7995 |
|  | 11.9902 | 12.2076 | 12.3890 | 12.5412 | 12.6694 | 12.7780 | 12.8702 | 12.9490 | 13.0166 | 13.0747 |
| 15 | 12.1380 | 12.3708 | 12.5667 | 12.7321 | 12.8724 | 12.9920 | 13.0943 | 13.1821 | 13.2578 | 13.3233 |
|  | 12.2666 | 12.5137 | 12.7229 | 12.9009 | 13.0528 | 13.1831 | 13.2951 | 13.3918 | 13.4755 | 13.5483 |
|  | 12.3790 | 12.6393 | 12.8610 | 13.0507 | 13.2136 | 13.3540 | 13.4755 | 13.5808 | 13.6725 | 13.7526 |
|  | 12.4777 | 12.7500 | 12.9833 | 13.1840 | 13.3573 | 13.5074 | 13.6379 | 13.7517 | 13.8511 | 13.9383 |
|  | 12.5648 | 12.8481 | 13.0921 | 13.3030 | 13.4861 | 13.6454 | 13.7846 | 13.9064 | 14.0134 | 14.1075 |
| 20 | 12.6419 | 12.9353 | 13.1891 | 13.4097 | 13.6019 | 13.7699 | 13.9173 | 14.0467 | 14.1611 | 14.2621 |
|  | 12.7104 | 13.0131 | 13.2760 | 13.5054 | 13.7062 | 13.8825 | 14.0377 | 14.1747 | 14.2959 | 14.4034 |
|  | 12.7715 | 13.0827 | 13.3540 | 13.5917 | 13.8005 | 13.9845 | 14.1471 | 14.2911 | 14.4191 | 14.5329 |
|  | 12.8263 | 13.1452 | 13.4243 | 13.6696 | 13.8858 | 14.0771 | 14.2467 | 14.3975 | 14.5318 | 14.6517 |
|  | 12.8755 | 13.2015 | 13.4877 | 13.7401 | 13.9634 | 14.1614 | 14.3377 | 14.4948 | 14.6352 | 14.7610 |
| 25 | 12.9198 | 13.2523 | 13.5452 | 13.8041 | 14.0339 | 14.2384 | 14.4208 | 14.5840 | 14.7302 | 14.8616 |
|  | 12.9598 | 13.2984 | 13.5974 | 13.8624 | 14.0983 | 14.3087 | 14.4970 | 14.6659 | 14.8177 | 14.9543 |
|  | 12.9961 | 13.3403 | 13.6449 | 13.9156 | 14.1571 | 14.3732 | 14.5670 | 14.7413 | 14.8983 | 15.0400 |
|  | 13.0291 | 13.3784 | 13.6882 | 13.9642 | 14.2110 | 14.4323 | 14.6313 | 14.8107 | 14.9727 | 15.1192 |
| 30 | 13.0592 | 13.4132 | 13.7278 | 14.0087 | 14.2604 | 14.4867 | 14.6906 | 14.8748 | 15.0415 | 15.1926 |

| $10F_2$ | $\beta=21$ | 22 | 23 | 24 | 25 | 26 | 27 | 28 | 29 | 30 |
|---|---|---|---|---|---|---|---|---|---|---|
| $\alpha=1$ | 0.0000 | 0.0000 | 0.0000 | 0.0000 | 0.0000 | 0.0000 | 0.0000 | 0.0000 | 0.0000 | 0.0000 |
| | 3.4645 | 3.4647 | 3.4648 | 3.4649 | 3.4650 | 3.4651 | 3.4651 | 3.4652 | 3.4653 | 3.4653 |
| | 5.4885 | 5.4891 | 5.4896 | 5.4900 | 5.4903 | 5.4906 | 5.4909 | 5.4911 | 5.4913 | 5.4915 |
| | 6.9205 | 6.9219 | 6.9231 | 6.9241 | 6.9249 | 6.9256 | 6.9262 | 6.9268 | 6.9272 | 6.9276 |
| 5 | 8.0260 | 8.0287 | 8.0309 | 8.0328 | 8.0344 | 8.0358 | 8.0370 | 8.0380 | 8.0389 | 8.0397 |
| | 8.9228 | 8.9273 | 8.9311 | 8.9343 | 8.9370 | 8.9393 | 8.9414 | 8.9431 | 8.9447 | 8.9460 |
| | 9.6736 | 9.6805 | 9.6863 | 9.6913 | 9.6955 | 9.6991 | 9.7023 | 9.7050 | 9.7073 | 9.7094 |
| | 10.3159 | 10.3258 | 10.3341 | 10.3412 | 10.3473 | 10.3526 | 10.3571 | 10.3611 | 10.3645 | 10.3676 |
| | 10.8737 | 10.8871 | 10.8985 | 10.9082 | 10.9166 | 10.9238 | 10.9301 | 10.9356 | 10.9404 | 10.9446 |
| 10 | 11.3637 | 11.3811 | 11.3960 | 11.4088 | 11.4198 | 11.4293 | 11.4377 | 11.4449 | 11.4513 | 11.4569 |
| | 11.7977 | 11.8196 | 11.8385 | 11.8547 | 11.8687 | 11.8809 | 11.8915 | 11.9008 | 11.9090 | 11.9163 |
| | 12.1846 | 12.2115 | 12.2346 | 12.2547 | 12.2720 | 12.2872 | 12.3004 | 12.3121 | 12.3223 | 12.3311 |
| | 12.5313 | 12.5635 | 12.5913 | 12.6155 | 12.6365 | 12.6549 | 12.6710 | 12.6852 | 12.6977 | 12.7088 |
| | 12.8432 | 12.8810 | 12.9138 | 12.9424 | 12.9673 | 12.9892 | 13.0084 | 13.0254 | 13.0404 | 13.0538 |
| 15 | 13.1250 | 13.1686 | 13.2065 | 13.2396 | 13.2687 | 13.2943 | 13.3168 | 13.3368 | 13.3545 | 13.3703 |
| | 13.3801 | 13.4296 | 13.4729 | 13.5108 | 13.5442 | 13.5737 | 13.5997 | 13.6229 | 13.6434 | 13.6618 |
| | 13.6118 | 13.6673 | 13.7160 | 13.7589 | 13.7967 | 13.8302 | 13.8599 | 13.8863 | 13.9103 | 13.9310 |
| | 13.8226 | 13.8842 | 13.9384 | 13.9862 | 14.0286 | 14.0662 | 14.0997 | 14.1296 | 14.1563 | 14.1803 |
| | 14.0149 | 14.0825 | 14.1422 | 14.1951 | 14.2421 | 14.2839 | 14.3213 | 14.3547 | 14.3846 | 14.4115 |
| 20 | 14.1906 | 14.2641 | 14.3293 | 14.3873 | 14.4389 | 14.4850 | 14.5263 | 14.5633 | 14.5965 | 14.6265 |
| | 14.3515 | 14.4308 | 14.5014 | 14.5644 | 14.6207 | 14.6711 | 14.7163 | 14.7570 | 14.7936 | 14.8267 |
| | 14.4989 | 14.5840 | 14.6600 | 14.7279 | 14.7888 | 14.8435 | 14.8927 | 14.9370 | 14.9771 | 15.0133 |
| | 14.6344 | 14.7251 | 14.8063 | 14.8791 | 14.9446 | 15.0035 | 15.0566 | 15.1047 | 15.1481 | 15.1876 |
| | 14.7590 | 14.8551 | 14.9414 | 15.0191 | 15.0890 | 15.1522 | 15.2092 | 15.2610 | 15.3079 | 15.3505 |
| 25 | 14.8738 | 14.9752 | 15.0665 | 15.1488 | 15.2232 | 15.2904 | 15.3514 | 15.4068 | 15.4571 | 15.5029 |
| | 14.9797 | 15.0862 | 15.1823 | 15.2692 | 15.3479 | 15.4192 | 15.4841 | 15.5430 | 15.5968 | 15.6458 |
| | 15.0776 | 15.1889 | 15.2897 | 15.3811 | 15.4640 | 15.5393 | 15.6079 | 15.6705 | 15.7276 | 15.7797 |
| | 15.1681 | 15.2842 | 15.3895 | 15.4851 | 15.5721 | 15.6514 | 15.7237 | 15.7898 | 15.8502 | 15.9055 |
| | 15.2521 | 15.3727 | 15.4823 | 15.5821 | 15.6731 | 15.7561 | 15.8321 | 15.9015 | 15.9652 | 16.0236 |
| 30 | 15.3299 | 15.4549 | 15.5687 | 15.6725 | 15.7673 | 15.8541 | 15.9335 | 16.0064 | 16.0733 | 16.1347 |

| $10F_2$ | $\beta=31$ | 32 | 33 | 34 | 35 | 36 | 37 | 38 | 39 | 40 |
|---|---|---|---|---|---|---|---|---|---|---|
| $\alpha=1$ | 0.0000 | 0.0000 | 0.0000 | 0.0000 | 0.0000 | 0.0000 | 0.0000 | 0.0000 | 0.0000 | 0.0000 |
| | 3.4653 | 3.4654 | 3.4654 | 3.4654 | 3.4655 | 3.4655 | 3.4655 | 3.4655 | 3.4655 | 3.4656 |
| | 5.4916 | 5.4918 | 5.4919 | 5.4920 | 5.4921 | 5.4921 | 5.4922 | 5.4923 | 5.4923 | 5.4924 |
| | 6.9280 | 6.9283 | 6.9286 | 6.9288 | 6.9291 | 6.9292 | 6.9294 | 6.9296 | 6.9297 | 6.9298 |
| 5 | 8.0404 | 8.0410 | 8.0416 | 8.0420 | 8.0425 | 8.0428 | 8.0432 | 8.0435 | 8.0438 | 8.0440 |
| | 8.9472 | 8.9482 | 8.9491 | 8.9499 | 8.9507 | 8.9513 | 8.9519 | 8.9524 | 8.9529 | 8.9533 |
| | 9.7113 | 9.7129 | 9.7143 | 9.7156 | 9.7167 | 9.7177 | 9.7187 | 9.7195 | 9.7202 | 9.7209 |
| | 10.3702 | 10.3726 | 10.3747 | 10.3766 | 10.3782 | 10.3797 | 10.3811 | 10.3823 | 10.3834 | 10.3844 |
| | 10.9483 | 10.9516 | 10.9545 | 10.9571 | 10.9594 | 10.9615 | 10.9634 | 10.9651 | 10.9666 | 10.9680 |
| 10 | 11.4618 | 11.4662 | 11.4701 | 11.4736 | 11.4768 | 11.4796 | 11.4821 | 11.4844 | 11.4864 | 11.4883 |
| | 11.9227 | 11.9283 | 11.9334 | 11.9379 | 11.9420 | 11.9457 | 11.9489 | 11.9519 | 11.9546 | 11.9571 |
| | 12.3394 | 12.3466 | 12.3530 | 12.3587 | 12.3638 | 12.3685 | 12.3726 | 12.3764 | 12.3798 | 12.3829 |
| | 12.7187 | 12.7275 | 12.7354 | 12.7425 | 12.7488 | 12.7546 | 12.7597 | 12.7644 | 12.7687 | 12.7725 |
| | 13.0657 | 13.0763 | 13.0858 | 13.0944 | 13.1021 | 13.1091 | 13.1154 | 13.1211 | 13.1262 | 13.1310 |
| 15 | 13.3844 | 13.3970 | 13.4084 | 13.4185 | 13.4277 | 13.4360 | 13.4436 | 13.4504 | 13.4566 | 13.4623 |
| | 13.6783 | 13.6930 | 13.7063 | 13.7182 | 13.7290 | 13.7388 | 13.7476 | 13.7557 | 13.7630 | 13.7697 |
| | 13.9500 | 13.9670 | 13.9823 | 13.9961 | 14.0086 | 14.0200 | 14.0303 | 14.0397 | 14.0482 | 14.0561 |
| | 14.2018 | 14.2212 | 14.2387 | 14.2545 | 14.2689 | 14.2819 | 14.2938 | 14.3046 | 14.3144 | 14.3235 |
| | 14.4358 | 14.4576 | 14.4774 | 14.4954 | 14.5116 | 14.5264 | 14.5399 | 14.5522 | 14.5635 | 14.5738 |
| 20 | 14.6535 | 14.6780 | 14.7001 | 14.7203 | 14.7385 | 14.7552 | 14.7704 | 14.7843 | 14.7970 | 14.8087 |
| | 14.8566 | 14.8837 | 14.9083 | 14.9306 | 14.9510 | 14.9696 | 14.9866 | 15.0021 | 15.0164 | 15.0295 |
| | 15.0461 | 15.0759 | 15.1030 | 15.1277 | 15.1503 | 15.1709 | 15.1897 | 15.2070 | 15.2228 | 15.2374 |
| | 15.2233 | 15.2559 | 15.2856 | 15.3126 | 15.3373 | 15.3600 | 15.3808 | 15.3999 | 15.4174 | 15.4335 |
| | 15.3892 | 15.4246 | 15.4568 | 15.4863 | 15.5133 | 15.5381 | 15.5608 | 15.5817 | 15.6009 | 15.6187 |
| 25 | 15.5447 | 15.5829 | 15.6177 | 15.6497 | 15.6790 | 15.7058 | 15.7306 | 15.7533 | 15.7743 | 15.7937 |
| | 15.6905 | 15.7315 | 15.7690 | 15.8034 | 15.8350 | 15.8641 | 15.8908 | 15.9155 | 15.9383 | 15.9593 |
| | 15.8275 | 15.8713 | 15.9114 | 15.9483 | 15.9822 | 16.0135 | 16.0423 | 16.0689 | 16.0935 | 16.1162 |
| | 15.9562 | 16.0028 | 16.0455 | 16.0849 | 16.1212 | 16.1547 | 16.1856 | 16.2141 | 16.2405 | 16.2650 |
| | 16.0773 | 16.1266 | 16.1720 | 16.2139 | 16.2525 | 16.2882 | 16.3211 | 16.3517 | 16.3800 | 16.4062 |
| 30 | 16.1913 | 16.2433 | 16.2914 | 16.3357 | 16.3766 | 16.4145 | 16.4496 | 16.4821 | 16.5123 | 16.5403 |

| $10F_2$ | $\beta=41$ | 42 | 43 | 44 | 45 | 46 | 47 | 48 | 49 | 50 |
|---|---|---|---|---|---|---|---|---|---|---|
| $\alpha=1$ | 0.0000 | 0.0000 | 0.0000 | 0.0000 | 0.0000 | 0.0000 | 0.0000 | 0.0000 | 0.0000 | 0.0000 |
|  | 3.4656 | 3.4656 | 3.4656 | 3.4656 | 3.4656 | 3.4656 | 3.4656 | 3.4656 | 3.4656 | 3.4656 |
|  | 5.4924 | 5.4925 | 5.4925 | 5.4926 | 5.4926 | 5.4926 | 5.4926 | 5.4927 | 5.4927 | 5.4927 |
|  | 6.9300 | 6.9301 | 6.9302 | 6.9302 | 6.9303 | 6.9304 | 6.9305 | 6.9305 | 6.9306 | 6.9306 |
| 5 | 8.0442 | 8.0444 | 8.0446 | 8.0448 | 8.0449 | 8.0451 | 8.0452 | 8.0453 | 8.0455 | 8.0456 |
|  | 8.9537 | 8.9540 | 8.9544 | 8.9547 | 8.9549 | 8.9552 | 8.9554 | 8.9556 | 8.9558 | 8.9560 |
|  | 9.7215 | 9.7220 | 9.7226 | 9.7230 | 9.7234 | 9.7238 | 9.7242 | 9.7245 | 9.7248 | 9.7251 |
|  | 10.3853 | 10.3861 | 10.3868 | 10.3875 | 10.3881 | 10.3887 | 10.3892 | 10.3897 | 10.3901 | 10.3905 |
|  | 10.9693 | 10.9704 | 10.9714 | 10.9724 | 10.9733 | 10.9741 | 10.9748 | 10.9755 | 10.9761 | 10.9767 |
| 10 | 11.4900 | 11.4915 | 11.4930 | 11.4943 | 11.4954 | 11.4965 | 11.4975 | 11.4984 | 11.4993 | 11.5001 |
|  | 11.9593 | 11.9613 | 11.9631 | 11.9648 | 11.9664 | 11.9678 | 11.9691 | 11.9703 | 11.9715 | 11.9725 |
|  | 12.3858 | 12.3883 | 12.3907 | 12.3929 | 12.3948 | 12.3967 | 12.3983 | 12.3999 | 12.4013 | 12.4026 |
|  | 12.7761 | 12.7793 | 12.7822 | 12.7849 | 12.7874 | 12.7897 | 12.7918 | 12.7937 | 12.7955 | 12.7971 |
|  | 13.1353 | 13.1392 | 13.1428 | 13.1461 | 13.1491 | 13.1519 | 13.1545 | 13.1569 | 13.1591 | 13.1611 |
| 15 | 13.4674 | 13.4722 | 13.4765 | 13.4805 | 13.4842 | 13.4875 | 13.4906 | 13.4935 | 13.4962 | 13.4986 |
|  | 13.7759 | 13.7815 | 13.7866 | 13.7914 | 13.7957 | 13.7997 | 13.8034 | 13.8068 | 13.8100 | 13.8130 |
|  | 14.0632 | 14.0698 | 14.0758 | 14.0814 | 14.0865 | 14.0912 | 14.0955 | 14.0995 | 14.1033 | 14.1068 |
|  | 14.3317 | 14.3393 | 14.3463 | 14.3527 | 14.3587 | 14.3641 | 14.3692 | 14.3739 | 14.3782 | 14.3822 |
|  | 14.5833 | 14.5920 | 14.6000 | 14.6073 | 14.6141 | 14.6204 | 14.6262 | 14.6316 | 14.6366 | 14.6413 |
| 20 | 14.8194 | 14.8293 | 14.8384 | 14.8467 | 14.8545 | 14.8616 | 14.8683 | 14.8744 | 14.8801 | 14.8855 |
|  | 15.0416 | 15.0526 | 15.0629 | 15.0723 | 15.0811 | 15.0891 | 15.0966 | 15.1036 | 15.1101 | 15.1161 |
|  | 15.2509 | 15.2632 | 15.2747 | 15.2852 | 15.2950 | 15.3041 | 15.3125 | 15.3203 | 15.3276 | 15.3344 |
|  | 15.4484 | 15.4621 | 15.4748 | 15.4865 | 15.4974 | 15.5075 | 15.5169 | 15.5255 | 15.5337 | 15.5413 |
|  | 15.6350 | 15.6501 | 15.6641 | 15.6771 | 15.6891 | 15.7003 | 15.7106 | 15.7203 | 15.7293 | 15.7377 |
| 25 | 15.8116 | 15.8281 | 15.8435 | 15.8577 | 15.8709 | 15.8832 | 15.8946 | 15.9052 | 15.9151 | 15.9244 |
|  | 15.9786 | 15.9968 | 16.0136 | 16.0291 | 16.0435 | 16.0569 | 16.0694 | 16.0811 | 16.0920 | 16.1021 |
|  | 16.1373 | 16.1569 | 16.1750 | 16.1919 | 16.2076 | 16.2222 | 16.2358 | 16.2485 | 16.2604 | 16.2714 |
|  | 16.2877 | 16.3088 | 16.3284 | 16.3466 | 16.3636 | 16.3794 | 16.3942 | 16.4080 | 16.4209 | 16.4329 |
|  | 16.4306 | 16.4532 | 16.4743 | 16.4939 | 16.5122 | 16.5293 | 16.5452 | 16.5601 | 16.5740 | 16.5871 |
| 30 | 16.5663 | 16.5905 | 16.6131 | 16.6342 | 16.6538 | 16.6721 | 16.6892 | 16.7053 | 16.7203 | 16.7344 |

| $-100F_3$ | $\beta=1$ | 2 | 3 | 4 | 5 | 6 | 7 | 8 | 9 | 10 |
|---|---|---|---|---|---|---|---|---|---|---|
| $\alpha=1$ | 0.0000 | 0.0000 | 0.0000 | 0.0000 | 0.0000 | 0.0000 | 0.0000 | 0.0000 | 0.0000 | 0.0000 |
| | 18.0994 | 6.6028 | 2.3176 | 0.9397 | 0.4368 | 0.2265 | 0.1279 | 0.0772 | 0.0492 | 0.0328 |
| | 25.0131 | 12.1648 | 5.3655 | 2.5217 | 1.2865 | 0.7083 | 0.4164 | 0.2586 | 0.1682 | 0.1137 |
| | 27.9761 | 15.6525 | 8.0063 | 4.2411 | 2.3624 | 1.3853 | 0.8521 | 0.5471 | 0.3647 | 0.2512 |
| 5 | 29.4656 | 17.7742 | 9.9814 | 5.7734 | 3.4601 | 2.1494 | 1.3824 | 0.9185 | 0.6288 | 0.4423 |
| | 30.3091 | 19.1093 | 11.3986 | 7.0221 | 4.4583 | 2.9093 | 1.9486 | 1.3381 | 0.9407 | 0.6760 |
| | 30.8299 | 19.9878 | 12.4149 | 8.0032 | 5.3128 | 3.6104 | 2.5052 | 1.7727 | 1.2781 | 0.9380 |
| | 31.1729 | 20.5908 | 13.1545 | 8.7659 | 6.0225 | 4.2296 | 3.0244 | 2.1978 | 1.6216 | 1.2140 |
| | 31.4105 | 21.0200 | 13.7032 | 9.3602 | 6.6045 | 4.7633 | 3.4928 | 2.5976 | 1.9567 | 1.4919 |
| 10 | 31.5816 | 21.3356 | 14.1186 | 9.8268 | 7.0800 | 5.2172 | 3.9071 | 2.9639 | 2.2740 | 1.7628 |
| | 31.7088 | 21.5736 | 14.4392 | 10.1971 | 7.4694 | 5.6013 | 4.2690 | 3.2941 | 2.5681 | 2.0207 |
| | 31.8060 | 21.7573 | 14.6909 | 10.4944 | 7.7898 | 5.9258 | 4.5832 | 3.5883 | 2.8370 | 2.2620 |
| | 31.8816 | 21.9019 | 14.8917 | 10.7356 | 8.0553 | 6.2006 | 4.8553 | 3.8489 | 3.0803 | 2.4849 |
| | 31.9421 | 22.0177 | 15.0542 | 10.9336 | 8.2767 | 6.4340 | 5.0908 | 4.0788 | 3.2992 | 2.6892 |
| 15 | 31.9908 | 22.1118 | 15.1874 | 11.0977 | 8.4627 | 6.6331 | 5.2950 | 4.2815 | 3.4953 | 2.8752 |
| | 32.0306 | 22.1892 | 15.2978 | 11.2351 | 8.6202 | 6.8037 | 5.4724 | 4.4602 | 3.6708 | 3.0441 |
| | 32.0639 | 22.2537 | 15.3903 | 11.3511 | 8.7544 | 6.9508 | 5.6274 | 4.5832 | 3.8276 | 3.1969 |
| | 32.0917 | 22.3080 | 15.4685 | 11.4498 | 8.8696 | 7.0781 | 5.7624 | 4.7573 | 3.9678 | 3.3350 |
| | 32.1153 | 22.3541 | 15.5352 | 11.5344 | 8.9690 | 7.1889 | 5.8812 | 4.8809 | 4.0932 | 3.4599 |
| 20 | 32.1354 | 22.3936 | 15.5925 | 11.6075 | 9.0553 | 7.2858 | 5.9859 | 4.9906 | 4.2056 | 3.5728 |
| | 32.1527 | 22.4276 | 15.6421 | 11.6710 | 9.1307 | 7.3709 | 6.0785 | 5.0884 | 4.3065 | 3.6749 |
| | 32.1678 | 22.4572 | 15.6853 | 11.7265 | 9.1970 | 7.4461 | 6.1607 | 5.1758 | 4.3973 | 3.7675 |
| | 32.1809 | 22.4830 | 15.7232 | 11.7753 | 9.2554 | 7.5127 | 6.2339 | 5.2541 | 4.4791 | 3.8514 |
| | 32.1924 | 22.5058 | 15.7565 | 11.8183 | 9.3071 | 7.5719 | 6.2993 | 5.3244 | 4.5530 | 3.9277 |
| 25 | 32.2026 | 22.5258 | 15.7860 | 11.8566 | 9.3532 | 7.6249 | 6.3581 | 5.3878 | 4.6200 | 3.9971 |
| | 32.2116 | 22.5437 | 15.8122 | 11.8907 | 9.3944 | 7.6723 | 6.4109 | 5.4451 | 4.6807 | 4.0604 |
| | 32.2196 | 22.5596 | 15.8357 | 11.9212 | 9.4314 | 7.7150 | 6.4586 | 5.4969 | 4.7359 | 4.1182 |
| | 32.2268 | 22.5738 | 15.8567 | 11.9485 | 9.4646 | 7.7536 | 6.5018 | 5.5440 | 4.7863 | 4.1711 |
| | 32.2333 | 22.5866 | 15.8756 | 11.9732 | 9.4947 | 7.7885 | 6.5410 | 5.5870 | 4.8323 | 4.2196 |
| 30 | 32.2391 | 22.5982 | 15.8927 | 11.9956 | 9.5219 | 7.8202 | 6.5766 | 5.6261 | 4.8744 | 4.2641 |

| $-100F_3$ | $\beta=11$ | 12 | 13 | 14 | 15 | 16 | 17 | 18 | 19 | 20 |
|---|---|---|---|---|---|---|---|---|---|---|
| $\alpha=1$ | 0.0000 | 0.0000 | 0.0000 | 0.0000 | 0.0000 | 0.0000 | 0.0000 | 0.0000 | 0.0000 | 0.0000 |
| | 0.0226 | 0.0161 | 0.0118 | 0.0088 | 0.0067 | 0.0052 | 0.0041 | 0.0033 | 0.0026 | 0.0022 |
| | 0.0794 | 0.0571 | 0.0420 | 0.0316 | 0.0242 | 0.0188 | 0.0148 | 0.0119 | 0.0096 | 0.0078 |
| | 0.1780 | 0.1294 | 0.0961 | 0.0728 | 0.0560 | 0.0438 | 0.0347 | 0.0279 | 0.0226 | 0.0185 |
| 5 | 0.3187 | 0.2347 | 0.1762 | 0.1346 | 0.1044 | 0.0822 | 0.0655 | 0.0528 | 0.0430 | 0.0354 |
| | 0.4957 | 0.3703 | 0.2813 | 0.2170 | 0.1698 | 0.1345 | 0.1078 | 0.0874 | 0.0715 | 0.0590 |
| | 0.7000 | 0.5306 | 0.4081 | 0.3181 | 0.2511 | 0.2005 | 0.1617 | 0.1318 | 0.1083 | 0.0898 |
| | 0.9215 | 0.7088 | 0.5519 | 0.4349 | 0.3464 | 0.2788 | 0.2265 | 0.1856 | 0.1534 | 0.1278 |
| | 1.1508 | 0.8976 | 0.7076 | 0.5635 | 0.4530 | 0.3675 | 0.3007 | 0.2480 | 0.2061 | 0.1725 |
| 10 | 1.3602 | 1.0908 | 0.8700 | 0.7000 | 0.5679 | 0.4645 | 0.3828 | 0.3177 | 0.2655 | 0.2233 |
| | 1.6037 | 1.2932 | 1.0349 | 0.8409 | 0.6384 | 0.5675 | 0.4709 | 0.3934 | 0.3306 | 0.2795 |
| | 1.8174 | 1.4708 | 1.1985 | 0.9831 | 0.8116 | 0.6742 | 0.5635 | 0.4736 | 0.4003 | 0.3402 |
| | 2.0188 | 1.6507 | 1.3581 | 1.1239 | 0.9354 | 0.7828 | 0.6587 | 0.5570 | 0.4735 | 0.4044 |
| | 2.2065 | 1.8213 | 1.5117 | 1.2614 | 1.0579 | 0.8916 | 0.7550 | 0.6423 | 0.5489 | 0.4712 |
| 15 | 2.3802 | 1.9815 | 1.6581 | 1.3941 | 1.1775 | 0.9990 | 0.8512 | 0.7283 | 0.6257 | 0.5397 |
| | 2.5401 | 2.1309 | 1.7963 | 1.5210 | 1.2933 | 1.1041 | 0.9463 | 0.8141 | 0.7029 | 0.6091 |
| | 2.6666 | 2.2696 | 1.9261 | 1.6415 | 1.4044 | 1.2059 | 1.0393 | 0.8987 | 0.7798 | 0.6788 |
| | 2.8206 | 2.3978 | 2.0474 | 1.7552 | 1.5103 | 1.3040 | 1.1296 | 0.9816 | 0.8557 | 0.7481 |
| | 2.9429 | 2.5159 | 2.1604 | 1.8622 | 1.6108 | 1.3978 | 1.2167 | 1.0623 | 0.9300 | 0.8165 |
| 20 | 3.0544 | 2.6247 | 2.2652 | 1.9624 | 1.7057 | 1.4872 | 1.3004 | 1.1402 | 1.0025 | 0.8836 |
| | 3.1562 | 2.7248 | 2.3625 | 2.0560 | 1.7951 | 1.5720 | 1.3804 | 1.2153 | 1.0727 | 0.9490 |
| | 3.2491 | 2.8168 | 2.4525 | 2.1433 | 1.8791 | 1.6522 | 1.4566 | 1.2873 | 1.1404 | 1.0125 |
| | 3.3339 | 2.9013 | 2.5359 | 2.2247 | 1.9579 | 1.7280 | 1.5290 | 1.3561 | 1.2055 | 1.0739 |
| | 3.4114 | 2.9790 | 2.6130 | 2.3004 | 2.0317 | 1.7994 | 1.5976 | 1.4217 | 1.2680 | 1.1331 |
| 25 | 3.4823 | 3.0506 | 2.6843 | 2.3709 | 2.1007 | 1.8665 | 1.6625 | 1.4842 | 1.3277 | 1.1900 |
| | 3.5473 | 3.1164 | 2.7503 | 2.4364 | 2.1653 | 1.9296 | 1.7239 | 1.5434 | 1.3847 | 1.2446 |
| | 3.6069 | 3.1771 | 2.8115 | 2.4974 | 2.2256 | 1.9889 | 1.7817 | 1.5996 | 1.4390 | 1.2968 |
| | 3.6617 | 3.2331 | 2.8681 | 2.5542 | 2.2821 | 2.0446 | 1.8363 | 1.6529 | 1.4906 | 1.3467 |
| | 3.7121 | 3.2848 | 2.9207 | 2.6071 | 2.3348 | 2.0969 | 1.8878 | 1.7033 | 1.5397 | 1.3944 |
| 30 | 3.7585 | 3.3327 | 2.9694 | 2.6563 | 2.3842 | 2.1460 | 1.9363 | 1.7509 | 1.5864 | 1.4398 |

| $-100F_3$ | 30 | 29 | 28 | 27 | 26 | 25 | 24 | 23 | 22 | $\beta=21$ |
|---|---|---|---|---|---|---|---|---|---|---|
| $\alpha=1$ | 0.0000 | 0.0000 | 0.0000 | 0.0000 | 0.0000 | 0.0000 | 0.0000 | 0.0000 | 0.0000 | 0.0000 |
| | 0.0004 | 0.0005 | 0.0006 | 0.0007 | 0.0008 | 0.0009 | 0.0010 | 0.0012 | 0.0015 | 0.0018 |
| | 0.0016 | 0.0018 | 0.0021 | 0.0024 | 0.0028 | 0.0033 | 0.0038 | 0.0045 | 0.0054 | 0.0065 |
| | 0.0038 | 0.0043 | 0.0050 | 0.0057 | 0.0067 | 0.0078 | 0.0091 | 0.0108 | 0.0128 | 0.0153 |
| 5 | 0.0073 | 0.0084 | 0.0096 | 0.0111 | 0.0128 | 0.0150 | 0.0175 | 0.0207 | 0.0245 | 0.0293 |
| | 0.0125 | 0.0143 | 0.0163 | 0.0188 | 0.0218 | 0.0253 | 0.0296 | 0.0348 | 0.0412 | 0.0491 |
| | 0.0195 | 0.0222 | 0.0254 | 0.0292 | 0.0337 | 0.0391 | 0.0456 | 0.0535 | 0.0631 | 0.0750 |
| | 0.0284 | 0.0324 | 0.0369 | 0.0424 | 0.0488 | 0.0565 | 0.0657 | 0.0769 | 0.0905 | 0.1072 |
| | 0.0395 | 0.0448 | 0.0511 | 0.0585 | 0.0672 | 0.0776 | 0.0900 | 0.1050 | 0.1232 | 0.1453 |
| 10 | 0.0526 | 0.0597 | 0.0679 | 0.0775 | 0.0889 | 0.1023 | 0.1184 | 0.1376 | 0.1608 | 0.1890 |
| | 0.0679 | 0.0768 | 0.0872 | 0.0994 | 0.1137 | 0.1305 | 0.1505 | 0.1744 | 0.2031 | 0.2376 |
| | 0.0853 | 0.0963 | 0.1091 | 0.1240 | 0.1414 | 0.1619 | 0.1862 | 0.2150 | 0.2493 | 0.2905 |
| | 0.1047 | 0.1179 | 0.1333 | 0.1511 | 0.1719 | 0.1963 | 0.2249 | 0.2588 | 0.2990 | 0.3469 |
| | 0.1260 | 0.1416 | 0.1596 | 0.1805 | 0.2048 | 0.2332 | 0.2664 | 0.3054 | 0.3515 | 0.4061 |
| 15 | 0.1490 | 0.1671 | 0.1880 | 0.2120 | 0.2399 | 0.2723 | 0.3100 | 0.3542 | 0.4061 | 0.4673 |
| | 0.1736 | 0.1943 | 0.2180 | 0.2453 | 0.2767 | 0.3131 | 0.3554 | 0.4047 | 0.4622 | 0.5297 |
| | 0.1997 | 0.2229 | 0.2495 | 0.2800 | 0.3151 | 0.3555 | 0.4022 | 0.4563 | 0.5193 | 0.5928 |
| | 0.2269 | 0.2528 | 0.2823 | 0.3160 | 0.3546 | 0.3988 | 0.4498 | 0.5087 | 0.5769 | 0.6560 |
| | 0.2552 | 0.2837 | 0.3160 | 0.3529 | 0.3949 | 0.4429 | 0.4981 | 0.5614 | 0.6344 | 0.7188 |
| 20 | 0.2844 | 0.3154 | 0.3506 | 0.3904 | 0.4358 | 0.4874 | 0.5465 | 0.6140 | 0.6916 | 0.7807 |
| | 0.3143 | 0.3478 | 0.3856 | 0.4284 | 0.4770 | 0.5320 | 0.5947 | 0.6662 | 0.7479 | 0.8415 |
| | 0.3446 | 0.3806 | 0.4210 | 0.4667 | 0.5182 | 0.5765 | 0.6426 | 0.7178 | 0.8033 | 0.9009 |
| | 0.3753 | 0.4136 | 0.4566 | 0.5049 | 0.5593 | 0.6206 | 0.6899 | 0.7684 | 0.8575 | 0.9587 |
| | 0.4062 | 0.4468 | 0.4921 | 0.5429 | 0.6000 | 0.6641 | 0.7364 | 0.8180 | 0.9102 | 1.0146 |
| 25 | 0.4372 | 0.4799 | 0.5275 | 0.5807 | 0.6402 | 0.7070 | 0.7820 | 0.8663 | 0.9613 | 1.0686 |
| | 0.4681 | 0.5128 | 0.5625 | 0.6179 | 0.6798 | 0.7490 | 0.8264 | 0.9133 | 1.0109 | 1.1207 |
| | 0.4989 | 0.5455 | 0.5972 | 0.6546 | 0.7186 | 0.7900 | 0.8697 | 0.9588 | 1.0587 | 1.1708 |
| | 0.5294 | 0.5777 | 0.6313 | 0.6907 | 0.7566 | 0.8300 | 0.9117 | 1.0029 | 1.1047 | 1.2188 |
| | 0.5595 | 0.6095 | 0.6648 | 0.7259 | 0.7937 | 0.8689 | 0.9524 | 1.0454 | 1.1490 | 1.2648 |
| 30 | 0.5892 | 0.6408 | 0.6976 | 0.7604 | 0.8298 | 0.9066 | 0.9918 | 1.0864 | 1.1916 | 1.3088 |

| $-100F_3$ | $\beta=31$ | 32 | 33 | 34 | 35 | 36 | 37 | 38 | 39 | 40 |
|---|---|---|---|---|---|---|---|---|---|---|
| $\alpha=1$ | 0.0000 | 0.0000 | 0.0000 | 0.0000 | 0.0000 | 0.0000 | 0.0000 | 0.0000 | 0.0000 | 0.0000 |
| | 0.0004 | 0.0003 | 0.0003 | 0.0003 | 0.0002 | 0.0002 | 0.0002 | 0.0002 | 0.0002 | 0.0001 |
| | 0.0014 | 0.0012 | 0.0011 | 0.0010 | 0.0009 | 0.0008 | 0.0007 | 0.0006 | 0.0006 | 0.0005 |
| | 0.0033 | 0.0029 | 0.0026 | 0.0023 | 0.0021 | 0.0018 | 0.0017 | 0.0015 | 0.0013 | 0.0012 |
| 5 | 0.0065 | 0.0057 | 0.0051 | 0.0045 | 0.0040 | 0.0036 | 0.0032 | 0.0029 | 0.0026 | 0.0024 |
| | 0.0110 | 0.0097 | 0.0086 | 0.0077 | 0.0069 | 0.0061 | 0.0055 | 0.0050 | 0.0045 | 0.0041 |
| | 0.0172 | 0.0152 | 0.0135 | 0.0120 | 0.0107 | 0.0096 | 0.0087 | 0.0078 | 0.0070 | 0.0064 |
| | 0.0251 | 0.0222 | 0.0198 | 0.0176 | 0.0158 | 0.0141 | 0.0127 | 0.0115 | 0.0104 | 0.0094 |
| | 0.0349 | 0.0310 | 0.0276 | 0.0246 | 0.0220 | 0.0198 | 0.0178 | 0.0161 | 0.0146 | 0.0132 |
| 10 | 0.0466 | 0.0414 | 0.0369 | 0.0330 | 0.0296 | 0.0266 | 0.0240 | 0.0217 | 0.0196 | 0.0178 |
| | 0.0603 | 0.0536 | 0.0479 | 0.0429 | 0.0385 | 0.0346 | 0.0312 | 0.0283 | 0.0256 | 0.0233 |
| | 0.0758 | 0.0676 | 0.0604 | 0.0542 | 0.0487 | 0.0439 | 0.0397 | 0.0359 | 0.0326 | 0.0296 |
| | 0.0932 | 0.0833 | 0.0746 | 0.0670' | 0.0603 | 0.0544 | 0.0492 | 0.0446 | 0.0405 | 0.0369 |
| | 0.1124 | 0.1006 | 0.0902 | 0.0811 | 0.0731 | 0.0661 | 0.0599 | 0.0543 | 0.0494 | 0.0450 |
| 15 | 0.1332 | 0.1194 | 0.1073 | 0.0967 | 0.0873 | 0.0790 | 0.0716 | 0.0651 | 0.0593 | 0.0541 |
| | 0.1556 | 0.1397 | 0.1258 | 0.1135 | 0.1026 | 0.0930 | 0.0845 | 0.0769 | 0.0701 | 0.0640 |
| | 0.1792 | 0.1613 | 0.1455 | 0.1315 | 0.1191 | 0.1081 | 0.0983 | 0.0896 | 0.0818 | 0.0748 |
| | 0.2042 | 0.1841 | 0.1663 | 0.1506 | 0.1366 | 0.1242 | 0.1131 | 0.1032 | 0.0943 | 0.0864 |
| | 0.2301 | 0.2079 | 0.1882 | 0.1707 | 0.1551 | 0.1412 | 0.1288 | 0.1177 | 0.1077 | 0.0987 |
| 20 | 0.2569 | 0.2326 | 0.2109 | 0.1916 | 0.1744 | 0.1591 | 0.1453 | 0.1329 | 0.1218 | 0.1118 |
| | 0.2845 | 0.2580 | 0.2344 | 0.2134 | 0.1945 | 0.1776 | 0.1625 | 0.1489 | 0.1366 | 0.1255 |
| | 0.3126 | 0.2841 | 0.2586 | 0.2357 | 0.2153 | 0.1969 | 0.1804 | 0.1655 | 0.1520 | 0.1399 |
| | 0.3411 | 0.3106 | 0.2832 | 0.2586 | 0.2366 | 0.2167 | 0.1988 | 0.1827 | 0.1680 | 0.1548 |
| | 0.3700 | 0.3375 | 0.3083 | 0.2820 | 0.2584 | 0.2370 | 0.2178 | 0.2003 | 0.1845 | 0.1702 |
| 25 | 0.3989 | 0.3645 | 0.3336 | 0.3057 | 0.2805 | 0.2577 | 0.2371 | 0.2184 | 0.2015 | 0.1861 |
| | 0.4569 | 0.4190 | 0.3847 | 0.3536 | 0.3255 | 0.3000 | 0.2768 | 0.2557 | 0.2364 | 0.2189 |
| | 0.4280 | 0.3918 | 0.3591 | 0.3296 | 0.3029 | 0.2787 | 0.2568 | 0.2369 | 0.2188 | 0.2023 |
| | 0.4857 | 0.4461 | 0.4103 | 0.3778 | 0.3482 | 0.3214 | 0.2969 | 0.2746 | 0.2543 | 0.2357 |
| | 0.5142 | 0.4731 | 0.4358 | 0.4019 | 0.3710 | 0.3429 | 0.3172 | 0.2938 | 0.2724 | 0.2528 |
| 30 | 0.5424 | 0.4998 | 0.4611 | 0.4259 | 0.3937 | 0.3644 | 0.3376 | 0.3130 | 0.2906 | 0.2700 |

| $-100F_3$ | 50 | 49 | 48 | 47 | 46 | 45 | 44 | 43 | 42 | $\beta=41$ |
|---|---|---|---|---|---|---|---|---|---|---|
| $\alpha=1$ | 0.0000 | 0.0000 | 0.0000 | 0.0000 | 0.0000 | 0.0000 | 0.0000 | 0.0000 | 0.0000 | 0.0000 |
|  | 0.0001 | 0.0001 | 0.0001 | 0.0001 | 0.0001 | 0.0001 | 0.0001 | 0.0001 | 0.0001 | 0.0001 |
|  | 0.0002 | 0.0002 | 0.0002 | 0.0003 | 0.0003 | 0.0003 | 0.0003 | 0.0004 | 0.0004 | 0.0005 |
|  | 0.0005 | 0.0005 | 0.0006 | 0.0006 | 0.0007 | 0.0008 | 0.0008 | 0.0009 | 0.0010 | 0.0011 |
|  | 0.0010 | 0.0011 | 0.0011 | 0.0012 | 0.0014 | 0.0015 | 0.0016 | 0.0018 | 0.0020 | 0.0021 |
| 5 | 0.0017 | 0.0018 | 0.0020 | 0.0022 | 0.0023 | 0.0026 | 0.0028 | 0.0031 | 0.0034 | 0.0037 |
|  | 0.0027 | 0.0029 | 0.0031 | 0.0034 | 0.0037 | 0.0040 | 0.0044 | 0.0048 | 0.0053 | 0.0058 |
|  | 0.0039 | 0.0043 | 0.0046 | 0.0050 | 0.0055 | 0.0059 | 0.0065 | 0.0071 | 0.0077 | 0.0085 |
|  | 0.0056 | 0.0060 | 0.0065 | 0.0071 | 0.0077 | 0.0084 | 0.0091 | 0.0100 | 0.0109 | 0.0120 |
|  | 0.0075 | 0.0081 | 0.0088 | 0.0096 | 0.0104 | 0.0113 | 0.0124 | 0.0135 | 0.0148 | 0.0162 |
| 10 | 0.0099 | 0.0107 | 0.0116 | 0.0126 | 0.0137 | 0.0149 | 0.0162 | 0.0177 | 0.0193 | 0.0212 |
|  | 0.0127 | 0.0137 | 0.0149 | 0.0161 | 0.0175 | 0.0190 | 0.0207 | 0.0226 | 0.0247 | 0.0270 |
|  | 0.0159 | 0.0172 | 0.0186 | 0.0201 | 0.0219 | 0.0237 | 0.0258 | 0.0282 | 0.0308 | 0.0337 |
|  | 0.0196 | 0.0211 | 0.0229 | 0.0247 | 0.0268 | 0.0291 | 0.0317 | 0.0345 | 0.0376 | 0.0411 |
|  | 0.0237 | 0.0256 | 0.0276 | 0.0299 | 0.0324 | 0.0351 | 0.0382 | 0.0415 | 0.0453 | 0.0494 |
| 15 | 0.0283 | 0.0305 | 0.0329 | 0.0356 | 0.0385 | 0.0418 | 0.0453 | 0.0493 | 0.0537 | 0.0586 |
|  | 0.0333 | 0.0359 | 0.0387 | 0.0419 | 0.0453 | 0.0490 | 0.0532 | 0.0578 | 0.0629 | 0.0685 |
|  | 0.0389 | 0.0418 | 0.0451 | 0.0487 | 0.0526 | 0.0569 | 0.0617 | 0.0669 | 0.0728 | 0.0792 |
|  | 0.0448 | 0.0482 | 0.0519 | 0.0560 | 0.0605 | 0.0654 | 0.0708 | 0.0768 | 0.0833 | 0.0906 |
|  | 0.0512 | 0.0551 | 0.0593 | 0.0639 | 0.0689 | 0.0744 | 0.0805 | 0.0872 | 0.0946 | 0.1028 |
| 20 | 0.0581 | 0.0624 | 0.0671 | 0.0722 | 0.0778 | 0.0840 | 0.0908 | 0.0983 | 0.1065 | 0.1155 |
|  | 0.0653 | 0.0701 | 0.0753 | 0.0810 | 0.0873 | 0.0941 | 0.1016 | 0.1099 | 0.1189 | 0.1289 |
|  | 0.0730 | 0.0783 | 0.0840 | 0.0903 | 0.0972 | 0.1047 | 0.1130 | 0.1220 | 0.1319 | 0.1428 |
|  | 0.0810 | 0.0868 | 0.0932 | 0.1001 | 0.1076 | 0.1158 | 0.1248 | 0.1346 | 0.1454 | 0.1572 |
|  | 0.0894 | 0.0958 | 0.1027 | 0.1102 | 0.1183 | 0.1273 | 0.1370 | 0.1476 | 0.1593 | 0.1721 |
| 25 | 0.0982 | 0.1051 | 0.1125 | 0.1207 | 0.1295 | 0.1391 | 0.1496 | 0.1611 | 0.1736 | 0.1873 |
|  | 0.1073 | 0.1147 | 0.1227 | 0.1315 | 0.1410 | 0.1513 | 0.1626 | 0.1748 | 0.1882 | 0.2029 |
|  | 0.1166 | 0.1246 | 0.1332 | 0.1426 | 0.1528 | 0.1638 | 0.1758 | 0.1889 | 0.2032 | 0.2187 |
|  | 0.1263 | 0.1348 | 0.1440 | 0.1540 | 0.1649 | 0.1766 | 0.1894 | 0.2033 | 0.2184 | 0.2348 |
| 30 | 0.1362 | 0.1453 | 0.1551 | 0.1657 | 0.1772 | 0.1896 | 0.2031 | 0.2178 | 0.2338 | 0.2511 |

$-100F_4 \mid \beta = 1$

| $\alpha$ | $\beta=1$ | 2 | 3 | 4 | 5 | 6 | 7 | 8 | 9 | 10 |
|---|---|---|---|---|---|---|---|---|---|---|
| 1 | 0.0000 | 0.0000 | 0.0000 | 0.0000 | 0.0000 | 0.0000 | 0.0000 | 0.0000 | 0.0000 | 0.0000 |
| 2 | 69.2992 | 63.4972 | 58.5175 | 57.0299 | 56.5588 | 56.3883 | 56.3185 | 56.2867 | 56.2710 | 56.2627 |
| 3 | 77.9705 | 76.7123 | 70.9271 | 68.4672 | 67.4813 | 67.0649 | 66.8758 | 66.7835 | 66.7356 | 66.7092 |
| 4 | 79.8286 | 80.8220 | 75.5789 | 72.9042 | 71.6334 | 71.0177 | 70.7076 | 70.5442 | 70.4542 | 70.4024 |
| 5 | 80.3887 | 82.3439 | 77.6345 | 75.0594 | 73.7092 | 72.9854 | 72.5870 | 72.3613 | 72.2295 | 72.1501 |
| 6 | 80.6000 | 82.9898 | 78.6270 | 76.2079 | 74.8797 | 74.1201 | 73.6730 | 73.4035 | 73.2375 | 73.1330 |
| 7 | 80.6932 | 83.2959 | 79.1416 | 76.8547 | 75.5806 | 74.8255 | 74.3599 | 74.0656 | 73.8759 | 73.7516 |
| 8 | 80.7392 | 83.4544 | 79.4254 | 77.2354 | 76.0169 | 75.2831 | 74.8175 | 74.5128 | 74.3092 | 74.1710 |
| 9 | 80.7640 | 83.5425 | 79.5905 | 77.4683 | 76.2967 | 75.5884 | 75.1321 | 74.8263 | 74.6164 | 74.4699 |
| 10 | 80.7782 | 83.5944 | 79.6911 | 77.6158 | 76.4811 | 75.7969 | 75.3532 | 75.0516 | 74.8405 | 74.6900 |
| 11 | 80.7869 | 83.6265 | 79.7550 | 77.7124 | 76.6057 | 75.9421 | 75.5114 | 75.2164 | 75.0073 | 74.8557 |
| 12 | 80.7924 | 83.6472 | 79.7970 | 77.7773 | 76.6917 | 76.0451 | 75.6263 | 75.3387 | 75.1333 | 74.9826 |
| 13 | 80.7961 | 83.6610 | 79.8254 | 77.8222 | 76.7524 | 76.1193 | 75.7110 | 75.4306 | 75.2295 | 75.0809 |
| 14 | 80.7986 | 83.6705 | 79.8451 | 77.8538 | 76.7960 | 76.1737 | 75.7742 | 75.5004 | 75.3038 | 75.1579 |
| 15 | 80.8003 | 83.6772 | 79.8592 | 77.8767 | 76.8280 | 76.2142 | 75.8220 | 75.5540 | 75.3616 | 75.2186 |
| 16 | 80.8016 | 83.6820 | 79.8694 | 77.8935 | 76.8517 | 76.2447 | 75.8585 | 75.5956 | 75.4071 | 75.2669 |
| 17 | 80.8025 | 83.6856 | 79.8770 | 77.9060 | 76.8697 | 76.2680 | 75.8867 | 75.6281 | 75.4432 | 75.3056 |
| 18 | 80.8032 | 83.6882 | 79.8827 | 77.9155 | 76.8834 | 76.2859 | 75.9088 | 75.6538 | 75.4719 | 75.3369 |
| 19 | 80.8037 | 83.6902 | 79.8870 | 77.9228 | 76.8940 | 76.3000 | 75.9262 | 75.6742 | 75.4951 | 75.3622 |
| 20 | 80.8041 | 83.6918 | 79.8904 | 77.9285 | 76.9023 | 76.3111 | 75.9401 | 75.6907 | 75.5138 | 75.3830 |
| 21 | 80.8044 | 83.6930 | 79.8930 | 77.9329 | 76.9089 | 76.3200 | 75.9512 | 75.7040 | 75.5291 | 75.4000 |
| 22 | 80.8046 | 83.6946 | 79.8951 | 77.9365 | 76.9142 | 76.3271 | 75.9602 | 75.7148 | 75.5417 | 75.4141 |
| 23 | 80.8048 | 83.6947 | 79.8968 | 77.9394 | 76.9184 | 76.3328 | 75.9675 | 75.7237 | 75.5520 | 75.4258 |
| 24 | 80.8050 | 83.6953 | 79.8981 | 77.9417 | 76.9219 | 76.3376 | 75.9735 | 75.7311 | 75.5606 | 75.4356 |
| 25 | 80.8051 | 83.6958 | 79.8992 | 77.9436 | 76.9247 | 76.3414 | 75.9785 | 75.7372 | 75.5678 | 75.4439 |
| 26 | 80.8052 | 83.6963 | 79.9001 | 77.9451 | 76.9271 | 76.3447 | 75.9827 | 75.7423 | 75.5739 | 75.4508 |
| 27 | 80.8053 | 83.6966 | 79.9009 | 77.9464 | 76.9290 | 76.3473 | 75.9862 | 75.7466 | 75.5790 | 75.4567 |
| 28 | 80.8054 | 83.6969 | 79.9015 | 77.9475 | 76.9306 | 76.3496 | 75.9891 | 75.7502 | 75.5833 | 75.4617 |
| 29 | 80.8054 | 83.6971 | 79.9020 | 77.9484 | 76.9320 | 76.3515 | 75.9916 | 75.7533 | 75.5870 | 75.4660 |
| 30 | 80.8055 | 83.6973 | 79.9025 | 77.9492 | 76.9332 | 76.3531 | 75.9937 | 75.7559 | 75.5902 | 75.4697 |

| $-100F_4 \mid \beta=11$ | 12 | 13 | 14 | 15 | 16 | 17 | 18 | 19 | 20 |
|---|---|---|---|---|---|---|---|---|---|
| $\alpha=1$  0.0000 | 0.0000 | 0.0000 | 0.0000 | 0.0000 | 0.0000 | 0.0000 | 0.0000 | 0.0000 | 0.0000 |
| 56.2580 | 56.2553 | 56.2536 | 56.2525 | 56.2518 | 56.2513 | 56.2510 | 56.2507 | 56.2506 | 56.2504 |
| 66.6940 | 66.6848 | 66.6791 | 66.6754 | 66.6729 | 66.6712 | 66.6701 | 66.6692 | 66.6686 | 66.6682 |
| 70.3715 | 70.3523 | 70.3401 | 70.3321 | 70.3267 | 70.3230 | 70.3203 | 70.3185 | 70.3171 | 70.3161 |
| 5  72.1009 | 72.0695 | 72.0489 | 72.0352 | 72.0257 | 72.0192 | 72.0145 | 72.0111 | 72.0086 | 72.0068 |
| 73.0657 | 73.0215 | 72.9918 | 72.9714 | 72.9572 | 72.9472 | 72.9399 | 72.9346 | 72.9307 | 72.9277 |
| 73.6687 | 73.6124 | 73.5737 | 73.5466 | 73.5273 | 73.5134 | 73.5033 | 73.4958 | 73.4901 | 73.4859 |
| 74.0760 | 74.0097 | 73.9629 | 73.9294 | 73.9051 | 73.8873 | 73.8741 | 73.8643 | 73.8568 | 73.8510 |
| 74.3663 | 74.2923 | 74.2388 | 74.1997 | 74.1708 | 74.1493 | 74.1332 | 74.1209 | 74.1115 | 74.1042 |
| 10  74.5811 | 74.5016 | 74.4429 | 74.3992 | 74.3664 | 74.3416 | 74.3227 | 74.3081 | 74.2968 | 74.2880 |
| 74.7442 | 74.6611 | 74.5988 | 74.5515 | 74.5155 | 74.4878 | 74.4664 | 74.4497 | 74.4366 | 74.4263 |
| 74.8702 | 74.7853 | 74.7205 | 74.6707 | 74.6322 | 74.6022 | 74.5786 | 74.5601 | 74.5454 | 74.5337 |
| 74.9689 | 74.8833 | 74.8172 | 74.7657 | 74.7253 | 74.6935 | 74.6683 | 74.6481 | 74.6320 | 74.6191 |
| 75.0471 | 74.9616 | 74.8949 | 74.8425 | 74.8009 | 74.7677 | 74.7411 | 74.7197 | 74.7024 | 74.6883 |
| 15  75.1095 | 75.0248 | 74.9581 | 74.9052 | 74.8628 | 74.8287 | 74.8012 | 74.7787 | 74.7604 | 74.7454 |
| 75.1597 | 75.0760 | 75.0098 | 74.9568 | 74.9141 | 74.8795 | 74.8512 | 74.8280 | 74.8089 | 74.7932 |
| 75.2003 | 75.1179 | 75.0524 | 74.9997 | 74.9569 | 74.9220 | 74.8933 | 74.8695 | 74.8499 | 74.8335 |
| 75.2334 | 75.1524 | 75.0877 | 75.0355 | 74.9929 | 74.9579 | 74.9289 | 74.9048 | 74.8847 | 74.8679 |
| 75.2606 | 75.1808 | 75.1171 | 75.0655 | 75.0232 | 74.9883 | 74.9592 | 74.9350 | 74.9146 | 74.8974 |
| 20  75.2829 | 75.2045 | 75.1417 | 75.0908 | 75.0489 | 75.0142 | 74.9852 | 74.9608 | 74.9403 | 74.9229 |
| 75.3015 | 75.2242 | 75.1624 | 75.1122 | 75.0708 | 75.0363 | 75.0075 | 74.9832 | 74.9626 | 74.9451 |
| 75.3169 | 75.2408 | 75.1799 | 75.1303 | 75.0894 | 75.0554 | 75.0268 | 75.0025 | 74.9820 | 74.9644 |
| 75.3298 | 75.2547 | 75.1947 | 75.1458 | 75.1055 | 75.0718 | 75.0434 | 75.0194 | 74.9988 | 74.9813 |
| 75.3407 | 75.2665 | 75.2073 | 75.1591 | 75.1192 | 75.0860 | 75.0579 | 75.0340 | 75.0136 | 74.9961 |
| 25  75.3499 | 75.2765 | 75.2180 | 75.1704 | 75.1311 | 75.0983 | 75.0705 | 75.0469 | 75.0266 | 75.0091 |
| 75.3576 | 75.2851 | 75.2272 | 75.1802 | 75.1414 | 75.1089 | 75.0815 | 75.0581 | 75.0380 | 75.0207 |
| 75.3643 | 75.2924 | 75.2352 | 75.1887 | 75.1503 | 75.1182 | 75.0911 | 75.0680 | 75.0481 | 75.0309 |
| 75.3699 | 75.2987 | 75.2420 | 75.1960 | 75.1581 | 75.1264 | 75.0996 | 75.0767 | 75.0570 | 75.0399 |
| 75.3748 | 75.3041 | 75.2479 | 75.2024 | 75.1649 | 75.1335 | 75.1070 | 75.0843 | 75.0648 | 75.0479 |
| 30  75.3790 | 75.3088 | 75.2531 | 75.2080 | 75.1708 | 75.1398 | 75.1135 | 75.0911 | 75.0718 | 75.0551 |

| $-100F_4$ $\alpha$ | $\beta=21$ | 22 | 23 | 24 | 25 | 26 | 27 | 28 | 29 | 30 |
|---|---|---|---|---|---|---|---|---|---|---|
| 1 | 0.0000 | 0.0000 | 0.0000 | 0.0000 | 0.0000 | 0.0000 | 0.0000 | 0.0000 | 0.0000 | 0.0000 |
|  | 56.2503 | 56.2503 | 56.2502 | 56.2502 | 56.2501 | 56.2501 | 56.2501 | 56.2501 | 56.2501 | 56.2501 |
|  | 66.6679 | 66.6676 | 66.6674 | 66.6673 | 66.6672 | 66.6671 | 66.6670 | 66.6670 | 66.6669 | 66.6669 |
|  | 70.3153 | 70.3148 | 70.3143 | 70.3140 | 70.3137 | 70.3135 | 70.3133 | 70.3132 | 70.3131 | 70.3130 |
| 5 | 72.0054 | 72.0043 | 72.0035 | 72.0028 | 72.0023 | 72.0019 | 72.0016 | 72.0013 | 72.0011 | 72.0010 |
|  | 72.9255 | 72.9238 | 72.9224 | 72.9214 | 72.9205 | 72.9199 | 72.9194 | 72.9189 | 72.9186 | 72.9183 |
|  | 73.4826 | 73.4801 | 73.4781 | 73.4765 | 73.4753 | 73.4743 | 73.4735 | 73.4729 | 73.4723 | 73.4719 |
|  | 73.8466 | 73.8431 | 73.8404 | 73.8383 | 73.8365 | 73.8351 | 73.8340 | 73.8331 | 73.8324 | 73.8317 |
|  | 74.0985 | 74.0941 | 74.0905 | 74.0877 | 74.0854 | 74.0836 | 74.0821 | 74.0809 | 74.0798 | 74.0790 |
| 10 | 74.2810 | 74.2755 | 74.2711 | 74.2675 | 74.2647 | 74.2623 | 74.2604 | 74.2589 | 74.2576 | 74.2565 |
|  | 74.4181 | 74.4115 | 74.4063 | 74.4020 | 74.3985 | 74.3957 | 74.3933 | 74.3914 | 74.3898 | 74.3884 |
|  | 74.5243 | 74.5167 | 74.5106 | 74.5055 | 74.5014 | 74.4981 | 74.4953 | 74.4929 | 74.4910 | 74.4894 |
|  | 74.6086 | 74.6000 | 74.5930 | 74.5873 | 74.5826 | 74.5787 | 74.5754 | 74.5727 | 74.5704 | 74.5685 |
|  | 74.6768 | 74.6674 | 74.6597 | 74.6533 | 74.6480 | 74.6435 | 74.6398 | 74.6367 | 74.6341 | 74.6319 |
| 15 | 74.7331 | 74.7229 | 74.7145 | 74.7074 | 74.7016 | 74.6967 | 74.6925 | 74.6890 | 74.6861 | 74.6836 |
|  | 74.7801 | 74.7693 | 74.7602 | 74.7526 | 74.7462 | 74.7408 | 74.7363 | 74.7324 | 74.7291 | 74.7263 |
|  | 74.8199 | 74.8084 | 74.7988 | 74.7907 | 74.7839 | 74.7781 | 74.7731 | 74.7689 | 74.7653 | 74.7623 |
|  | 74.8538 | 74.8419 | 74.8318 | 74.8232 | 74.8160 | 74.8098 | 74.8045 | 74.8000 | 74.7961 | 74.7928 |
|  | 74.8829 | 74.8706 | 74.8602 | 74.8513 | 74.8436 | 74.8371 | 74.8315 | 74.8267 | 74.8226 | 74.8190 |
| 20 | 74.9081 | 74.8956 | 74.8848 | 74.8756 | 74.8677 | 74.8608 | 74.8550 | 74.8499 | 74.8455 | 74.8417 |
|  | 74.9301 | 74.9173 | 74.9063 | 74.8968 | 74.8886 | 74.8816 | 74.8755 | 74.8701 | 74.8655 | 74.8615 |
|  | 74.9493 | 74.9363 | 74.9251 | 74.9155 | 74.9071 | 74.8998 | 74.8935 | 74.8880 | 74.8832 | 74.8789 |
|  | 74.9661 | 74.9530 | 74.9417 | 74.9319 | 74.9234 | 74.9159 | 74.9094 | 74.9037 | 74.8987 | 74.8944 |
|  | 74.9809 | 74.9678 | 74.9564 | 74.9465 | 74.9378 | 74.9302 | 74.9236 | 74.9178 | 74.9126 | 74.9081 |
| 25 | 74.9940 | 74.9809 | 74.9694 | 74.9594 | 74.9507 | 74.9430 | 74.9362 | 74.9303 | 74.9250 | 74.9204 |
|  | 75.0056 | 74.9925 | 74.9810 | 74.9710 | 74.9622 | 74.9544 | 74.9476 | 74.9415 | 74.9361 | 74.9314 |
|  | 75.0159 | 75.0028 | 74.9914 | 74.9813 | 74.9725 | 74.9646 | 74.9577 | 74.9516 | 74.9462 | 74.9413 |
|  | 75.0250 | 75.0120 | 75.0006 | 74.9906 | 74.9817 | 74.9739 | 74.9669 | 74.9607 | 74.9552 | 74.9503 |
|  | 75.0332 | 75.0203 | 75.0089 | 74.9989 | 74.9900 | 74.9821 | 74.9752 | 74.9689 | 74.9634 | 74.9584 |
| 30 | 75.0405 | 75.0276 | 75.0163 | 75.0064 | 74.9975 | 74.9896 | 74.9826 | 74.9764 | 74.9708 | 74.9658 |

| $-100F_4$ $\alpha$ | $\beta=31$ | 32 | 33 | 34 | 35 | 36 | 37 | 38 | 39 | 40 |
|---|---|---|---|---|---|---|---|---|---|---|
| 1 | 0.0000 | 0.0000 | 0.0000 | 0.0000 | 0.0000 | 0.0000 | 0.0000 | 0.0000 | 0.0000 | 0.0000 |
| 2 | 56.2500 | 56.2500 | 56.2500 | 56.2500 | 56.2500 | 56.2500 | 56.2500 | 56.2500 | 56.2500 | 56.2500 |
| 3 | 66.6668 | 66.6668 | 66.6668 | 66.6668 | 66.6667 | 66.6668 | 66.6667 | 66.6667 | 66.6667 | 66.6667 |
| 4 | 70.3129 | 70.3129 | 70.3128 | 70.3128 | 70.3127 | 70.3127 | 70.3127 | 70.3127 | 70.3126 | 70.3126 |
| 5 | 72.0008 | 72.0007 | 72.0006 | 72.0005 | 72.0005 | 72.0004 | 72.0003 | 72.0003 | 72.0003 | 72.0002 |
| 6 | 72.9180 | 72.9179 | 72.9177 | 72.9175 | 72.9174 | 72.9173 | 72.9173 | 72.9172 | 72.9171 | 72.9171 |
| 7 | 73.4715 | 73.4712 | 73.4710 | 73.4708 | 73.4706 | 73.4704 | 73.4703 | 73.4702 | 73.4701 | 73.4700 |
| 8 | 73.8312 | 73.8308 | 73.8304 | 73.8301 | 73.8299 | 73.8296 | 73.8295 | 73.8293 | 73.8292 | 73.8290 |
| 9 | 74.0783 | 74.0777 | 74.0772 | 74.0768 | 74.0765 | 74.0762 | 74.0759 | 74.0757 | 74.0755 | 74.0753 |
| 10 | 74.2556 | 74.2548 | 74.2542 | 74.2537 | 74.2532 | 74.2528 | 74.2525 | 74.2522 | 74.2519 | 74.2517 |
| 11 | 74.3873 | 74.3863 | 74.3855 | 74.3848 | 74.3843 | 74.3838 | 74.3833 | 74.3830 | 74.3826 | 74.3824 |
| 12 | 74.4880 | 74.4868 | 74.4858 | 74.4850 | 74.4843 | 74.4837 | 74.4831 | 74.4827 | 74.4823 | 74.4819 |
| 13 | 74.5669 | 74.5655 | 74.5643 | 74.5633 | 74.5625 | 74.5617 | 74.5611 | 74.5605 | 74.5601 | 74.5596 |
| 14 | 74.6300 | 74.6284 | 74.6271 | 74.6259 | 74.6248 | 74.6240 | 74.6232 | 74.6226 | 74.6220 | 74.6215 |
| 15 | 74.6814 | 74.6796 | 74.6780 | 74.6766 | 74.6755 | 74.6745 | 74.6736 | 74.6728 | 74.6722 | 74.6716 |
| 16 | 74.7239 | 74.7219 | 74.7201 | 74.7186 | 74.7172 | 74.7161 | 74.7151 | 74.7142 | 74.7134 | 74.7128 |
| 17 | 74.7596 | 74.7573 | 74.7553 | 74.7536 | 74.7521 | 74.7509 | 74.7497 | 74.7487 | 74.7479 | 74.7471 |
| 18 | 74.7899 | 74.7874 | 74.7852 | 74.7833 | 74.7817 | 74.7802 | 74.7790 | 74.7779 | 74.7769 | 74.7761 |
| 19 | 74.8159 | 74.8131 | 74.8108 | 74.8087 | 74.8069 | 74.8054 | 74.8040 | 74.8028 | 74.8017 | 74.8008 |
| 20 | 74.8383 | 74.8354 | 74.8329 | 74.8307 | 74.8288 | 74.8270 | 74.8255 | 74.8242 | 74.8230 | 74.8220 |
| 21 | 74.8580 | 74.8549 | 74.8522 | 74.8498 | 74.8477 | 74.8459 | 74.8443 | 74.8429 | 74.8416 | 74.8405 |
| 22 | 74.8752 | 74.8720 | 74.8691 | 74.8665 | 74.8644 | 74.8625 | 74.8607 | 74.8592 | 74.8578 | 74.8566 |
| 23 | 74.8905 | 74.8871 | 74.8841 | 74.8815 | 74.8791 | 74.8771 | 74.8752 | 74.8736 | 74.8721 | 74.8708 |
| 24 | 74.9041 | 74.9006 | 74.8975 | 74.8947 | 74.8922 | 74.8900 | 74.8881 | 74.8864 | 74.8848 | 74.8834 |
| 25 | 74.9163 | 74.9126 | 74.9094 | 74.9065 | 74.9039 | 74.9016 | 74.8996 | 74.8978 | 74.8962 | 74.8947 |
| 26 | 74.9272 | 74.9234 | 74.9201 | 74.9171 | 74.9144 | 74.9121 | 74.9099 | 74.9080 | 74.9063 | 74.9048 |
| 27 | 74.9370 | 74.9332 | 74.9297 | 74.9267 | 74.9239 | 74.9214 | 74.9192 | 74.9173 | 74.9155 | 74.9139 |
| 28 | 74.9459 | 74.9420 | 74.9385 | 74.9353 | 74.9325 | 74.9299 | 74.9277 | 74.9256 | 74.9238 | 74.9221 |
| 29 | 74.9539 | 74.9500 | 74.9464 | 74.9432 | 74.9403 | 74.9377 | 74.9353 | 74.9332 | 74.9313 | 74.9296 |
| 30 | 74.9613 | 74.9572 | 74.9536 | 74.9503 | 74.9474 | 74.9447 | 74.9423 | 74.9401 | 74.9382 | 74.9364 |

| $-100F_4$ $\alpha$ | 50 | 49 | 48 | 47 | 46 | 45 | 44 | 43 | 42 | $\beta=41$ |
|---|---|---|---|---|---|---|---|---|---|---|
| 1 | 0.0000 | 0.0000 | 0.0000 | 0.0000 | 0.0000 | 0.0000 | 0.0000 | 0.0000 | 0.0000 | 0.0000 |
| 2 | 56.2500 | 56.2500 | 56.2500 | 56.2500 | 56.2500 | 56.2500 | 56.2500 | 56.2500 | 56.2500 | 56.2500 |
| 3 | 66.6667 | 66.6667 | 66.6667 | 66.6667 | 66.6667 | 66.6667 | 66.6667 | 66.6667 | 66.6667 | 66.6667 |
| 4 | 70.3125 | 70.3125 | 70.3125 | 70.3126 | 70.3126 | 70.3126 | 70.3126 | 70.3126 | 70.3126 | 70.3126 |
| 5 | 72.0001 | 72.0001 | 72.0001 | 72.0001 | 72.0001 | 72.0001 | 72.0001 | 72.0002 | 72.0002 | 72.0002 |
| 6 | 72.9168 | 72.9168 | 72.9168 | 72.9168 | 72.9169 | 72.9169 | 72.9169 | 72.9169 | 72.9170 | 72.9170 |
| 7 | 73.4696 | 73.4696 | 73.4696 | 73.4696 | 73.4697 | 73.4698 | 73.4698 | 73.4698 | 73.4699 | 73.4699 |
| 8 | 73.8284 | 73.8285 | 73.8285 | 73.8285 | 73.8286 | 73.8286 | 73.8287 | 73.8288 | 73.8288 | 73.8289 |
| 9 | 74.0745 | 74.0746 | 74.0746 | 74.0747 | 74.0747 | 74.0748 | 74.0749 | 74.0750 | 74.0751 | 74.0752 |
| 10 | 74.2506 | 74.2506 | 74.2507 | 74.2508 | 74.2509 | 74.2510 | 74.2511 | 74.2512 | 74.2514 | 74.2515 |
| 11 | 74.3809 | 74.3810 | 74.3811 | 74.3812 | 74.3813 | 74.3814 | 74.3816 | 74.3817 | 74.3819 | 74.3821 |
| 12 | 74.4801 | 74.4802 | 74.4803 | 74.4805 | 74.4806 | 74.4808 | 74.4809 | 74.4812 | 74.4814 | 74.4816 |
| 13 | 74.5574 | 74.5575 | 74.5577 | 74.5578 | 74.5580 | 74.5582 | 74.5584 | 74.5587 | 74.5590 | 74.5593 |
| 14 | 74.6188 | 74.6190 | 74.6191 | 74.6193 | 74.6195 | 74.6198 | 74.6200 | 74.6203 | 74.6207 | 74.6210 |
| 15 | 74.6684 | 74.6686 | 74.6688 | 74.6690 | 74.6693 | 74.6696 | 74.6699 | 74.6702 | 74.6706 | 74.6711 |
| 16 | 74.7091 | 74.7093 | 74.7096 | 74.7098 | 74.7101 | 74.7104 | 74.7108 | 74.7112 | 74.7117 | 74.7122 |
| 17 | 74.7430 | 74.7432 | 74.7434 | 74.7437 | 74.7441 | 74.7444 | 74.7448 | 74.7453 | 74.7458 | 74.7464 |
| 18 | 74.7714 | 74.7716 | 74.7719 | 74.7723 | 74.7726 | 74.7731 | 74.7735 | 74.7740 | 74.7746 | 74.7753 |
| 19 | 74.7955 | 74.7958 | 74.7961 | 74.7965 | 74.7969 | 74.7974 | 74.7979 | 74.7985 | 74.7992 | 74.7999 |
| 20 | 74.8162 | 74.8165 | 74.8169 | 74.8173 | 74.8178 | 74.8183 | 74.8189 | 74.8195 | 74.8203 | 74.8211 |
| 21 | 74.8341 | 74.8344 | 74.8348 | 74.8353 | 74.8358 | 74.8364 | 74.8370 | 74.8378 | 74.8386 | 74.8394 |
| 22 | 74.8496 | 74.8500 | 74.8505 | 74.8510 | 74.8516 | 74.8522 | 74.8529 | 74.8537 | 74.8545 | 74.8555 |
| 23 | 74.8633 | 74.8637 | 74.8642 | 74.8648 | 74.8654 | 74.8661 | 74.8668 | 74.8677 | 74.8686 | 74.8697 |
| 24 | 74.8754 | 74.8759 | 74.8764 | 74.8770 | 74.8776 | 74.8784 | 74.8792 | 74.8801 | 74.8811 | 74.8822 |
| 25 | 74.8861 | 74.8866 | 74.8872 | 74.8878 | 74.8885 | 74.8893 | 74.8902 | 74.8911 | 74.8922 | 74.8934 |
| 26 | 74.8957 | 74.8962 | 74.8968 | 74.8975 | 74.8983 | 74.8991 | 74.9000 | 74.9010 | 74.9021 | 74.9034 |
| 27 | 74.9042 | 74.9048 | 74.9055 | 74.9062 | 74.9070 | 74.9079 | 74.9089 | 74.9099 | 74.9111 | 74.9124 |
| 28 | 74.9120 | 74.9126 | 74.9133 | 74.9141 | 74.9149 | 74.9159 | 74.9169 | 74.9180 | 74.9192 | 74.9206 |
| 29 | 74.9190 | 74.9197 | 74.9204 | 74.9212 | 74.9221 | 74.9231 | 74.9241 | 74.9253 | 74.9266 | 74.9280 |
| 30 | 74.9254 | 74.9261 | 74.9269 | 74.9277 | 74.9286 | 74.9296 | 74.9307 | 74.9320 | 74.9333 | 74.9348 |

## TABLES FOR $K_1$, $K_2$, $K_3$ AND $K_4$:

### (see also Ch. 3, § 1.2)

$$K_1 = \tfrac{1}{2} \ln \frac{\alpha\{\beta + (\beta^2 + 1)^{\frac{1}{2}}\}}{\beta + (\beta^2 + \alpha^2)^{\frac{1}{2}}} =$$

$$= \frac{1}{2}\left(\operatorname{arcsinh} \beta - \operatorname{arcsinh} \frac{\beta}{\alpha}\right);$$

$$K_2 = \frac{1}{2}\left\{\frac{1}{(\alpha^2 + \beta^2)^{\frac{1}{2}}} - \frac{1}{(1 + \beta^2)^{\frac{1}{2}}} - \frac{1}{\alpha} + 1\right\};$$

$$K_3 = \frac{1}{2}\left\{\frac{\beta}{(1 + \beta^2)^{\frac{3}{2}}} - \frac{\beta}{(\alpha^2 + \beta^2)^{\frac{3}{2}}}\right\};$$

$$K_4 = \frac{1}{2}\left\{\frac{\alpha^2 - 2\beta^2}{(\alpha^2 + \beta^2)^{\frac{5}{2}}} - \frac{1 - 2\beta^2}{(1 + \beta^2)^{\frac{5}{2}}} - \frac{1}{\alpha^3} + 1\right\}.$$

For a coil extending from $-\beta$ to $0$:

$$K_1 = \quad K_1(\alpha, \beta); \qquad K_3 = \quad K_3(\alpha, \beta);$$
$$K_2 = - K_2(\alpha, \beta); \qquad K_4 = - K_4(\alpha, \beta).$$

An example of how to use the tables is given in Appendix 3.

$10K_1$

| $\alpha$ | $\beta=1$ | 2 | 3 | 4 | 5 | 6 | 7 | 8 | 9 | 10 |
|---|---|---|---|---|---|---|---|---|---|---|
| 1 | 0.0000 | 0.0000 | 0.0000 | 0.0000 | 0.0000 | 0.0000 | 0.0000 | 0.0000 | 0.0000 | 0.0000 |
| 2 | 2.0008 | 2.8113 | 3.1184 | 3.2554 | 3.3260 | 3.3667 | 3.3920 | 3.4088 | 3.4205 | 3.4289 |
| 3 | 2.7696 | 4.0925 | 4.6854 | 4.9805 | 5.1432 | 5.2407 | 5.3032 | 5.3453 | 5.3750 | 5.3966 |
| 4 | 3.1695 | 4.8121 | 5.6265 | 6.0667 | 6.3243 | 6.4851 | 6.5911 | 6.6642 | 6.7164 | 6.7550 |
| 5 | 3.4134 | 5.2680 | 6.2481 | 6.8102 | 7.1553 | 7.3790 | 7.5307 | 7.6374 | 7.7150 | 7.7729 |
| 6 | 3.5773 | 5.5809 | 6.6862 | 7.3478 | 7.7698 | 8.0520 | 8.2483 | 8.3893 | 8.4934 | 8.5721 |
| 7 | 3.6950 | 5.8084 | 7.0101 | 7.7527 | 8.2405 | 8.5755 | 8.8137 | 8.9880 | 9.1187 | 9.2187 |
| 8 | 3.7835 | 5.9808 | 7.2586 | 8.0675 | 8.6115 | 8.9932 | 9.2698 | 9.4755 | 9.6319 | 9.7531 |
| 9 | 3.8524 | 6.1160 | 7.4550 | 8.3187 | 8.9105 | 9.3332 | 9.6445 | 9.8794 | 10.0604 | 10.2021 |
| 10 | 3.9077 | 6.2247 | 7.6139 | 8.5234 | 9.1561 | 9.6148 | 9.9573 | 10.2190 | 10.4229 | 10.5842 |
| 11 | 3.9529 | 6.3140 | 7.7450 | 8.6932 | 9.3612 | 9.8514 | 10.2218 | 10.5080 | 10.7332 | 10.9131 |
| 12 | 3.9907 | 6.3887 | 7.8549 | 8.8363 | 9.5349 | 10.0528 | 10.4482 | 10.7566 | 11.0015 | 11.1987 |
| 13 | 4.0226 | 6.4519 | 7.9484 | 8.9584 | 9.6836 | 10.2262 | 10.6439 | 10.9725 | 11.2355 | 11.4488 |
| 14 | 4.0500 | 6.5063 | 8.0288 | 9.0637 | 9.8124 | 10.3767 | 10.8145 | 11.1615 | 11.4411 | 11.6695 |
| 15 | 4.0738 | 6.5535 | 8.0988 | 9.1555 | 9.9249 | 10.5087 | 10.9646 | 11.3282 | 11.6231 | 11.8654 |
| 16 | 4.0946 | 6.5948 | 8.1601 | 9.2362 | 10.0241 | 10.6253 | 11.0975 | 11.4763 | 11.7852 | 12.0404 |
| 17 | 4.1129 | 6.6311 | 8.2144 | 9.3071 | 10.1120 | 10.7289 | 11.2159 | 11.6086 | 11.9304 | 12.1976 |
| 18 | 4.1292 | 6.6638 | 8.2627 | 9.3714 | 10.1906 | 10.8216 | 11.3221 | 11.7275 | 12.0612 | 12.3394 |
| 19 | 4.1438 | 6.6928 | 8.3060 | 9.4286 | 10.2611 | 10.9051 | 11.4178 | 11.8348 | 12.1795 | 12.4680 |
| 20 | 4.1570 | 6.7190 | 8.3450 | 9.4801 | 10.3249 | 10.9805 | 11.5045 | 11.9322 | 12.2870 | 12.5851 |
| 21 | 4.1689 | 6.7427 | 8.3804 | 9.5268 | 10.3827 | 11.0491 | 11.5834 | 12.0209 | 12.3851 | 12.6920 |
| 22 | 4.1797 | 6.7643 | 8.4125 | 9.5694 | 10.4354 | 11.1116 | 11.6554 | 12.1020 | 12.4749 | 12.7902 |
| 23 | 4.1895 | 6.7839 | 8.4419 | 9.6083 | 10.4836 | 11.1689 | 11.7214 | 12.1765 | 12.5575 | 12.8804 |
| 24 | 4.1986 | 6.8020 | 8.4688 | 9.6440 | 10.5279 | 11.2216 | 11.7822 | 12.2451 | 12.6336 | 12.9638 |
| 25 | 4.2069 | 6.8186 | 8.4937 | 9.6769 | 10.5687 | 11.2701 | 11.8383 | 12.3085 | 12.7040 | 13.0409 |
| 26 | 4.2146 | 6.8339 | 8.5166 | 9.7073 | 10.6065 | 11.3151 | 11.8902 | 12.3672 | 12.7693 | 13.1125 |
| 27 | 4.2217 | 6.8481 | 8.5378 | 9.7355 | 10.6415 | 11.3567 | 11.9384 | 12.4217 | 12.8300 | 13.1792 |
| 28 | 4.2283 | 6.8613 | 8.5575 | 9.7617 | 10.6740 | 11.3955 | 11.9833 | 12.4725 | 12.8865 | 13.2413 |
| 29 | 4.2345 | 6.8736 | 8.5759 | 9.7861 | 10.7043 | 11.4317 | 12.0251 | 12.5200 | 12.9394 | 13.2994 |
| 30 | 4.2402 | 6.8851 | 8.5931 | 9.8089 | 10.7327 | 11.4654 | 12.0643 | 12.5643 | 12.9889 | 13.3539 |

| $10K_1$ | $\beta=11$ | 12 | 13 | 14 | 15 | 16 | 17 | 18 | 19 | 20 |
|---|---|---|---|---|---|---|---|---|---|---|
| $\alpha=1$ | 0.0000 | 0.0000 | 0.0000 | 0.0000 | 0.0000 | 0.0000 | 0.0000 | 0.0000 | 0.0000 | 0.0000 |
| | 3.4352 | 3.4400 | 3.4438 | 3.4468 | 3.4492 | 3.4512 | 3.4528 | 3.4542 | 3.4554 | 3.4564 |
| | 5.4129 | 5.4254 | 5.4352 | 5.4430 | 5.4493 | 5.4546 | 5.4589 | 5.4625 | 5.4656 | 5.4683 |
| | 6.7841 | 6.8067 | 6.8245 | 6.8388 | 6.8504 | 6.8600 | 6.8680 | 6.8747 | 6.8804 | 6.8853 |
| 5 | 7.8172 | 7.8517 | 7.8791 | 7.9012 | 7.9193 | 7.9342 | 7.9467 | 7.9573 | 7.9662 | 7.9740 |
| | 8.6329 | 8.6807 | 8.7190 | 8.7499 | 8.7754 | 8.7965 | 8.8142 | 8.8292 | 8.8420 | 8.8530 |
| | 9.2968 | 9.3587 | 9.4086 | 9.4492 | 9.4827 | 9.5107 | 9.5343 | 9.5543 | 9.5714 | 9.5861 |
| | 9.8487 | 9.9251 | 9.9871 | 10.0379 | 10.0801 | 10.1154 | 10.1452 | 10.1707 | 10.1925 | 10.2114 |
| | 10.3149 | 10.4059 | 10.4801 | 10.5414 | 10.5926 | 10.6356 | 10.6721 | 10.7033 | 10.7301 | 10.7534 |
| 10 | 10.7138 | 10.8191 | 10.9056 | 10.9775 | 11.0377 | 11.0886 | 11.1320 | 11.1692 | 11.2014 | 11.2293 |
| | 11.0586 | 11.1778 | 11.2765 | 11.3588 | 11.4282 | 11.4871 | 11.5375 | 11.5809 | 11.6186 | 11.6513 |
| | 11.3595 | 11.4921 | 11.6024 | 11.6951 | 11.7736 | 11.8405 | 11.8980 | 11.9476 | 11.9908 | 12.0285 |
| | 11.6240 | 11.7693 | 11.8910 | 11.9937 | 12.0811 | 12.1559 | 12.2205 | 12.2764 | 12.3252 | 12.3680 |
| | 11.8581 | 12.0156 | 12.1481 | 12.2605 | 12.3566 | 12.4392 | 12.5107 | 12.5729 | 12.6273 | 12.6751 |
| 15 | 12.0667 | 12.2356 | 12.3784 | 12.5002 | 12.6047 | 12.6949 | 12.7732 | 12.8416 | 12.9016 | 12.9545 |
| | 12.2535 | 12.4332 | 12.5859 | 12.7165 | 12.8291 | 12.9267 | 13.0117 | 13.0862 | 13.1517 | 13.2096 |
| | 12.4217 | 12.6115 | 12.7735 | 12.9127 | 13.0331 | 13.1377 | 13.2293 | 13.3096 | 13.3806 | 13.4434 |
| | 12.5739 | 12.7732 | 12.9440 | 13.0913 | 13.2191 | 13.3306 | 13.4284 | 13.5146 | 13.5908 | 13.6585 |
| | 12.7121 | 12.9204 | 13.0994 | 13.2544 | 13.3894 | 13.5075 | 13.6114 | 13.7031 | 13.7845 | 13.8570 |
| 20 | 12.8381 | 13.0546 | 13.2417 | 13.4041 | 13.5458 | 13.6702 | 13.7799 | 13.8771 | 13.9635 | 14.0407 |
| | 12.9535 | 13.1781 | 13.3724 | 13.5417 | 13.6899 | 13.8203 | 13.9357 | 14.0381 | 14.1294 | 14.2110 |
| | 13.0595 | 13.2915 | 13.4928 | 13.6686 | 13.8230 | 13.9592 | 14.0800 | 14.1874 | 14.2834 | 14.3695 |
| | 13.1571 | 13.3961 | 13.6040 | 13.7861 | 13.9463 | 14.0880 | 14.2140 | 14.3263 | 14.4268 | 14.5172 |
| | 13.2473 | 13.4929 | 13.7070 | 13.8950 | 14.0608 | 14.2078 | 14.3387 | 14.4557 | 14.5607 | 14.6551 |
| 25 | 13.3309 | 13.5827 | 13.8027 | 13.9963 | 14.1674 | 14.3195 | 14.4551 | 14.5766 | 14.6857 | 14.7842 |
| | 13.4086 | 13.6662 | 13.8918 | 14.0907 | 14.2669 | 14.4237 | 14.5639 | 14.6897 | 14.8029 | 14.9052 |
| | 13.4810 | 13.7440 | 13.9749 | 14.1788 | 14.3598 | 14.5212 | 14.6658 | 14.7957 | 14.9129 | 15.0189 |
| | 13.5485 | 13.8168 | 14.0527 | 14.2613 | 14.4469 | 14.6127 | 14.7614 | 14.8953 | 15.0163 | 15.1259 |
| | 13.6117 | 13.8849 | 14.1255 | 14.3387 | 14.5286 | 14.6986 | 14.8513 | 14.9890 | 15.1136 | 15.2267 |
| 30 | 13.6710 | 13.9488 | 14.1938 | 14.4114 | 14.6055 | 14.7794 | 14.9360 | 15.0773 | 15.2054 | 15.3218 |

| $10K_1$ | $\beta=21$ | 22 | 23 | 24 | 25 | 26 | 27 | 28 | 29 | 30 |
|---|---|---|---|---|---|---|---|---|---|---|
| $\alpha=1$ | 0.0000 | 0.0000 | 0.0000 | 0.0000 | 0.0000 | 0.0000 | 0.0000 | 0.0000 | 0.0000 | 0.0000 |
| | 3.4573 | 3.4580 | 3.4587 | 3.4592 | 3.4598 | 3.4602 | 3.4606 | 3.4610 | 3.4613 | 3.4616 |
| | 5.4706 | 5.4726 | 5.4743 | 5.4758 | 5.4772 | 5.4783 | 5.4794 | 5.4804 | 5.4812 | 5.4820 |
| | 6.8896 | 6.8932 | 6.8964 | 6.8993 | 6.9018 | 6.9040 | 6.9060 | 6.9077 | 6.9093 | 6.9108 |
| 5 | 7.9806 | 7.9864 | 7.9915 | 7.9960 | 7.9999 | 8.0034 | 8.0066 | 8.0094 | 8.0119 | 8.0142 |
| | 8.8626 | 8.8709 | 8.8782 | 8.8846 | 8.8903 | 8.8954 | 8.8999 | 8.9040 | 8.9076 | 8.9109 |
| | 9.5989 | 9.6101 | 9.6200 | 9.6286 | 9.6363 | 9.6432 | 9.6493 | 9.6548 | 9.6597 | 9.6642 |
| | 10.2278 | 10.2421 | 10.2548 | 10.2659 | 10.2759 | 10.2847 | 10.2926 | 10.2997 | 10.3062 | 10.3120 |
| | 10.7737 | 10.7915 | 10.8072 | 10.8211 | 10.8335 | 10.8445 | 10.8544 | 10.8633 | 10.8713 | 10.8786 |
| 10 | 11.2538 | 11.2752 | 11.2942 | 11.3110 | 11.3260 | 11.3394 | 11.3514 | 11.3622 | 11.3720 | 11.3809 |
| | 11.6801 | 11.7054 | 11.7277 | 11.7476 | 11.7654 | 11.7813 | 11.7956 | 11.8084 | 11.8201 | 11.8307 |
| | 12.0617 | 12.0910 | 12.1169 | 12.1400 | 12.1606 | 12.1792 | 12.1958 | 12.2109 | 12.2246 | 12.2370 |
| | 12.4056 | 12.4390 | 12.4686 | 12.4950 | 12.5186 | 12.5399 | 12.5591 | 12.5764 | 12.5921 | 12.6064 |
| | 12.7174 | 12.7548 | 12.7882 | 12.8180 | 12.8447 | 12.8688 | 12.8905 | 12.9102 | 12.9280 | 12.9443 |
| 15 | 13.0013 | 13.0429 | 13.0800 | 13.1133 | 13.1431 | 13.1701 | 13.1944 | 13.2165 | 13.2366 | 13.2549 |
| | 13.2609 | 13.3067 | 13.3476 | 13.3844 | 13.4174 | 13.4473 | 13.4743 | 13.4989 | 13.5212 | 13.5416 |
| | 13.4993 | 13.5492 | 13.5940 | 13.6342 | 13.6704 | 13.7032 | 13.7330 | 13.7600 | 13.7847 | 13.8073 |
| | 13.7189 | 13.7729 | 13.8214 | 13.8651 | 13.9046 | 13.9403 | 13.9728 | 14.0024 | 14.0294 | 14.0541 |
| | 13.9218 | 13.9798 | 14.0321 | 14.0792 | 14.1219 | 14.1606 | 14.1958 | 14.2280 | 14.2573 | 14.2842 |
| 20 | 14.1097 | 14.1718 | 14.2277 | 14.2783 | 14.3241 | 14.3658 | 14.4038 | 14.4384 | 14.4702 | 14.4993 |
| | 14.2843 | 14.3503 | 14.4099 | 14.4638 | 14.5128 | 14.5574 | 14.5981 | 14.6353 | 14.6694 | 14.7007 |
| | 14.4469 | 14.5167 | 14.5798 | 14.6371 | 14.6892 | 14.7367 | 14.7801 | 14.8198 | 14.8563 | 14.8898 |
| | 14.5985 | 14.6721 | 14.7387 | 14.7992 | 14.8544 | 14.9047 | 14.9508 | 14.9931 | 15.0319 | 15.0676 |
| | 14.7403 | 14.8175 | 14.8876 | 14.9513 | 15.0095 | 15.0626 | 15.1113 | 15.1561 | 15.1972 | 15.2351 |
| 25 | 14.8732 | 14.9539 | 15.0273 | 15.0942 | 15.1552 | 15.2112 | 15.2625 | 15.3097 | 15.3531 | 15.3932 |
| | 14.9979 | 15.0820 | 15.1586 | 15.2286 | 15.2925 | 15.3512 | 15.4051 | 15.4547 | 15.5004 | 15.5427 |
| | 15.1151 | 15.2026 | 15.2823 | 15.3552 | 15.4220 | 15.4834 | 15.5398 | 15.5917 | 15.6397 | 15.6841 |
| | 15.2254 | 15.3162 | 15.3990 | 15.4748 | 15.5444 | 15.6083 | 15.6672 | 15.7215 | 15.7717 | 15.8182 |
| | 15.3295 | 15.4234 | 15.5092 | 15.5878 | 15.6601 | 15.7266 | 15.7878 | 15.8445 | 15.8968 | 15.9454 |
| 30 | 15.4278 | 15.5247 | 15.6134 | 15.6948 | 15.7697 | 15.8386 | 15.9023 | 15.9612 | 16.0157 | 16.0662 |

| $10K_1$ | $\beta=31$ | 32 | 33 | 34 | 35 | 36 | 37 | 38 | 39 | 40 |
|---|---|---|---|---|---|---|---|---|---|---|
| $\alpha=1$ | 0.0000 | 0.0000 | 0.0000 | 0.0000 | 0.0000 | 0.0000 | 0.0000 | 0.0000 | 0.0000 | 0.0000 |
| | 3.4618 | 3.4621 | 3.4623 | 3.4625 | 3.4627 | 3.4628 | 3.4630 | 3.4631 | 3.4633 | 3.4634 |
| | 5.4827 | 5.4833 | 5.4839 | 5.4844 | 5.4849 | 5.4854 | 5.4858 | 5.4862 | 5.4865 | 5.4868 |
| | 6.9121 | 6.9133 | 6.9144 | 6.9153 | 6.9162 | 6.9171 | 6.9178 | 6.9185 | 6.9192 | 6.9198 |
| 5 | 8.0163 | 8.0182 | 8.0199 | 8.0215 | 8.0229 | 8.0242 | 8.0254 | 8.0266 | 8.0276 | 8.0286 |
| | 8.9139 | 8.9166 | 8.9191 | 8.9214 | 8.9235 | 8.9254 | 8.9272 | 8.9288 | 8.9303 | 8.9317 |
| | 9.6683 | 9.6720 | 9.6754 | 9.6785 | 9.6813 | 9.6839 | 9.6863 | 9.6885 | 9.6906 | 9.6925 |
| | 10.3173 | 10.3221 | 10.3265 | 10.3305 | 10.3342 | 10.3376 | 10.3407 | 10.3436 | 10.3462 | 10.3487 |
| | 10.8852 | 10.8913 | 10.8968 | 10.9018 | 10.9065 | 10.9107 | 10.9147 | 10.9183 | 10.9217 | 10.9248 |
| 10 | 11.3890 | 11.3963 | 11.4031 | 11.4092 | 11.4149 | 11.4201 | 11.4249 | 11.4294 | 11.4335 | 11.4374 |
| | 11.8403 | 11.8491 | 11.8572 | 11.8646 | 11.8714 | 11.8776 | 11.8834 | 11.8887 | 11.8937 | 11.8983 |
| | 12.2483 | 12.2586 | 12.2680 | 12.2767 | 12.2847 | 12.2921 | 12.2989 | 12.3052 | 12.3110 | 12.3164 |
| | 12.6194 | 12.6314 | 12.6423 | 12.6524 | 12.6616 | 12.6701 | 12.6780 | 12.6853 | 12.6921 | 12.6984 |
| | 12.9592 | 12.9728 | 12.9853 | 12.9968 | 13.0073 | 13.0171 | 13.0261 | 13.0345 | 13.0423 | 13.0495 |
| 15 | 13.2717 | 13.2870 | 13.3011 | 13.3141 | 13.3261 | 13.3371 | 13.3473 | 13.3568 | 13.3657 | 13.3739 |
| | 13.5603 | 13.5775 | 13.5932 | 13.6077 | 13.6211 | 13.6335 | 13.6450 | 13.6556 | 13.6655 | 13.6748 |
| | 13.8279 | 13.8469 | 13.8643 | 13.8804 | 13.8953 | 13.9091 | 13.9218 | 13.9337 | 13.9447 | 13.9550 |
| | 14.0768 | 14.0976 | 14.1168 | 14.1346 | 14.1509 | 14.1661 | 14.1802 | 14.1933 | 14.2055 | 14.2168 |
| | 14.3090 | 14.3317 | 14.3527 | 14.3720 | 14.3910 | 14.4066 | 14.4220 | 14.4364 | 14.4497 | 14.4622 |
| 20 | 14.5261 | 14.5507 | 14.5735 | 14.5945 | 14.6140 | 14.6321 | 14.6489 | 14.6645 | 14.6791 | 14.6927 |
| | 14.7296 | 14.7561 | 14.7807 | 14.8034 | 14.8245 | 14.8441 | 14.8623 | 14.8792 | 14.8951 | 14.9098 |
| | 14.9207 | 14.9492 | 14.9756 | 15.0000 | 15.0227 | 15.0438 | 15.0634 | 15.0817 | 15.0988 | 15.1147 |
| | 15.1006 | 15.1310 | 15.1593 | 15.1854 | 15.2097 | 15.2323 | 15.2533 | 15.2730 | 15.2913 | 15.3085 |
| | 15.2702 | 15.3026 | 15.3326 | 15.3605 | 15.3864 | 15.4105 | 15.4330 | 15.4539 | 15.4736 | 15.4919 |
| 25 | 15.4303 | 15.4646 | 15.4965 | 15.5261 | 15.5536 | 15.5792 | 15.6031 | 15.6255 | 15.6464 | 15.6660 |
| | 15.5818 | 15.6180 | 15.6517 | 15.6830 | 15.7121 | 15.7393 | 15.7646 | 15.7883 | 15.8105 | 15.8314 |
| | 15.7252 | 15.7634 | 15.7988 | 15.8318 | 15.8625 | 15.8912 | 15.9180 | 15.9431 | 15.9666 | 15.9887 |
| | 15.8613 | 15.9013 | 15.9385 | 15.9732 | 16.0055 | 16.0357 | 16.0640 | 16.0904 | 16.1152 | 16.1385 |
| | 15.9904 | 16.0323 | 16.0713 | 16.1077 | 16.1416 | 16.1733 | 16.2030 | 16.2308 | 16.2569 | 16.2814 |
| 30 | 16.1132 | 16.1569 | 16.1977 | 16.2357 | 16.2712 | 16.3044 | 16.3355 | 16.3647 | 16.3921 | 16.4179 |

| $10K_1$ $\alpha$ | $\beta=50$ | 49 | 48 | 47 | 46 | 45 | 44 | 43 | 42 | $\beta=41$ |
|---|---|---|---|---|---|---|---|---|---|---|
| 1 | 0.0000 | 0.0000 | 0.0000 | 0.0000 | 0.0000 | 0.0000 | 0.0000 | 0.0000 | 0.0000 | 0.0000 |
|  | 3.4642 | 3.4642 | 3.4641 | 3.4640 | 3.4640 | 3.4639 | 3.4638 | 3.4637 | 3.4636 | 3.4635 |
|  | 5.4891 | 5.4889 | 5.4887 | 5.4885 | 5.4883 | 5.4881 | 5.4879 | 5.4877 | 5.4874 | 5.4871 |
|  | 6.9240 | 6.9237 | 6.9234 | 6.9230 | 6.9226 | 6.9222 | 6.9218 | 6.9214 | 6.9209 | 6.9204 |
| 5 | 8.0352 | 8.0347 | 8.0342 | 8.0337 | 8.0331 | 8.0324 | 8.0318 | 8.0310 | 8.0303 | 8.0294 |
|  | 8.9414 | 8.9407 | 8.9399 | 8.9391 | 8.9383 | 8.9373 | 8.9364 | 8.9353 | 8.9342 | 8.9330 |
|  | 9.7057 | 9.7048 | 9.7037 | 9.7026 | 9.7014 | 9.7002 | 9.6989 | 9.6974 | 9.6959 | 9.6942 |
|  | 10.3660 | 10.3647 | 10.3634 | 10.3619 | 10.3604 | 10.3588 | 10.3570 | 10.3552 | 10.3532 | 10.3510 |
|  | 10.9466 | 10.9450 | 10.9433 | 10.9415 | 10.9395 | 10.9375 | 10.9353 | 10.9329 | 10.9304 | 10.9277 |
| 10 | 11.4642 | 11.4622 | 11.4601 | 11.4578 | 11.4555 | 11.4529 | 11.4502 | 11.4473 | 11.4442 | 11.4409 |
|  | 11.9305 | 11.9282 | 11.9256 | 11.9229 | 11.9201 | 11.9170 | 11.9138 | 11.9103 | 11.9066 | 11.9026 |
|  | 12.3545 | 12.3517 | 12.3487 | 12.3455 | 12.3422 | 12.3385 | 12.3347 | 12.3306 | 12.3262 | 12.3215 |
|  | 12.7428 | 12.7395 | 12.7360 | 12.7323 | 12.7284 | 12.7242 | 12.7197 | 12.7149 | 12.7098 | 12.7043 |
|  | 13.1005 | 13.0968 | 13.0927 | 13.0885 | 13.0839 | 13.0791 | 13.0739 | 13.0684 | 13.0626 | 13.0563 |
| 15 | 13.4319 | 13.4275 | 13.4230 | 13.4181 | 13.4129 | 13.4074 | 13.4016 | 13.3953 | 13.3886 | 13.3815 |
|  | 13.7401 | 13.7352 | 13.7301 | 13.7246 | 13.7187 | 13.7125 | 13.7059 | 13.6989 | 13.6911 | 13.6834 |
|  | 14.0280 | 14.0225 | 14.0167 | 14.0106 | 14.0041 | 13.9971 | 13.9898 | 13.9819 | 13.9735 | 13.9646 |
|  | 14.2977 | 14.2916 | 14.2852 | 14.2784 | 14.2712 | 14.2635 | 14.2553 | 14.2466 | 14.2373 | 14.2274 |
|  | 14.5513 | 14.5446 | 14.5375 | 14.5300 | 14.5220 | 14.5135 | 14.5045 | 14.4950 | 14.4848 | 14.4739 |
| 20 | 14.7902 | 14.7829 | 14.7751 | 14.7669 | 14.7581 | 14.7489 | 14.7390 | 14.7285 | 14.7174 | 14.7055 |
|  | 15.0159 | 15.0079 | 14.9994 | 14.9905 | 14.9810 | 14.9709 | 14.9602 | 14.9488 | 14.9366 | 14.9237 |
|  | 15.2296 | 15.2209 | 15.2117 | 15.2020 | 15.1917 | 15.1808 | 15.1692 | 15.1568 | 15.1437 | 15.1297 |
|  | 15.4323 | 15.4229 | 15.4130 | 15.4025 | 15.3914 | 15.3796 | 15.3670 | 15.3537 | 15.3396 | 15.3245 |
|  | 15.6249 | 15.6148 | 15.6041 | 15.5928 | 15.5809 | 15.5682 | 15.5548 | 15.5405 | 15.5253 | 15.5092 |
| 25 | 15.8082 | 15.7973 | 15.7859 | 15.7738 | 15.7610 | 15.7475 | 15.7331 | 15.7178 | 15.7016 | 15.6844 |
|  | 15.9829 | 15.9713 | 15.9591 | 15.9462 | 15.9325 | 15.9181 | 15.9028 | 15.8865 | 15.8692 | 15.8509 |
|  | 16.1496 | 16.1373 | 16.1243 | 16.1106 | 16.0960 | 16.0807 | 16.0644 | 16.0472 | 16.0288 | 16.0094 |
|  | 16.3089 | 16.2959 | 16.2821 | 16.2675 | 16.2521 | 16.2359 | 16.2186 | 16.2004 | 16.1810 | 16.1604 |
|  | 16.4614 | 16.4475 | 16.4329 | 16.4175 | 16.4013 | 16.3841 | 16.3659 | 16.3466 | 16.3262 | 16.3045 |
| 30 | 16.6074 | 16.5928 | 16.5774 | 16.5611 | 16.5440 | 16.5258 | 16.5067 | 16.4864 | 16.4649 | 16.4421 |

$100K_2$

| α | β=1 | 2 | 3 | 4 | 5 | 6 | 7 | 8 | 9 | 10 |
|---|---|---|---|---|---|---|---|---|---|---|
| 1 | 0.0000 | 0.0000 | 0.0000 | 0.0000 | 0.0000 | 0.0000 | 0.0000 | 0.0000 | 0.0000 | 0.0000 |
| 2 | 12.0053 | 20.3170 | 23.0561 | 24.0536 | 24.4790 | 24.6857 | 24.7970 | 24.8617 | 24.9017 | 24.9277 |
| 3 | 13.7894 | 24.8402 | 29.3071 | 31.2066 | 32.1025 | 32.5669 | 32.8276 | 32.9837 | 33.0822 | 33.1473 |
| 4 | 14.2714 | 26.3197 | 31.6886 | 35.2121 | 35.5029 | 36.2138 | 36.6307 | 36.8884 | 37.0552 | 37.1672 |
| 5 | 14.4505 | 26.9241 | 32.7635 | 35.6819 | 37.2653 | 38.1819 | 38.7413 | 39.0983 | 39.3349 | 39.4970 |
| 6 | 14.5313 | 27.2117 | 33.3088 | 36.4736 | 38.2627 | 39.3393 | 40.0189 | 40.4649 | 40.7676 | 40.9789 |
| 7 | 14.5729 | 27.3645 | 33.6111 | 36.9321 | 38.8637 | 40.0605 | 40.8368 | 41.3590 | 41.7209 | 41.9781 |
| 8 | 14.5964 | 27.4527 | 33.7907 | 37.2134 | 39.2442 | 40.5301 | 41.3825 | 41.9677 | 42.3807 | 42.6792 |
| 9 | 14.6107 | 27.5070 | 33.9035 | 37.3944 | 39.4951 | 40.8470 | 41.7587 | 42.3950 | 42.8512 | 43.1857 |
| 10 | 14.6198 | 27.5422 | 33.9777 | 37.5156 | 39.6663 | 41.0675 | 42.0251 | 42.7026 | 43.1949 | 43.5603 |
| 11 | 14.6260 | 27.5660 | 34.0284 | 37.5996 | 39.7868 | 41.2250 | 42.2183 | 42.9289 | 43.4510 | 43.8427 |
| 12 | 14.6303 | 27.5826 | 34.0642 | 37.6594 | 39.8737 | 41.3402 | 42.3613 | 43.0613 | 43.6451 | 44.0591 |
| 13 | 14.6333 | 27.5946 | 34.0901 | 37.7031 | 39.9378 | 41.4260 | 42.4692 | 43.2277 | 43.7945 | 44.2272 |
| 14 | 14.6356 | 27.6034 | 34.1093 | 37.7358 | 39.9861 | 41.4913 | 42.5519 | 43.3277 | 43.9112 | 44.3596 |
| 15 | 14.6373 | 27.6101 | 34.1239 | 37.7607 | 40.0231 | 41.5416 | 42.6162 | 43.4061 | 44.0034 | 44.4650 |
| 16 | 14.6386 | 27.6152 | 34.1351 | 37.7799 | 40.0519 | 41.5811 | 42.6669 | 43.4683 | 44.0771 | 44.5498 |
| 17 | 14.6396 | 27.6192 | 34.1439 | 37.7950 | 40.0747 | 41.6124 | 42.7074 | 43.5183 | 44.1366 | 44.6187 |
| 18 | 14.6404 | 27.6223 | 34.1508 | 37.8071 | 40.0929 | 41.6375 | 42.7401 | 43.5589 | 44.1852 | 44.6753 |
| 19 | 14.6410 | 27.6249 | 34.1564 | 37.8168 | 40.1075 | 41.6579 | 42.7667 | 43.5920 | 44.2251 | 44.7220 |
| 20 | 14.6415 | 27.6269 | 34.1610 | 37.8247 | 40.1195 | 41.6746 | 42.7886 | 43.6195 | 44.2582 | 44.7609 |
| 21 | 14.6420 | 27.6286 | 34.1647 | 37.8312 | 40.1294 | 41.6884 | 42.8067 | 43.6423 | 44.2859 | 44.7935 |
| 22 | 14.6423 | 27.6300 | 34.1678 | 37.8366 | 40.1377 | 41.7000 | 42.8219 | 43.6614 | 44.3092 | 44.8211 |
| 23 | 14.6426 | 27.6311 | 34.1704 | 37.8411 | 40.1446 | 41.7097 | 42.8347 | 43.6776 | 44.3290 | 44.8445 |
| 24 | 14.6429 | 27.6321 | 34.1725 | 37.8449 | 40.1504 | 41.7178 | 42.8456 | 43.6914 | 44.3458 | 44.8646 |
| 25 | 14.6431 | 27.6330 | 34.1744 | 37.8481 | 40.1554 | 41.7248 | 42.8549 | 43.7031 | 44.3602 | 44.8818 |
| 26 | 14.6432 | 27.6337 | 34.1759 | 37.8509 | 40.1596 | 41.7308 | 42.8628 | 43.7132 | 44.3726 | 44.8966 |
| 27 | 14.6434 | 27.6343 | 34.1773 | 37.8532 | 40.1632 | 41.7360 | 42.8697 | 43.7220 | 44.3834 | 44.9095 |
| 28 | 14.6435 | 27.6348 | 34.1784 | 37.8553 | 40.1664 | 41.7404 | 42.8756 | 43.7296 | 44.3928 | 44.9208 |
| 29 | 14.6436 | 27.6352 | 34.1795 | 37.8570 | 40.1691 | 41.7443 | 42.8808 | 43.7362 | 44.4009 | 44.9306 |
| 30 | 14.6437 | 27.6356 | 34.1803 | 37.8586 | 40.1715 | 41.7477 | 42.8853 | 43.7420 | 44.4081 | 44.9393 |

$100K_2$

| $\alpha$ | $\beta=11$ | 12 | 13 | 14 | 15 | 16 | 17 | 18 | 19 | 20 |
|---|---|---|---|---|---|---|---|---|---|---|
| 1 | 0.0000 | 0.0000 | 0.0000 | 0.0000 | 0.0000 | 0.0000 | 0.0000 | 0.0000 | 0.0000 | 0.0000 |
|  | 24.9453 | 24.9577 | 24.9666 | 24.9732 | 24.9781 | 24.9820 | 24.9849 | 24.9873 | 24.9892 | 24.9907 |
|  | 33.1918 | 33.2233 | 33.2462 | 33.2631 | 33.2760 | 33.2859 | 33.2937 | 33.2998 | 33.3048 | 33.3088 |
|  | 37.2450 | 37.3006 | 37.3412 | 37.3717 | 37.3946 | 37.4128 | 37.4269 | 37.4381 | 37.4472 | 37.4546 |
| 5 | 39.6112 | 39.6939 | 39.7550 | 39.8010 | 39.8363 | 39.8638 | 39.8856 | 39.9029 | 39.9170 | 39.9285 |
|  | 41.1303 | 41.2412 | 41.3240 | 41.3870 | 41.4356 | 41.4738 | 41.5041 | 41.5284 | 41.5482 | 41.5644 |
|  | 42.1652 | 42.3039 | 42.4087 | 42.4892 | 42.5518 | 42.6012 | 42.6407 | 42.6725 | 42.6985 | 42.7199 |
|  | 42.8993 | 43.0646 | 43.1908 | 43.2885 | 43.3652 | 43.4262 | 43.4751 | 43.5149 | 43.5474 | 43.5743 |
|  | 43.4356 | 43.6255 | 43.7719 | 43.8863 | 43.9768 | 44.0492 | 44.1077 | 44.1555 | 44.1948 | 44.2274 |
| 10 | 43.8366 | 44.0486 | 44.2137 | 44.3438 | 44.4476 | 44.5311 | 44.5990 | 44.6547 | 44.7008 | 44.7392 |
|  | 44.1419 | 44.3737 | 44.5558 | 44.7005 | 44.8166 | 44.9108 | 44.9878 | 45.0513 | 45.1040 | 45.1482 |
|  | 44.3780 | 44.6273 | 44.8247 | 44.9826 | 45.1103 | 45.2144 | 45.3001 | 45.3711 | 45.4304 | 45.4802 |
|  | 44.5632 | 44.8277 | 45.0387 | 45.2086 | 45.3469 | 45.4603 | 45.5541 | 45.6322 | 45.6978 | 45.7531 |
|  | 44.7101 | 44.9879 | 45.2109 | 45.3916 | 45.5395 | 45.6615 | 45.7629 | 45.8477 | 45.9192 | 45.9798 |
| 15 | 44.8279 | 45.1173 | 45.3508 | 45.5412 | 45.6977 | 45.8276 | 45.9360 | 46.0271 | 46.1042 | 46.1698 |
|  | 44.9233 | 45.2227 | 45.4655 | 45.6644 | 45.8289 | 45.9658 | 46.0807 | 46.1776 | 46.2600 | 46.3303 |
|  | 45.0014 | 45.3094 | 45.5603 | 45.7669 | 45.9383 | 46.0817 | 46.2024 | 46.3048 | 46.3920 | 46.4668 |
|  | 45.0657 | 45.3812 | 45.6393 | 45.8525 | 46.0302 | 46.1794 | 46.3056 | 46.4129 | 46.5047 | 46.5836 |
|  | 45.1191 | 45.4411 | 45.7055 | 45.9246 | 46.1080 | 46.2624 | 46.3935 | 46.5053 | 46.6013 | 46.6840 |
| 20 | 45.1638 | 45.4915 | 45.7613 | 45.9857 | 46.1740 | 46.3333 | 46.4687 | 46.5847 | 46.6846 | 46.7709 |
|  | 45.2014 | 45.5340 | 45.8087 | 46.0378 | 46.2306 | 46.3940 | 46.5335 | 46.6533 | 46.7567 | 46.8463 |
|  | 45.2333 | 45.5702 | 45.8491 | 46.0823 | 46.2791 | 46.4464 | 46.5895 | 46.7128 | 46.8194 | 46.9121 |
|  | 45.2605 | 45.6012 | 45.8838 | 46.1207 | 46.3210 | 46.4917 | 46.6382 | 46.7646 | 46.8741 | 46.9697 |
|  | 45.2838 | 45.6278 | 45.9137 | 46.1539 | 46.3574 | 46.5312 | 46.6806 | 46.8098 | 46.9222 | 47.0202 |
| 25 | 45.3038 | 45.6508 | 45.9396 | 46.1827 | 46.3890 | 46.5656 | 46.7178 | 46.8496 | 46.9644 | 47.0649 |
|  | 45.3212 | 45.6707 | 45.9622 | 46.2078 | 46.4167 | 46.5958 | 46.7504 | 46.8846 | 47.0017 | 47.1043 |
|  | 45.3363 | 45.6881 | 45.9818 | 46.2298 | 46.4410 | 46.6224 | 46.7791 | 46.9155 | 47.0347 | 47.1393 |
|  | 45.3496 | 45.7033 | 45.9991 | 46.2491 | 46.4624 | 46.6458 | 46.8046 | 46.9429 | 47.0640 | 47.1705 |
|  | 45.3611 | 45.7167 | 46.0143 | 46.2662 | 46.4813 | 46.6666 | 46.8272 | 46.9673 | 47.0901 | 47.1983 |
| 30 | 45.3713 | 45.7285 | 46.0278 | 46.2813 | 46.4981 | 46.6850 | 46.8473 | 46.9890 | 47.1134 | 47.2232 |

$100K_2$, $\beta = 21$

| $\alpha$ | 21 | 22 | 23 | 24 | 25 | 26 | 27 | 28 | 29 | 30 |
|---|---|---|---|---|---|---|---|---|---|---|
| 1 | 0.0000 | 0.0000 | 0.0000 | 0.0000 | 0.0000 | 0.0000 | 0.0000 | 0.0000 | 0.0000 | 0.0000 |
|  | 24.9920 | 24.9930 | 24.9939 | 24.9946 | 24.9952 | 24.9958 | 24.9962 | 24.9966 | 24.9969 | 24.9972 |
|  | 33.3121 | 33.3148 | 33.3171 | 33.3191 | 33.3207 | 33.3221 | 33.3233 | 33.3243 | 33.3252 | 33.3260 |
|  | 37.4606 | 37.4657 | 37.4699 | 37.4735 | 37.4765 | 37.4791 | 37.4813 | 37.4832 | 37.4849 | 37.4863 |
| 5 | 39.9379 | 39.9458 | 39.9524 | 39.9580 | 39.9628 | 39.9668 | 39.9703 | 39.9733 | 39.9760 | 39.9782 |
|  | 41.5778 | 41.5889 | 41.5983 | 41.6063 | 41.6130 | 41.6188 | 41.6238 | 41.6282 | 41.6319 | 41.6352 |
|  | 42.7377 | 42.7525 | 42.7650 | 42.7756 | 42.7847 | 42.7924 | 42.7991 | 42.8050 | 42.8100 | 42.8145 |
|  | 43.5967 | 43.6155 | 43.6314 | 43.6449 | 43.6564 | 43.6664 | 43.6750 | 43.6824 | 43.6889 | 43.6947 |
|  | 44.2546 | 44.2776 | 44.2970 | 44.3136 | 44.3278 | 44.3401 | 44.3507 | 44.3599 | 44.3680 | 44.3751 |
| 10 | 44.7714 | 44.7986 | 44.8218 | 44.8415 | 44.8586 | 44.8732 | 44.8860 | 44.8971 | 44.9068 | 44.9154 |
|  | 45.1854 | 45.2170 | 45.2438 | 45.2669 | 45.2868 | 45.3040 | 45.3189 | 45.3320 | 45.3435 | 45.3536 |
|  | 45.5223 | 45.5582 | 45.5888 | 45.6152 | 45.6380 | 45.6578 | 45.6750 | 45.6901 | 45.7034 | 45.7151 |
|  | 45.8000 | 45.8401 | 45.8745 | 45.9042 | 45.9299 | 45.9522 | 45.9718 | 45.9889 | 46.0040 | 46.0174 |
|  | 46.0314 | 46.0756 | 46.1137 | 46.1466 | 46.1752 | 46.2001 | 46.2220 | 46.2412 | 46.2581 | 46.2731 |
| 15 | 46.2259 | 46.2741 | 46.3157 | 46.3518 | 46.3833 | 46.4108 | 46.4349 | 46.4562 | 46.4750 | 46.4916 |
|  | 46.3906 | 46.4427 | 46.4877 | 46.5269 | 46.5611 | 46.5911 | 46.6175 | 46.6409 | 46.6615 | 46.6798 |
|  | 46.5311 | 46.5868 | 46.6352 | 46.6774 | 46.7143 | 46.7467 | 46.7753 | 46.8007 | 46.8231 | 46.8431 |
|  | 46.6517 | 46.7108 | 46.7623 | 46.8074 | 46.8469 | 46.8817 | 46.9125 | 46.9398 | 46.9640 | 46.9856 |
|  | 46.7557 | 46.8181 | 46.8726 | 46.9203 | 46.9623 | 46.9994 | 47.0323 | 47.0615 | 47.0875 | 47.1107 |
| 20 | 46.8459 | 46.9113 | 46.9686 | 47.0189 | 47.0633 | 47.1026 | 47.1375 | 47.1685 | 47.1962 | 47.2210 |
|  | 46.9244 | 46.9927 | 47.0526 | 47.1054 | 47.1521 | 47.1934 | 47.2302 | 47.2630 | 47.2924 | 47.3187 |
|  | 46.9930 | 47.0640 | 47.1264 | 47.1815 | 47.2303 | 47.2737 | 47.3123 | 47.3468 | 47.3778 | 47.4055 |
|  | 47.0532 | 47.1267 | 47.1914 | 47.2487 | 47.2995 | 47.3448 | 47.3852 | 47.4205 | 47.4538 | 47.4830 |
|  | 47.1063 | 47.1820 | 47.2489 | 47.3083 | 47.3610 | 47.4081 | 47.4502 | 47.4879 | 47.5218 | 47.5524 |
| 25 | 47.1532 | 47.2310 | 47.3000 | 47.3612 | 47.4158 | 47.4646 | 47.5082 | 47.5475 | 47.5828 | 47.6146 |
|  | 47.1947 | 47.2746 | 47.3454 | 47.4085 | 47.4647 | 47.5151 | 47.5603 | 47.6009 | 47.6375 | 47.6707 |
|  | 47.2317 | 47.3134 | 47.3860 | 47.4507 | 47.5086 | 47.5604 | 47.6070 | 47.6490 | 47.6869 | 47.7212 |
|  | 47.2646 | 47.3480 | 47.4223 | 47.4886 | 47.5479 | 47.6012 | 47.6491 | 47.6924 | 47.7315 | 47.7670 |
|  | 47.2941 | 47.3791 | 47.4549 | 47.5226 | 47.5833 | 47.6379 | 47.6872 | 47.7316 | 47.7719 | 47.8084 |
| 30 | 47.3205 | 47.4070 | 47.4841 | 47.5533 | 47.6153 | 47.6712 | 47.7216 | 47.7672 | 47.8085 | 47.8461 |

| $100K_2$ $\alpha=1$ | $\beta=31$ | 32 | 33 | 34 | 35 | 36 | 37 | 38 | 39 | 40 |
|---|---|---|---|---|---|---|---|---|---|---|
| 1 | 0.0000 | 0.0000 | 0.0000 | 0.0000 | 0.0000 | 0.0000 | 0.0000 | 0.0000 | 0.0000 | 0.0000 |
| | 24.9975 | 24.9977 | 24.9979 | 24.9981 | 24.9983 | 24.9984 | 24.9985 | 24.9986 | 24.9987 | 24.9988 |
| | 33.3267 | 33.3273 | 33.3278 | 33.3283 | 33.3287 | 33.3291 | 33.3294 | 33.3297 | 33.3300 | 33.3302 |
| | 37.4876 | 37.4887 | 37.4897 | 37.4906 | 37.4913 | 37.4920 | 37.4927 | 37.4932 | 37.4937 | 37.4942 |
| 5 | 39.9803 | 39.9820 | 39.9836 | 39.9850 | 39.9862 | 39.9873 | 39.9883 | 39.9892 | 39.9900 | 39.9907 |
| | 41.6381 | 41.6407 | 41.6429 | 41.6449 | 41.6467 | 41.6483 | 41.6497 | 41.6510 | 41.6522 | 41.6532 |
| | 42.8184 | 42.8218 | 42.8249 | 42.8276 | 42.8300 | 42.8321 | 42.8341 | 42.8358 | 42.8374 | 42.8388 |
| | 43.6997 | 43.7041 | 43.7080 | 43.7115 | 43.7147 | 43.7175 | 43.7200 | 43.7222 | 43.7243 | 43.7261 |
| | 44.3813 | 44.3868 | 44.3918 | 44.3961 | 44.4000 | 44.4035 | 44.4067 | 44.4095 | 44.4120 | 44.4143 |
| 10 | 44.9229 | 44.9296 | 44.9356 | 44.9409 | 44.9456 | 44.9499 | 44.9537 | 44.9571 | 44.9602 | 44.9631 |
| | 45.3625 | 45.3704 | 45.3775 | 45.3838 | 45.3894 | 45.3945 | 45.3990 | 45.4031 | 45.4068 | 45.4102 |
| | 45.7254 | 45.7346 | 45.7428 | 45.7501 | 45.7567 | 45.7626 | 45.7679 | 45.7727 | 45.7771 | 45.7810 |
| | 46.0292 | 46.0397 | 46.0491 | 46.0575 | 46.0650 | 46.0718 | 46.0779 | 46.0835 | 46.0885 | 46.0930 |
| | 46.2865 | 46.2983 | 46.3089 | 46.3184 | 46.3270 | 46.3347 | 46.3416 | 46.3479 | 46.3536 | 46.3588 |
| 15 | 46.5065 | 46.5197 | 46.5316 | 46.5422 | 46.5517 | 46.5604 | 46.5682 | 46.5752 | 46.5816 | 46.5875 |
| | 46.6962 | 46.7108 | 46.7239 | 46.7357 | 46.7463 | 46.7558 | 46.7645 | 46.7723 | 46.7795 | 46.7860 |
| | 46.8610 | 46.8770 | 46.8913 | 46.9042 | 46.9158 | 46.9264 | 46.9359 | 46.9460 | 46.9524 | 46.9596 |
| | 47.0050 | 47.0223 | 47.0379 | 47.0520 | 47.0646 | 47.0761 | 47.0865 | 47.0960 | 47.1046 | 47.1125 |
| | 47.1315 | 47.1502 | 47.1670 | 47.1822 | 47.1959 | 47.2084 | 47.2197 | 47.2300 | 47.2393 | 47.2479 |
| 20 | 47.2433 | 47.2633 | 47.2813 | 47.2976 | 47.3124 | 47.3258 | 47.3379 | 47.3490 | 47.3592 | 47.3684 |
| | 47.3423 | 47.3636 | 47.3829 | 47.4003 | 47.4160 | 47.4304 | 47.4434 | 47.4553 | 47.4662 | 47.4762 |
| | 47.4305 | 47.4531 | 47.4735 | 47.4920 | 47.5088 | 47.5240 | 47.5379 | 47.5507 | 47.5623 | 47.5729 |
| | 47.5093 | 47.5331 | 47.5547 | 47.5742 | 47.5920 | 47.6081 | 47.6229 | 47.6364 | 47.6488 | 47.6601 |
| | 47.5800 | 47.6049 | 47.6276 | 47.6481 | 47.6669 | 47.6839 | 47.6995 | 47.7138 | 47.7269 | 47.7389 |
| 25 | 47.6434 | 47.6696 | 47.6933 | 47.7148 | 47.7345 | 47.7524 | 47.7689 | 47.7839 | 47.7977 | 47.8104 |
| | 47.7007 | 47.7279 | 47.7526 | 47.7751 | 47.7957 | 47.8145 | 47.8317 | 47.8475 | 47.8620 | 47.8754 |
| | 47.7523 | 47.7806 | 47.8064 | 47.8298 | 47.8518 | 47.8709 | 47.8889 | 47.9054 | 47.9206 | 47.9346 |
| | 47.7992 | 47.8284 | 47.8551 | 47.8795 | 47.9018 | 47.9223 | 47.9410 | 47.9582 | 47.9741 | 47.9887 |
| | 47.8417 | 47.8719 | 47.8995 | 47.9248 | 47.9479 | 47.9691 | 47.9886 | 48.0065 | 48.0230 | 48.0383 |
| 30 | 47.8803 | 47.9115 | 47.9400 | 47.9661 | 47.9900 | 48.0120 | 48.0321 | 48.0507 | 48.0679 | 48.0837 |

| $100K_2$ $\alpha=$ | $\beta=41$ | 42 | 43 | 44 | 45 | 46 | 47 | 48 | 49 | 50 |
|---|---|---|---|---|---|---|---|---|---|---|
| 1 | 0.0000 | 0.0000 | 0.0000 | 0.0000 | 0.0000 | 0.0000 | 0.0000 | 0.0000 | 0.0000 | 0.0000 |
|  | 24.9989 | 24.9990 | 24.9991 | 24.9991 | 24.9992 | 24.9992 | 24.9993 | 24.9993 | 24.9994 | 24.9994 |
|  | 33.3304 | 33.3306 | 33.3308 | 33.3310 | 33.3311 | 33.3313 | 33.3314 | 33.3315 | 33.3316 | 33.3311 |
|  | 37.4946 | 37.4950 | 37.4953 | 37.4956 | 37.4959 | 37.4962 | 37.4964 | 37.4966 | 37.4968 | 37.4970 |
| 5 | 39.9914 | 39.9920 | 39.9925 | 39.9930 | 39.9935 | 39.9939 | 39.9943 | 39.9946 | 39.9949 | 39.9952 |
|  | 41.6542 | 41.6550 | 41.6558 | 41.6565 | 41.6572 | 41.6578 | 41.6583 | 41.6588 | 41.6593 | 41.6597 |
|  | 42.8401 | 42.8413 | 42.8423 | 42.8433 | 42.8442 | 42.8450 | 42.8458 | 42.8465 | 42.8471 | 42.8477 |
|  | 43.7278 | 43.7293 | 43.7307 | 43.7320 | 43.7331 | 43.7342 | 43.7352 | 43.7361 | 43.7369 | 43.7376 |
|  | 44.4164 | 44.4184 | 44.4201 | 44.4217 | 44.4231 | 44.4245 | 44.4257 | 44.4268 | 44.4279 | 44.4288 |
| 10 | 44.9656 | 44.9680 | 44.9701 | 44.9720 | 44.9736 | 44.9754 | 44.9769 | 44.9783 | 44.9796 | 44.9808 |
|  | 45.4133 | 45.4160 | 45.4186 | 45.4209 | 45.4230 | 45.4250 | 45.4268 | 45.4285 | 45.4300 | 45.4314 |
|  | 45.7846 | 45.7879 | 45.7909 | 45.7936 | 45.7961 | 45.7984 | 45.8005 | 45.8025 | 45.8043 | 45.8059 |
|  | 46.0972 | 46.1010 | 46.1044 | 46.1076 | 46.1105 | 46.1131 | 46.1156 | 46.1178 | 46.1199 | 46.1219 |
|  | 46.3635 | 46.3678 | 46.3718 | 46.3754 | 46.3787 | 46.3817 | 46.3845 | 46.3871 | 46.3895 | 46.3917 |
| 15 | 46.5928 | 46.5976 | 46.6021 | 46.6062 | 46.6099 | 46.6134 | 46.6165 | 46.6195 | 46.6222 | 46.6247 |
|  | 46.7919 | 46.7973 | 46.8023 | 46.8069 | 46.8111 | 46.8149 | 46.8185 | 46.8218 | 46.8248 | 46.8276 |
|  | 46.9662 | 46.9722 | 46.9777 | 46.9828 | 46.9874 | 46.9917 | 46.9956 | 46.9993 | 47.0027 | 47.0058 |
|  | 47.1197 | 47.1263 | 47.1324 | 47.1379 | 47.1430 | 47.1477 | 47.1521 | 47.1561 | 47.1599 | 47.1633 |
|  | 47.2557 | 47.2629 | 47.2695 | 47.2756 | 47.2812 | 47.2864 | 47.2911 | 47.2955 | 47.2996 | 47.3034 |
| 20 | 47.3769 | 47.3847 | 47.3919 | 47.3984 | 47.4045 | 47.4101 | 47.4153 | 47.4201 | 47.4245 | 47.4287 |
|  | 47.4853 | 47.4937 | 47.5014 | 47.5085 | 47.5151 | 47.5211 | 47.5267 | 47.5328 | 47.5368 | 47.5412 |
|  | 47.5827 | 47.5917 | 47.6000 | 47.6076 | 47.6146 | 47.6212 | 47.6272 | 47.6328 | 47.6380 | 47.6428 |
|  | 47.6705 | 47.6801 | 47.6889 | 47.6971 | 47.7046 | 47.7116 | 47.7180 | 47.7240 | 47.7296 | 47.7348 |
|  | 47.7500 | 47.7602 | 47.7695 | 47.7782 | 47.7862 | 47.7936 | 47.8005 | 47.8069 | 47.8129 | 47.8184 |
| 25 | 47.8221 | 47.8328 | 47.8428 | 47.8519 | 47.8604 | 47.8683 | 47.8756 | 47.8824 | 47.8887 | 47.8946 |
|  | 47.8877 | 47.8990 | 47.9095 | 47.9192 | 47.9282 | 47.9365 | 47.9442 | 47.9514 | 47.9581 | 47.9643 |
|  | 47.9475 | 47.9594 | 47.9704 | 47.9806 | 47.9901 | 47.9989 | 48.0070 | 48.0146 | 48.0217 | 48.0283 |
|  | 48.0022 | 48.0147 | 48.0262 | 48.0369 | 48.0468 | 48.0561 | 48.0646 | 48.0726 | 48.0801 | 48.0870 |
|  | 48.0523 | 48.0654 | 48.0774 | 48.0886 | 48.0990 | 48.1086 | 48.1176 | 48.1260 | 48.1338 | 48.1411 |
| 30 | 48.0984 | 48.1119 | 48.1245 | 48.1362 | 48.1470 | 48.1571 | 48.1665 | 48.1752 | 48.1834 | 48.1910 |

| $\alpha$ | $100K_3$ $\beta=1$ / 1 | 2 | 3 | 4 | 5 | 6 | 7 | 8 | 9 | 10 |
|---|---|---|---|---|---|---|---|---|---|---|
| | 0.0000 | 0.0000 | 0.0000 | 0.0000 | 0.0000 | 0.0000 | 0.0000 | 0.0000 | 0.0000 | 0.0000 |
| | 13.2055 | 4.5249 | 1.5432 | 0.6173 | 0.2849 | 0.1471 | 0.0829 | 0.0500 | 0.0318 | 0.0212 |
| | 16.0965 | 6.8108 | 2.7792 | 1.2534 | 0.6247 | 0.3392 | 0.1976 | 0.1220 | 0.0790 | 0.0532 |
| | 16.9643 | 7.8262 | 3.5434 | 1.7485 | 0.9335 | 0.5329 | 0.3221 | 0.2043 | 0.1350 | 0.0924 |
| 5 | 17.3005 | 8.3039 | 3.9868 | 2.0915 | 1.1786 | 0.7033 | 0.4401 | 0.2869 | 0.1937 | 0.1348 |
| | 17.4555 | 8.5490 | 4.2465 | 2.3200 | 1.3610 | 0.8419 | 0.5433 | 0.3633 | 0.2504 | 0.1773 |
| | 17.5362 | 8.6851 | 4.4038 | 2.4717 | 1.4930 | 0.9501 | 0.6292 | 0.4303 | 0.3024 | 0.2177 |
| | 17.5823 | 8.7659 | 4.5029 | 2.5739 | 1.5880 | 1.0330 | 0.6986 | 0.4871 | 0.3483 | 0.2545 |
| | 17.6103 | 8.8167 | 4.5677 | 2.6440 | 1.6567 | 1.0959 | 0.7538 | 0.5342 | 0.3878 | 0.2873 |
| 10 | 17.6284 | 8.8500 | 4.6116 | 2.6933 | 1.7068 | 1.1438 | 0.7975 | 0.5728 | 0.4212 | 0.3158 |
| | 17.6406 | 8.8727 | 4.6422 | 2.7286 | 1.7440 | 1.1805 | 0.8320 | 0.6043 | 0.4493 | 0.3404 |
| | 17.6490 | 8.8887 | 4.6642 | 2.7545 | 1.7719 | 1.2087 | 0.8594 | 0.6299 | 0.4727 | 0.3614 |
| | 17.6551 | 8.9003 | 4.6803 | 2.7739 | 1.7932 | 1.2308 | 0.8812 | 0.6508 | 0.4922 | 0.3793 |
| | 17.6596 | 8.9089 | 4.6923 | 2.7886 | 1.8096 | 1.2481 | 0.8987 | 0.6679 | 0.5084 | 0.3944 |
| 15 | 17.6630 | 8.9154 | 4.7015 | 2.7999 | 1.8225 | 1.2618 | 0.9128 | 0.6819 | 0.5220 | 0.4073 |
| | 17.6655 | 8.9204 | 4.7086 | 2.8088 | 1.8327 | 1.2728 | 0.9242 | 0.6934 | 0.5333 | 0.4182 |
| | 17.6675 | 8.9243 | 4.7143 | 2.8158 | 1.8408 | 1.2818 | 0.9336 | 0.7030 | 0.5428 | 0.4274 |
| | 17.6691 | 8.9274 | 4.7187 | 2.8215 | 1.8474 | 1.2890 | 0.9414 | 0.7110 | 0.5508 | 0.4353 |
| | 17.6704 | 8.9299 | 4.7223 | 2.8260 | 1.8528 | 1.2950 | 0.9478 | 0.7176 | 0.5576 | 0.4421 |
| 20 | 17.6714 | 8.9320 | 4.7253 | 2.8298 | 1.8572 | 1.3000 | 0.9532 | 0.7233 | 0.5634 | 0.4479 |
| | 17.6723 | 8.9336 | 4.7277 | 2.8329 | 1.8609 | 1.3042 | 0.9577 | 0.7280 | 0.5683 | 0.4529 |
| | 17.6730 | 8.9350 | 4.7297 | 2.8355 | 1.8640 | 1.3077 | 0.9615 | 0.7321 | 0.5725 | 0.4572 |
| | 17.6736 | 8.9361 | 4.7314 | 2.8376 | 1.8666 | 1.3106 | 0.9648 | 0.7356 | 0.5762 | 0.4609 |
| | 17.6741 | 8.9371 | 4.7328 | 2.8395 | 1.8688 | 1.3131 | 0.9675 | 0.7386 | 0.5793 | 0.4641 |
| 25 | 17.6745 | 8.9379 | 4.7340 | 2.8410 | 1.8706 | 1.3153 | 0.9699 | 0.7412 | 0.5820 | 0.4670 |
| | 17.6748 | 8.9386 | 4.7350 | 2.8424 | 1.8723 | 1.3172 | 0.9720 | 0.7434 | 0.5844 | 0.4695 |
| | 17.6751 | 8.9392 | 4.7359 | 2.8435 | 1.8737 | 1.3188 | 0.9738 | 0.7454 | 0.5865 | 0.4716 |
| | 17.6754 | 8.9398 | 4.7367 | 2.8445 | 1.8749 | 1.3202 | 0.9754 | 0.7471 | 0.5883 | 0.4736 |
| | 17.6756 | 8.9402 | 4.7374 | 2.8454 | 1.8759 | 1.3214 | 0.9768 | 0.7486 | 0.5900 | 0.4753 |
| 30 | 17.6758 | 8.9406 | 4.7379 | 2.8461 | 1.8768 | 1.3225 | 0.9780 | 0.7499 | 0.5914 | 0.4768 |

| $100K_3$ | $\beta=11$ | 12 | 13 | 14 | 15 | 16 | 17 | 18 | 19 | 20 |
|---|---|---|---|---|---|---|---|---|---|---|
| $\alpha=1$ | 0.0000 | 0.0000 | 0.0000 | 0.0000 | 0.0000 | 0.0000 | 0.0000 | 0.0000 | 0.0000 | 0.0000 |
|  | 0.0146 | 0.0104 | 0.0076 | 0.0057 | 0.0043 | 0.0034 | 0.0026 | 0.0021 | 0.0017 | 0.0014 |
|  | 0.0371 | 0.0266 | 0.0195 | 0.0147 | 0.0112 | 0.0087 | 0.0069 | 0.0055 | 0.0044 | 0.0036 |
|  | 0.0652 | 0.0472 | 0.0349 | 0.0264 | 0.0203 | 0.0158 | 0.0125 | 0.0101 | 0.0081 | 0.0067 |
|  | 0.0964 | 0.0705 | 0.0527 | 0.0401 | 0.0310 | 0.0243 | 0.0194 | 0.0156 | 0.0127 | 0.0104 |
| 5 | 0.1286 | 0.0952 | 0.0718 | 0.0551 | 0.0429 | 0.0338 | 0.0270 | 0.0218 | 0.0178 | 0.0147 |
|  | 0.1600 | 0.1199 | 0.0913 | 0.0706 | 0.0554 | 0.0440 | 0.0353 | 0.0287 | 0.0235 | 0.0194 |
|  | 0.1896 | 0.1436 | 0.1105 | 0.0862 | 0.0681 | 0.0544 | 0.0440 | 0.0359 | 0.0295 | 0.0245 |
|  | 0.2166 | 0.1659 | 0.1288 | 0.1013 | 0.0806 | 0.0649 | 0.0527 | 0.0432 | 0.0357 | 0.0297 |
|  | 0.2407 | 0.1862 | 0.1459 | 0.1157 | 0.0927 | 0.0751 | 0.0613 | 0.0505 | 0.0420 | 0.0351 |
| 10 | 0.2621 | 0.2046 | 0.1616 | 0.1291 | 0.1042 | 0.0849 | 0.0697 | 0.0577 | 0.0482 | 0.0404 |
|  | 0.2807 | 0.2209 | 0.1759 | 0.1415 | 0.1149 | 0.0942 | 0.0778 | 0.0647 | 0.0542 | 0.0457 |
|  | 0.2968 | 0.2353 | 0.1886 | 0.1528 | 0.1248 | 0.1029 | 0.0854 | 0.0714 | 0.0601 | 0.0509 |
|  | 0.3107 | 0.2479 | 0.2000 | 0.1630 | 0.1339 | 0.1109 | 0.0925 | 0.0777 | 0.0657 | 0.0558 |
|  | 0.3227 | 0.2590 | 0.2101 | 0.1721 | 0.1422 | 0.1183 | 0.0992 | 0.0836 | 0.0710 | 0.0605 |
| 15 | 0.3330 | 0.2686 | 0.2191 | 0.1803 | 0.1497 | 0.1251 | 0.1053 | 0.0892 | 0.0759 | 0.0650 |
|  | 0.3419 | 0.2770 | 0.2269 | 0.1876 | 0.1564 | 0.1313 | 0.1109 | 0.0943 | 0.0806 | 0.0692 |
|  | 0.3496 | 0.2844 | 0.2339 | 0.1941 | 0.1624 | 0.1369 | 0.1161 | 0.0990 | 0.0849 | 0.0732 |
|  | 0.3562 | 0.2908 | 0.2400 | 0.1999 | 0.1679 | 0.1420 | 0.1208 | 0.1034 | 0.0890 | 0.0769 |
|  | 0.3619 | 0.2963 | 0.2454 | 0.2051 | 0.1727 | 0.1466 | 0.1251 | 0.1074 | 0.0927 | 0.0803 |
| 20 | 0.3669 | 0.3012 | 0.2501 | 0.2096 | 0.1771 | 0.1507 | 0.1290 | 0.1111 | 0.0961 | 0.0835 |
|  | 0.3712 | 0.3055 | 0.2543 | 0.2137 | 0.1810 | 0.1544 | 0.1326 | 0.1144 | 0.0993 | 0.0865 |
|  | 0.3750 | 0.3093 | 0.2580 | 0.2173 | 0.1845 | 0.1578 | 0.1358 | 0.1175 | 0.1022 | 0.0892 |
|  | 0.3783 | 0.3126 | 0.2613 | 0.2205 | 0.1877 | 0.1608 | 0.1387 | 0.1203 | 0.1048 | 0.0917 |
|  | 0.3812 | 0.3155 | 0.2642 | 0.2234 | 0.1905 | 0.1636 | 0.1414 | 0.1228 | 0.1072 | 0.0941 |
| 25 | 0.3837 | 0.3181 | 0.2668 | 0.2260 | 0.1930 | 0.1661 | 0.1438 | 0.1251 | 0.1095 | 0.0962 |
|  | 0.3860 | 0.3204 | 0.2691 | 0.2283 | 0.1953 | 0.1683 | 0.1459 | 0.1273 | 0.1115 | 0.0982 |
|  | 0.3880 | 0.3224 | 0.2712 | 0.2303 | 0.1973 | 0.1703 | 0.1479 | 0.1292 | 0.1134 | 0.1000 |
|  | 0.3897 | 0.3242 | 0.2730 | 0.2322 | 0.1992 | 0.1722 | 0.1497 | 0.1310 | 0.1151 | 0.1017 |
| 30 | 0.3913 | 0.3258 | 0.2747 | 0.2339 | 0.2009 | 0.1738 | 0.1514 | 0.1326 | 0.1167 | 0.1032 |

| $100K_3$ | $\beta=21$ | 22 | 23 | 24 | 25 | 26 | 27 | 28 | 29 | 30 |
|---|---|---|---|---|---|---|---|---|---|---|
| $\alpha=1$ | 0.0000 | 0.0000 | 0.0000 | 0.0000 | 0.0000 | 0.0000 | 0.0000 | 0.0000 | 0.0000 | 0.0000 |
|  | 0.0011 | 0.0009 | 0.0008 | 0.0007 | 0.0006 | 0.0005 | 0.0004 | 0.0004 | 0.0003 | 0.0003 |
|  | 0.0030 | 0.0025 | 0.0021 | 0.0018 | 0.0015 | 0.0013 | 0.0011 | 0.0010 | 0.0008 | 0.0007 |
|  | 0.0055 | 0.0046 | 0.0039 | 0.0033 | 0.0028 | 0.0024 | 0.0021 | 0.0018 | 0.0016 | 0.0014 |
| 5 | 0.0086 | 0.0072 | 0.0061 | 0.0051 | 0.0044 | 0.0038 | 0.0032 | 0.0028 | 0.0024 | 0.0021 |
|  | 0.0122 | 0.0102 | 0.0086 | 0.0073 | 0.0063 | 0.0054 | 0.0046 | 0.0040 | 0.0035 | 0.0031 |
|  | 0.0162 | 0.0136 | 0.0115 | 0.0098 | 0.0084 | 0.0072 | 0.0062 | 0.0054 | 0.0047 | 0.0042 |
|  | 0.0205 | 0.0172 | 0.0146 | 0.0125 | 0.0107 | 0.0092 | 0.0080 | 0.0070 | 0.0061 | 0.0053 |
|  | 0.0250 | 0.0211 | 0.0179 | 0.0153 | 0.0132 | 0.0114 | 0.0099 | 0.0086 | 0.0076 | 0.0066 |
| 10 | 0.0296 | 0.0250 | 0.0214 | 0.0183 | 0.0158 | 0.0137 | 0.0119 | 0.0104 | 0.0091 | 0.0080 |
|  | 0.0342 | 0.0291 | 0.0249 | 0.0214 | 0.0185 | 0.0160 | 0.0140 | 0.0122 | 0.0108 | 0.0095 |
|  | 0.0388 | 0.0331 | 0.0284 | 0.0245 | 0.0212 | 0.0184 | 0.0161 | 0.0141 | 0.0124 | 0.0110 |
|  | 0.0433 | 0.0371 | 0.0319 | 0.0276 | 0.0239 | 0.0209 | 0.0183 | 0.0161 | 0.0142 | 0.0125 |
|  | 0.0477 | 0.0410 | 0.0353 | 0.0306 | 0.0267 | 0.0233 | 0.0205 | 0.0180 | 0.0159 | 0.0141 |
| 15 | 0.0519 | 0.0447 | 0.0387 | 0.0336 | 0.0294 | 0.0257 | 0.0226 | 0.0200 | 0.0177 | 0.0157 |
|  | 0.0559 | 0.0483 | 0.0420 | 0.0366 | 0.0320 | 0.0281 | 0.0248 | 0.0219 | 0.0194 | 0.0173 |
|  | 0.0598 | 0.0518 | 0.0451 | 0.0394 | 0.0346 | 0.0304 | 0.0269 | 0.0238 | 0.0212 | 0.0189 |
|  | 0.0634 | 0.0551 | 0.0481 | 0.0421 | 0.0371 | 0.0327 | 0.0289 | 0.0257 | 0.0229 | 0.0204 |
|  | 0.0668 | 0.0582 | 0.0509 | 0.0447 | 0.0394 | 0.0349 | 0.0309 | 0.0275 | 0.0246 | 0.0220 |
| 20 | 0.0699 | 0.0611 | 0.0536 | 0.0472 | 0.0417 | 0.0370 | 0.0329 | 0.0293 | 0.0262 | 0.0235 |
|  | 0.0729 | 0.0639 | 0.0562 | 0.0496 | 0.0439 | 0.0390 | 0.0347 | 0.0310 | 0.0278 | 0.0249 |
|  | 0.0757 | 0.0665 | 0.0586 | 0.0518 | 0.0460 | 0.0409 | 0.0365 | 0.0326 | 0.0293 | 0.0263 |
|  | 0.0782 | 0.0689 | 0.0608 | 0.0539 | 0.0479 | 0.0427 | 0.0382 | 0.0342 | 0.0308 | 0.0277 |
|  | 0.0806 | 0.0711 | 0.0629 | 0.0559 | 0.0498 | 0.0445 | 0.0398 | 0.0357 | 0.0322 | 0.0290 |
| 25 | 0.0828 | 0.0732 | 0.0649 | 0.0577 | 0.0515 | 0.0461 | 0.0414 | 0.0372 | 0.0335 | 0.0303 |
|  | 0.0849 | 0.0751 | 0.0668 | 0.0595 | 0.0532 | 0.0477 | 0.0428 | 0.0386 | 0.0348 | 0.0315 |
|  | 0.0868 | 0.0769 | 0.0685 | 0.0611 | 0.0547 | 0.0491 | 0.0442 | 0.0399 | 0.0360 | 0.0326 |
|  | 0.0885 | 0.0786 | 0.0701 | 0.0627 | 0.0562 | 0.0505 | 0.0455 | 0.0411 | 0.0372 | 0.0338 |
|  | 0.0901 | 0.0802 | 0.0716 | 0.0641 | 0.0575 | 0.0518 | 0.0467 | 0.0423 | 0.0383 | 0.0348 |
| 30 | 0.0916 | 0.0816 | 0.0730 | 0.0654 | 0.0588 | 0.0530 | 0.0479 | 0.0434 | 0.0394 | 0.0358 |

| $100K_3$ | $\beta=31$ | 32 | 33 | 34 | 35 | 36 | 37 | 38 | 39 | 40 |
|---|---|---|---|---|---|---|---|---|---|---|
| $\alpha=1$ | 0.0000 | 0.0000 | 0.0000 | 0.0000 | 0.0000 | 0.0000 | 0.0000 | 0.0000 | 0.0000 | 0.0000 |
| | 0.0002 | 0.0002 | 0.0002 | 0.0002 | 0.0001 | 0.0001 | 0.0001 | 0.0001 | 0.0001 | 0.0001 |
| | 0.0006 | 0.0006 | 0.0005 | 0.0004 | 0.0004 | 0.0004 | 0.0003 | 0.0003 | 0.0003 | 0.0002 |
| | 0.0012 | 0.0011 | 0.0009 | 0.0008 | 0.0007 | 0.0007 | 0.0006 | 0.0005 | 0.0005 | 0.0004 |
| 5 | 0.0019 | 0.0017 | 0.0015 | 0.0013 | 0.0012 | 0.0010 | 0.0009 | 0.0008 | 0.0008 | 0.0007 |
| | 0.0027 | 0.0024 | 0.0021 | 0.0019 | 0.0017 | 0.0015 | 0.0014 | 0.0012 | 0.0011 | 0.0010 |
| | 0.0037 | 0.0032 | 0.0029 | 0.0026 | 0.0023 | 0.0020 | 0.0018 | 0.0017 | 0.0015 | 0.0014 |
| | 0.0047 | 0.0042 | 0.0037 | 0.0033 | 0.0030 | 0.0026 | 0.0024 | 0.0021 | 0.0019 | 0.0018 |
| | 0.0059 | 0.0052 | 0.0046 | 0.0041 | 0.0037 | 0.0033 | 0.0030 | 0.0027 | 0.0024 | 0.0022 |
| 10 | 0.0071 | 0.0063 | 0.0056 | 0.0050 | 0.0045 | 0.0040 | 0.0036 | 0.0033 | 0.0030 | 0.0027 |
| | 0.0084 | 0.0075 | 0.0066 | 0.0059 | 0.0053 | 0.0048 | 0.0043 | 0.0039 | 0.0035 | 0.0032 |
| | 0.0098 | 0.0087 | 0.0077 | 0.0069 | 0.0062 | 0.0056 | 0.0050 | 0.0046 | 0.0041 | 0.0038 |
| | 0.0111 | 0.0099 | 0.0089 | 0.0079 | 0.0071 | 0.0064 | 0.0058 | 0.0053 | 0.0048 | 0.0043 |
| | 0.0126 | 0.0112 | 0.0100 | 0.0090 | 0.0081 | 0.0073 | 0.0066 | 0.0060 | 0.0054 | 0.0049 |
| 15 | 0.0140 | 0.0125 | 0.0112 | 0.0101 | 0.0091 | 0.0082 | 0.0074 | 0.0067 | 0.0061 | 0.0056 |
| | 0.0154 | 0.0138 | 0.0124 | 0.0112 | 0.0101 | 0.0091 | 0.0082 | 0.0075 | 0.0068 | 0.0062 |
| | 0.0169 | 0.0151 | 0.0136 | 0.0122 | 0.0111 | 0.0100 | 0.0091 | 0.0083 | 0.0075 | 0.0069 |
| | 0.0183 | 0.0164 | 0.0148 | 0.0133 | 0.0121 | 0.0109 | 0.0099 | 0.0090 | 0.0082 | 0.0075 |
| | 0.0197 | 0.0177 | 0.0160 | 0.0144 | 0.0131 | 0.0118 | 0.0108 | 0.0098 | 0.0090 | 0.0082 |
| 20 | 0.0211 | 0.0190 | 0.0171 | 0.0155 | 0.0141 | 0.0128 | 0.0116 | 0.0106 | 0.0097 | 0.0089 |
| | 0.0224 | 0.0202 | 0.0183 | 0.0166 | 0.0150 | 0.0137 | 0.0125 | 0.0114 | 0.0104 | 0.0095 |
| | 0.0237 | 0.0214 | 0.0194 | 0.0176 | 0.0160 | 0.0146 | 0.0133 | 0.0121 | 0.0111 | 0.0102 |
| | 0.0250 | 0.0226 | 0.0205 | 0.0186 | 0.0169 | 0.0154 | 0.0141 | 0.0129 | 0.0118 | 0.0109 |
| | 0.0262 | 0.0238 | 0.0216 | 0.0196 | 0.0179 | 0.0163 | 0.0149 | 0.0137 | 0.0125 | 0.0115 |
| 25 | 0.0274 | 0.0249 | 0.0226 | 0.0206 | 0.0188 | 0.0172 | 0.0157 | 0.0144 | 0.0132 | 0.0122 |
| | 0.0285 | 0.0259 | 0.0236 | 0.0215 | 0.0197 | 0.0180 | 0.0165 | 0.0151 | 0.0139 | 0.0128 |
| | 0.0296 | 0.0270 | 0.0246 | 0.0224 | 0.0205 | 0.0188 | 0.0172 | 0.0158 | 0.0146 | 0.0134 |
| | 0.0307 | 0.0279 | 0.0255 | 0.0233 | 0.0213 | 0.0196 | 0.0180 | 0.0165 | 0.0152 | 0.0140 |
| | 0.0317 | 0.0289 | 0.0264 | 0.0241 | 0.0221 | 0.0203 | 0.0187 | 0.0172 | 0.0159 | 0.0146 |
| 30 | 0.0326 | 0.0298 | 0.0272 | 0.0250 | 0.0229 | 0.0210 | 0.0194 | 0.0178 | 0.0165 | 0.0152 |

| $100K_3$ | $\beta=41$ | 42 | 43 | 44 | 45 | 46 | 47 | 48 | 49 | 50 |
|---|---|---|---|---|---|---|---|---|---|---|
| $\alpha=1$ | 0.0000 | 0.0000 | 0.0000 | 0.0000 | 0.0000 | 0.0000 | 0.0000 | 0.0000 | 0.0000 | 0.0000 |
| | 0.0001 | 0.0001 | 0.0001 | 0.0001 | 0.0001 | 0.0001 | 0.0001 | 0.0001 | 0.0000 | 0.0000 |
| | 0.0002 | 0.0002 | 0.0002 | 0.0002 | 0.0001 | 0.0001 | 0.0001 | 0.0001 | 0.0001 | 0.0001 |
| | 0.0004 | 0.0004 | 0.0003 | 0.0003 | 0.0003 | 0.0002 | 0.0002 | 0.0002 | 0.0002 | 0.0002 |
| | 0.0006 | 0.0006 | 0.0005 | 0.0005 | 0.0004 | 0.0004 | 0.0004 | 0.0003 | 0.0003 | 0.0003 |
| 5 | 0.0009 | 0.0008 | 0.0007 | 0.0007 | 0.0006 | 0.0006 | 0.0005 | 0.0005 | 0.0004 | 0.0004 |
| | 0.0012 | 0.0011 | 0.0010 | 0.0009 | 0.0009 | 0.0008 | 0.0007 | 0.0007 | 0.0006 | 0.0006 |
| | 0.0016 | 0.0015 | 0.0013 | 0.0012 | 0.0011 | 0.0010 | 0.0009 | 0.0009 | 0.0008 | 0.0007 |
| | 0.0020 | 0.0018 | 0.0017 | 0.0015 | 0.0014 | 0.0013 | 0.0012 | 0.0011 | 0.0010 | 0.0009 |
| | 0.0024 | 0.0022 | 0.0020 | 0.0019 | 0.0017 | 0.0016 | 0.0014 | 0.0013 | 0.0012 | 0.0011 |
| 10 | 0.0029 | 0.0027 | 0.0024 | 0.0022 | 0.0020 | 0.0019 | 0.0017 | 0.0016 | 0.0015 | 0.0014 |
| | 0.0034 | 0.0031 | 0.0029 | 0.0026 | 0.0024 | 0.0022 | 0.0020 | 0.0019 | 0.0017 | 0.0016 |
| | 0.0040 | 0.0036 | 0.0033 | 0.0030 | 0.0028 | 0.0026 | 0.0024 | 0.0022 | 0.0020 | 0.0019 |
| | 0.0045 | 0.0041 | 0.0038 | 0.0035 | 0.0032 | 0.0029 | 0.0027 | 0.0025 | 0.0023 | 0.0021 |
| | 0.0051 | 0.0046 | 0.0043 | 0.0039 | 0.0036 | 0.0033 | 0.0030 | 0.0028 | 0.0026 | 0.0024 |
| 15 | 0.0057 | 0.0052 | 0.0048 | 0.0044 | 0.0040 | 0.0037 | 0.0034 | 0.0032 | 0.0029 | 0.0027 |
| | 0.0063 | 0.0057 | 0.0053 | 0.0048 | 0.0045 | 0.0041 | 0.0038 | 0.0035 | 0.0033 | 0.0030 |
| | 0.0069 | 0.0063 | 0.0058 | 0.0053 | 0.0049 | 0.0045 | 0.0042 | 0.0039 | 0.0036 | 0.0033 |
| | 0.0075 | 0.0069 | 0.0063 | 0.0058 | 0.0054 | 0.0050 | 0.0046 | 0.0042 | 0.0039 | 0.0037 |
| | 0.0081 | 0.0075 | 0.0069 | 0.0063 | 0.0058 | 0.0054 | 0.0050 | 0.0046 | 0.0043 | 0.0040 |
| 20 | 0.0087 | 0.0080 | 0.0074 | 0.0068 | 0.0063 | 0.0058 | 0.0054 | 0.0050 | 0.0046 | 0.0043 |
| | 0.0094 | 0.0086 | 0.0079 | 0.0073 | 0.0068 | 0.0063 | 0.0058 | 0.0054 | 0.0050 | 0.0047 |
| | 0.0100 | 0.0092 | 0.0085 | 0.0078 | 0.0072 | 0.0067 | 0.0062 | 0.0058 | 0.0054 | 0.0050 |
| | 0.0106 | 0.0098 | 0.0090 | 0.0083 | 0.0077 | 0.0071 | 0.0066 | 0.0062 | 0.0057 | 0.0053 |
| | 0.0112 | 0.0103 | 0.0095 | 0.0088 | 0.0082 | 0.0076 | 0.0070 | 0.0065 | 0.0061 | 0.0057 |
| 25 | 0.0118 | 0.0109 | 0.0101 | 0.0093 | 0.0086 | 0.0080 | 0.0075 | 0.0069 | 0.0065 | 0.0060 |
| | 0.0124 | 0.0114 | 0.0106 | 0.0098 | 0.0091 | 0.0085 | 0.0079 | 0.0073 | 0.0068 | 0.0064 |
| | 0.0130 | 0.0120 | 0.0111 | 0.0103 | 0.0096 | 0.0089 | 0.0083 | 0.0077 | 0.0072 | 0.0067 |
| | 0.0135 | 0.0125 | 0.0116 | 0.0108 | 0.0100 | 0.0093 | 0.0087 | 0.0081 | 0.0075 | 0.0070 |
| 30 | 0.0141 | 0.0130 | 0.0121 | 0.0112 | 0.0105 | 0.0097 | 0.0091 | 0.0085 | 0.0079 | 0.0074 |

| $100K_4$ $\alpha$ | $\beta=1$ | 2 | 3 | 4 | 5 | 6 | 7 | 8 | 9 | 10 |
|---|---|---|---|---|---|---|---|---|---|---|
| 1 | 0.0000 | 0.0000 | 0.0000 | 0.0000 | 0.0000 | 0.0000 | 0.0000 | 0.0000 | 0.0000 | 0.0000 |
|  | 54.3777 | 48.9061 | 45.2891 | 44.2682 | 43.9529 | 43.8403 | 43.7945 | 43.7738 | 43.7636 | 43.7582 |
|  | 58.0938 | 54.4912 | 51.5087 | 49.0809 | 48.5548 | 48.3426 | 48.2488 | 48.2039 | 48.1808 | 48.1682 |
|  | 58.6450 | 55.7033 | 51.8747 | 50.3814 | 49.7716 | 49.5015 | 49.3727 | 49.3073 | 49.2722 | 49.2523 |
| 5 | 58.7725 | 56.0487 | 52.3399 | 50.8683 | 50.2401 | 49.9454 | 49.7969 | 49.7175 | 49.6730 | 49.6470 |
|  | 58.8115 | 56.1679 | 52.5227 | 51.0796 | 50.4552 | 50.1539 | 49.9963 | 49.9089 | 49.8582 | 49.8276 |
|  | 58.8260 | 56.2155 | 52.6027 | 51.1800 | 50.5639 | 50.2633 | 50.1028 | 50.0115 | 49.9571 | 49.9234 |
|  | 58.8322 | 56.2368 | 52.6408 | 51.2311 | 50.6225 | 50.3247 | 50.1642 | 50.0715 | 50.0152 | 49.9797 |
|  | 58.8351 | 56.2472 | 52.6603 | 51.2586 | 50.6556 | 50.3608 | 50.2014 | 50.1085 | 50.0515 | 50.0150 |
| 10 | 58.8366 | 56.2527 | 52.6710 | 51.2743 | 50.6751 | 50.3828 | 50.2247 | 50.1324 | 50.0752 | 50.0382 |
|  | 58.8375 | 56.2558 | 52.6771 | 51.2835 | 50.6870 | 50.3967 | 50.2398 | 50.1481 | 50.0911 | 50.0540 |
|  | 58.8379 | 56.2576 | 52.6808 | 51.2892 | 50.6945 | 50.4057 | 50.2499 | 50.1588 | 50.1021 | 50.0651 |
|  | 58.8382 | 56.2587 | 52.6830 | 51.2928 | 50.6994 | 50.4116 | 50.2567 | 50.1661 | 50.1098 | 50.0730 |
|  | 58.8384 | 56.2594 | 52.6845 | 51.2951 | 50.7026 | 50.4156 | 50.2614 | 50.1713 | 50.1153 | 50.0787 |
| 15 | 58.8385 | 56.2598 | 52.6855 | 51.2967 | 50.7048 | 50.4184 | 50.2647 | 50.1750 | 50.1193 | 50.0829 |
|  | 58.8386 | 56.2602 | 52.6861 | 51.2978 | 50.7064 | 50.4204 | 50.2670 | 50.1777 | 50.1223 | 50.0860 |
|  | 58.8387 | 56.2604 | 52.6866 | 51.2985 | 50.7074 | 50.4219 | 50.2687 | 50.1797 | 50.1244 | 50.0884 |
|  | 58.8387 | 56.2605 | 52.6869 | 51.2991 | 50.7082 | 50.4229 | 50.2700 | 50.1812 | 50.1261 | 50.0902 |
|  | 58.8387 | 56.2606 | 52.6872 | 51.2995 | 50.7088 | 50.4236 | 50.2709 | 50.1823 | 50.1273 | 50.0915 |
| 20 | 58.8388 | 56.2607 | 52.6873 | 51.2998 | 50.7092 | 50.4242 | 50.2716 | 50.1831 | 50.1283 | 50.0926 |
|  | 58.8388 | 56.2608 | 52.6875 | 51.3000 | 50.7095 | 50.4246 | 50.2722 | 50.1838 | 50.1291 | 50.0934 |
|  | 58.8388 | 56.2609 | 52.6876 | 51.3001 | 50.7098 | 50.4250 | 50.2726 | 50.1843 | 50.1296 | 50.0941 |
|  | 58.8388 | 56.2609 | 52.6876 | 51.3003 | 50.7100 | 50.4252 | 50.2729 | 50.1847 | 50.1301 | 50.0946 |
|  | 58.8388 | 56.2609 | 52.6877 | 51.3004 | 50.7101 | 50.4254 | 50.2732 | 50.1850 | 50.1305 | 50.0950 |
| 25 | 58.8388 | 56.2609 | 52.6877 | 51.3004 | 50.7102 | 50.4256 | 50.2734 | 50.1852 | 50.1308 | 50.0954 |
|  | 58.8388 | 56.2609 | 52.6878 | 51.3005 | 50.7103 | 50.4257 | 50.2736 | 50.1854 | 50.1310 | 50.0956 |
|  | 58.8388 | 56.2609 | 52.6878 | 51.3006 | 50.7104 | 50.4258 | 50.2737 | 50.1856 | 50.1312 | 50.0959 |
|  | 58.8388 | 56.2609 | 52.6878 | 51.3006 | 50.7105 | 50.4259 | 50.2738 | 50.1857 | 50.1313 | 50.0960 |
|  | 58.8388 | 56.2609 | 52.6878 | 51.3006 | 50.7105 | 50.4259 | 50.2739 | 50.1858 | 50.1315 | 50.0962 |
| 30 | 58.8388 | 56.2610 | 52.6879 | 51.3007 | 50.7106 | 50.4260 | 50.2740 | 50.1859 | 50.1316 | 50.0963 |

$100K_4$

| $\alpha$ | $\beta=11$ | 12 | 13 | 14 | 15 | 16 | 17 | 18 | 19 | 20 |
|---|---|---|---|---|---|---|---|---|---|---|
| 1 | 0.0000 | 0.0000 | 0.0000 | 0.0000 | 0.0000 | 0.0000 | 0.0000 | 0.0000 | 0.0000 | 0.0000 |
| | 43.7552 | 43.7534 | 43.7523 | 43.7516 | 43.7511 | 43.7508 | 43.7506 | 43.7505 | 43.7504 | 43.7503 |
| | 48.1610 | 48.1567 | 48.1540 | 48.1522 | 48.1511 | 48.1503 | 48.1497 | 48.1493 | 48.1491 | 48.1489 |
| | 49.2406 | 49.2334 | 49.2289 | 49.2259 | 49.2239 | 49.2226 | 49.2216 | 49.2209 | 49.2204 | 49.2201 |
| 5 | 49.6312 | 49.6213 | 49.6149 | 49.6106 | 49.6077 | 49.6057 | 49.6043 | 49.6033 | 49.6026 | 49.6020 |
| | 49.8085 | 49.7962 | 49.7881 | 49.7827 | 49.7789 | 49.7763 | 49.7744 | 49.7731 | 49.7721 | 49.7713 |
| | 49.9019 | 49.8878 | 49.8784 | 49.8719 | 49.8673 | 49.8641 | 49.8618 | 49.8601 | 49.8588 | 49.8578 |
| | 49.9565 | 49.9411 | 49.9305 | 49.9232 | 49.9180 | 49.9142 | 49.9115 | 49.9095 | 49.9080 | 49.9068 |
| | 49.9908 | 49.9745 | 49.9631 | 49.9551 | 49.9494 | 49.9452 | 49.9421 | 49.9398 | 49.9381 | 49.9367 |
| 10 | 50.0135 | 49.9966 | 49.9847 | 49.9762 | 49.9700 | 49.9655 | 49.9621 | 49.9596 | 49.9576 | 49.9561 |
| | 50.0291 | 50.0118 | 49.9996 | 49.9908 | 49.9843 | 49.9795 | 49.9759 | 49.9731 | 49.9710 | 49.9694 |
| | 50.0401 | 50.0226 | 50.0102 | 50.0011 | 49.9945 | 49.9894 | 49.9856 | 49.9827 | 49.9805 | 49.9787 |
| | 50.0480 | 50.0305 | 50.0179 | 50.0088 | 50.0019 | 49.9968 | 49.9928 | 49.9898 | 49.9874 | 49.9856 |
| | 50.0538 | 50.0363 | 50.0237 | 50.0144 | 50.0075 | 50.0023 | 49.9982 | 49.9951 | 49.9926 | 49.9907 |
| 15 | 50.0581 | 50.0407 | 50.0281 | 50.0188 | 50.0118 | 50.0065 | 50.0024 | 49.9992 | 49.9967 | 49.9946 |
| | 50.0613 | 50.0440 | 50.0314 | 50.0221 | 50.0151 | 50.0098 | 50.0056 | 50.0024 | 49.9998 | 49.9977 |
| | 50.0638 | 50.0465 | 50.0340 | 50.0247 | 50.0177 | 50.0123 | 50.0082 | 50.0049 | 50.0023 | 50.0002 |
| | 50.0657 | 50.0485 | 50.0360 | 50.0268 | 50.0198 | 50.0144 | 50.0102 | 50.0069 | 50.0043 | 50.0021 |
| | 50.0672 | 50.0500 | 50.0376 | 50.0284 | 50.0214 | 50.0160 | 50.0118 | 50.0085 | 50.0059 | 50.0037 |
| 20 | 50.0683 | 50.0512 | 50.0389 | 50.0297 | 50.0227 | 50.0174 | 50.0132 | 50.0099 | 50.0072 | 50.0051 |
| | 50.0692 | 50.0522 | 50.0399 | 50.0307 | 50.0238 | 50.0185 | 50.0143 | 50.0110 | 50.0083 | 50.0061 |
| | 50.0699 | 50.0530 | 50.0407 | 50.0316 | 50.0247 | 50.0193 | 50.0152 | 50.0119 | 50.0092 | 50.0070 |
| | 50.0705 | 50.0536 | 50.0413 | 50.0323 | 50.0254 | 50.0201 | 50.0159 | 50.0126 | 50.0099 | 50.0078 |
| | 50.0710 | 50.0541 | 50.0419 | 50.0328 | 50.0260 | 50.0207 | 50.0165 | 50.0132 | 50.0106 | 50.0084 |
| 25 | 50.0714 | 50.0545 | 50.0423 | 50.0333 | 50.0265 | 50.0212 | 50.0170 | 50.0137 | 50.0111 | 50.0089 |
| | 50.0717 | 50.0548 | 50.0427 | 50.0337 | 50.0269 | 50.0216 | 50.0175 | 50.0142 | 50.0115 | 50.0094 |
| | 50.0719 | 50.0551 | 50.0430 | 50.0340 | 50.0272 | 50.0219 | 50.0178 | 50.0146 | 50.0119 | 50.0098 |
| | 50.0721 | 50.0553 | 50.0432 | 50.0343 | 50.0275 | 50.0222 | 50.0181 | 50.0149 | 50.0123 | 50.0101 |
| | 50.0723 | 50.0555 | 50.0434 | 50.0345 | 50.0277 | 50.0225 | 50.0184 | 50.0151 | 50.0125 | 50.0104 |
| 30 | 50.0724 | 50.0557 | 50.0436 | 50.0347 | 50.0279 | 50.0227 | 50.0186 | 50.0154 | 50.0128 | 50.0106 |

| $100K_4$ $\big/$ $\alpha$ | $\beta=21$ | 22 | 23 | 24 | 25 | 26 | 27 | 28 | 29 | 30 |
|---|---|---|---|---|---|---|---|---|---|---|
| $\alpha=1$ | 0.0000 | 0.0000 | 0.0000 | 0.0000 | 0.0000 | 0.0000 | 0.0000 | 0.0000 | 0.0000 | 0.0000 |
|  | 43.7502 | 43.7502 | 43.7501 | 43.7501 | 43.7501 | 43.7501 | 43.7501 | 43.7501 | 43.7500 | 43.7500 |
|  | 48.1487 | 48.1486 | 48.1485 | 48.1484 | 48.1484 | 48.1483 | 48.1483 | 48.1483 | 48.1483 | 48.1482 |
|  | 49.2198 | 49.2196 | 49.2194 | 49.2193 | 49.2192 | 49.2191 | 49.2191 | 49.2190 | 49.2190 | 49.2189 |
| 5 | 49.6016 | 49.6013 | 49.6010 | 49.6008 | 49.6007 | 49.6006 | 49.6005 | 49.6004 | 49.6003 | 49.6003 |
|  | 49.7707 | 49.7703 | 49.7700 | 49.7697 | 49.7695 | 49.7693 | 49.7692 | 49.7691 | 49.7690 | 49.7689 |
|  | 49.8571 | 49.8566 | 49.8561 | 49.8558 | 49.8555 | 49.8553 | 49.8551 | 49.8550 | 49.8549 | 49.8548 |
|  | 49.9059 | 49.9052 | 49.9047 | 49.9043 | 49.9040 | 49.9037 | 49.9035 | 49.9033 | 49.9031 | 49.9030 |
|  | 49.9357 | 49.9348 | 49.9343 | 49.9338 | 49.9333 | 49.9330 | 49.9328 | 49.9326 | 49.9324 | 49.9323 |
| 10 | 49.9550 | 49.9541 | 49.9533 | 49.9528 | 49.9523 | 49.9519 | 49.9516 | 49.9514 | 49.9512 | 49.9510 |
|  | 49.9681 | 49.9671 | 49.9663 | 49.9656 | 49.9651 | 49.9647 | 49.9643 | 49.9640 | 49.9638 | 49.9636 |
|  | 49.9773 | 49.9762 | 49.9753 | 49.9746 | 49.9741 | 49.9736 | 49.9732 | 49.9729 | 49.9726 | 49.9724 |
|  | 49.9841 | 49.9829 | 49.9820 | 49.9812 | 49.9806 | 49.9801 | 49.9796 | 49.9793 | 49.9790 | 49.9788 |
|  | 49.9892 | 49.9879 | 49.9869 | 49.9861 | 49.9854 | 49.9849 | 49.9844 | 49.9840 | 49.9837 | 49.9835 |
| 15 | 49.9930 | 49.9917 | 49.9907 | 49.9898 | 49.9891 | 49.9885 | 49.9881 | 49.9876 | 49.9873 | 49.9870 |
|  | 49.9961 | 49.9947 | 49.9936 | 49.9927 | 49.9920 | 49.9914 | 49.9909 | 49.9905 | 49.9901 | 49.9898 |
|  | 49.9985 | 49.9971 | 49.9960 | 49.9951 | 49.9943 | 49.9936 | 49.9931 | 49.9927 | 49.9923 | 49.9920 |
|  | 50.0004 | 49.9990 | 49.9979 | 49.9969 | 49.9961 | 49.9955 | 49.9949 | 49.9944 | 49.9940 | 49.9937 |
|  | 50.0020 | 50.0006 | 49.9994 | 49.9984 | 49.9976 | 49.9969 | 49.9964 | 49.9959 | 49.9955 | 49.9951 |
| 20 | 50.0033 | 50.0019 | 50.0007 | 49.9997 | 49.9989 | 49.9982 | 49.9976 | 49.9971 | 49.9967 | 49.9963 |
|  | 50.0044 | 50.0029 | 50.0017 | 50.0007 | 49.9999 | 49.9992 | 49.9986 | 49.9981 | 49.9976 | 49.9973 |
|  | 50.0053 | 50.0038 | 50.0026 | 50.0016 | 50.0007 | 50.0000 | 49.9994 | 49.9989 | 49.9985 | 49.9981 |
|  | 50.0060 | 50.0046 | 50.0033 | 50.0023 | 50.0015 | 50.0007 | 50.0001 | 49.9996 | 49.9991 | 49.9988 |
|  | 50.0066 | 50.0052 | 50.0040 | 50.0029 | 50.0021 | 50.0013 | 50.0007 | 50.0002 | 49.9997 | 49.9993 |
| 25 | 50.0072 | 50.0057 | 50.0045 | 50.0035 | 50.0026 | 50.0019 | 50.0012 | 50.0007 | 50.0002 | 49.9998 |
|  | 50.0076 | 50.0062 | 50.0049 | 50.0039 | 50.0031 | 50.0023 | 50.0017 | 50.0011 | 50.0007 | 50.0003 |
|  | 50.0080 | 50.0066 | 50.0053 | 50.0043 | 50.0034 | 50.0027 | 50.0021 | 50.0015 | 50.0011 | 50.0007 |
|  | 50.0084 | 50.0069 | 50.0057 | 50.0046 | 50.0038 | 50.0030 | 50.0024 | 50.0019 | 50.0014 | 50.0010 |
|  | 50.0086 | 50.0072 | 50.0060 | 50.0049 | 50.0041 | 50.0033 | 50.0027 | 50.0021 | 50.0017 | 50.0013 |
| 30 | 50.0089 | 50.0074 | 50.0062 | 50.0052 | 50.0043 | 50.0036 | 50.0029 | 50.0024 | 50.0019 | 50.0015 |

| $100K_4$ | $\beta=31$ | 32 | 33 | 34 | 35 | 36 | 37 | 38 | 39 | 40 |
|---|---|---|---|---|---|---|---|---|---|---|
| $\alpha=1$ | 0.0000 | 0.0000 | 0.0000 | 0.0000 | 0.0000 | 0.0000 | 0.0000 | 0.0000 | 0.0000 | 0.0000 |
| | 43.7500 | 43.7500 | 43.7500 | 43.7500 | 43.7500 | 43.7500 | 43.7500 | 43.7500 | 43.7500 | 43.7500 |
| | 48.1482 | 48.1482 | 48.1482 | 48.1482 | 48.1482 | 48.1482 | 48.1482 | 48.1482 | 48.1482 | 48.1482 |
| | 49.2189 | 49.2189 | 49.2189 | 49.2188 | 49.2188 | 49.2188 | 49.2188 | 49.2188 | 49.2188 | 49.2188 |
| | 49.6002 | 49.6002 | 49.6002 | 49.6001 | 49.6001 | 49.6001 | 49.6001 | 49.6001 | 49.6001 | 49.6001 |
| 5 | 49.7689 | 49.7688 | 49.7688 | 49.7687 | 49.7687 | 49.7687 | 49.7687 | 49.7686 | 49.7686 | 49.7686 |
| | 49.8547 | 49.8546 | 49.8546 | 49.8545 | 49.8544 | 49.8544 | 49.8544 | 49.8544 | 49.8544 | 49.8544 |
| | 49.9029 | 49.9028 | 49.9028 | 49.9027 | 49.9027 | 49.9026 | 49.9026 | 49.9026 | 49.9025 | 49.9025 |
| | 49.9321 | 49.9320 | 49.9319 | 49.9319 | 49.9318 | 49.9318 | 49.9317 | 49.9317 | 49.9317 | 49.9316 |
| | 49.9509 | 49.9507 | 49.9506 | 49.9506 | 49.9505 | 49.9504 | 49.9504 | 49.9503 | 49.9503 | 49.9503 |
| 10 | 49.9634 | 49.9633 | 49.9632 | 49.9631 | 49.9630 | 49.9629 | 49.9629 | 49.9628 | 49.9628 | 49.9627 |
| | 49.9722 | 49.9721 | 49.9719 | 49.9718 | 49.9717 | 49.9716 | 49.9716 | 49.9715 | 49.9715 | 49.9714 |
| | 49.9785 | 49.9784 | 49.9782 | 49.9781 | 49.9780 | 49.9779 | 49.9778 | 49.9778 | 49.9777 | 49.9776 |
| | 49.9832 | 49.9830 | 49.9829 | 49.9827 | 49.9826 | 49.9825 | 49.9824 | 49.9824 | 49.9823 | 49.9822 |
| | 49.9868 | 49.9866 | 49.9864 | 49.9863 | 49.9861 | 49.9860 | 49.9859 | 49.9858 | 49.9858 | 49.9857 |
| 15 | 49.9895 | 49.9893 | 49.9891 | 49.9890 | 49.9888 | 49.9887 | 49.9886 | 49.9885 | 49.9884 | 49.9884 |
| | 49.9917 | 49.9915 | 49.9913 | 49.9911 | 49.9909 | 49.9908 | 49.9907 | 49.9906 | 49.9905 | 49.9904 |
| | 49.9934 | 49.9932 | 49.9930 | 49.9928 | 49.9926 | 49.9925 | 49.9924 | 49.9923 | 49.9922 | 49.9921 |
| | 49.9948 | 49.9946 | 49.9944 | 49.9942 | 49.9940 | 49.9939 | 49.9937 | 49.9936 | 49.9935 | 49.9934 |
| | 49.9960 | 49.9957 | 49.9955 | 49.9953 | 49.9951 | 49.9950 | 49.9948 | 49.9947 | 49.9946 | 49.9945 |
| 20 | 49.9969 | 49.9967 | 49.9964 | 49.9962 | 49.9960 | 49.9959 | 49.9957 | 49.9956 | 49.9955 | 49.9954 |
| | 49.9977 | 49.9975 | 49.9972 | 49.9970 | 49.9968 | 49.9967 | 49.9965 | 49.9964 | 49.9963 | 49.9962 |
| | 49.9984 | 49.9981 | 49.9979 | 49.9977 | 49.9975 | 49.9973 | 49.9972 | 49.9970 | 49.9969 | 49.9968 |
| | 49.9990 | 49.9987 | 49.9984 | 49.9982 | 49.9980 | 49.9979 | 49.9977 | 49.9976 | 49.9975 | 49.9973 |
| | 49.9995 | 49.9992 | 49.9989 | 49.9987 | 49.9985 | 49.9983 | 49.9982 | 49.9980 | 49.9979 | 49.9978 |
| 25 | 49.9999 | 49.9996 | 49.9994 | 49.9991 | 49.9991 | 49.9987 | 49.9986 | 49.9984 | 49.9983 | 49.9982 |
| | 50.0003 | 50.0000 | 49.9997 | 49.9995 | 49.9995 | 49.9991 | 49.9989 | 49.9988 | 49.9987 | 49.9985 |
| | 50.0006 | 50.0003 | 50.0000 | 49.9998 | 49.9996 | 49.9994 | 49.9992 | 49.9991 | 49.9990 | 49.9988 |
| | 50.0009 | 50.0006 | 50.0003 | 50.0000 | 49.9999 | 49.9997 | 49.9995 | 49.9994 | 49.9992 | 49.9991 |
| 30 | 50.0012 | 50.0008 | 50.0006 | 50.0003 | 50.0001 | 49.9999 | 49.9997 | 49.9996 | 49.9995 | 49.9993 |

| $100K_4$ $\backslash$ | 50 | 49 | 48 | 47 | 46 | 45 | 44 | 43 | 42 | $\beta=41$ |
|---|---|---|---|---|---|---|---|---|---|---|
| $\alpha=1$ | 0.0000 | 0.0000 | 0.0000 | 0.0000 | 0.0000 | 0.0000 | 0.0000 | 0.0000 | 0.0000 | 0.0000 |
| | 43.7500 | 43.7500 | 43.7500 | 43.7500 | 43.7500 | 43.7500 | 43.7500 | 43.7500 | 43.7500 | 43.7500 |
| | 48.1482 | 48.1482 | 48.1482 | 48.1482 | 48.1482 | 48.1482 | 48.1482 | 48.1482 | 48.1482 | 48.1482 |
| | 49.2188 | 49.2188 | 49.2188 | 49.2188 | 49.2188 | 49.2188 | 49.2188 | 49.2188 | 49.2188 | 49.2188 |
| | 49.6000 | 49.6000 | 49.6000 | 49.6000 | 49.6000 | 49.6000 | 49.6000 | 49.6000 | 49.6001 | 49.6001 |
| 5 | 49.7686 | 49.7686 | 49.7686 | 49.7686 | 49.7686 | 49.7686 | 49.7686 | 49.7686 | 49.7686 | 49.7686 |
| | 49.8543 | 49.8543 | 49.8543 | 49.8543 | 49.8543 | 49.8543 | 49.8543 | 49.8543 | 49.8543 | 49.8543 |
| | 49.9024 | 49.9024 | 49.9024 | 49.9024 | 49.9024 | 49.9024 | 49.9025 | 49.9025 | 49.9025 | 49.9025 |
| | 49.9315 | 49.9315 | 49.9315 | 49.9315 | 49.9315 | 49.9315 | 49.9315 | 49.9316 | 49.9316 | 49.9316 |
| | 49.9501 | 49.9501 | 49.9501 | 49.9501 | 49.9501 | 49.9501 | 49.9502 | 49.9502 | 49.9502 | 49.9502 |
| 10 | 49.9625 | 49.9626 | 49.9626 | 49.9626 | 49.9626 | 49.9626 | 49.9626 | 49.9627 | 49.9627 | 49.9627 |
| | 49.9712 | 49.9712 | 49.9712 | 49.9712 | 49.9712 | 49.9713 | 49.9713 | 49.9713 | 49.9713 | 49.9714 |
| | 49.9774 | 49.9774 | 49.9774 | 49.9774 | 49.9775 | 49.9775 | 49.9775 | 49.9775 | 49.9776 | 49.9776 |
| | 49.9819 | 49.9820 | 49.9820 | 49.9820 | 49.9820 | 49.9820 | 49.9821 | 49.9821 | 49.9821 | 49.9822 |
| | 49.9854 | 49.9854 | 49.9854 | 49.9854 | 49.9855 | 49.9855 | 49.9855 | 49.9856 | 49.9856 | 49.9856 |
| 15 | 49.9880 | 49.9880 | 49.9880 | 49.9881 | 49.9881 | 49.9881 | 49.9882 | 49.9882 | 49.9882 | 49.9883 |
| | 49.9900 | 49.9901 | 49.9901 | 49.9901 | 49.9902 | 49.9902 | 49.9902 | 49.9903 | 49.9903 | 49.9904 |
| | 49.9917 | 49.9917 | 49.9917 | 49.9918 | 49.9918 | 49.9918 | 49.9919 | 49.9919 | 49.9920 | 49.9920 |
| | 49.9930 | 49.9930 | 49.9930 | 49.9931 | 49.9931 | 49.9931 | 49.9932 | 49.9932 | 49.9933 | 49.9934 |
| | 49.9940 | 49.9941 | 49.9941 | 49.9941 | 49.9942 | 49.9942 | 49.9943 | 49.9943 | 49.9944 | 49.9944 |
| 20 | 49.9949 | 49.9949 | 49.9950 | 49.9950 | 49.9951 | 49.9951 | 49.9952 | 49.9952 | 49.9953 | 49.9953 |
| | 49.9956 | 49.9957 | 49.9957 | 49.9957 | 49.9958 | 49.9958 | 49.9959 | 49.9959 | 49.9960 | 49.9961 |
| | 49.9962 | 49.9963 | 49.9963 | 49.9964 | 49.9964 | 49.9965 | 49.9965 | 49.9966 | 49.9966 | 49.9967 |
| | 49.9968 | 49.9968 | 49.9968 | 49.9969 | 49.9969 | 49.9970 | 49.9970 | 49.9971 | 49.9972 | 49.9973 |
| | 49.9972 | 49.9972 | 49.9973 | 49.9973 | 49.9974 | 49.9974 | 49.9975 | 49.9976 | 49.9976 | 49.9977 |
| 25 | 49.9976 | 49.9976 | 49.9977 | 49.9977 | 49.9977 | 49.9978 | 49.9979 | 49.9979 | 49.9980 | 49.9981 |
| | 49.9979 | 49.9979 | 49.9980 | 49.9980 | 49.9981 | 49.9981 | 49.9982 | 49.9983 | 49.9984 | 49.9984 |
| | 49.9982 | 49.9982 | 49.9983 | 49.9983 | 49.9984 | 49.9984 | 49.9985 | 49.9986 | 49.9987 | 49.9987 |
| | 49.9984 | 49.9985 | 49.9985 | 49.9986 | 49.9986 | 49.9987 | 49.9987 | 49.9988 | 49.9989 | 49.9990 |
| 30 | 49.9986 | 49.9987 | 49.9987 | 49.9988 | 49.9988 | 49.9989 | 49.9990 | 49.9991 | 49.9991 | 49.9992 |

**TABLE FOR $G_1$:**

(see also Ch. 3, § 1.3)

$$G_1 = \frac{1}{2\pi}\left(\frac{\pi\beta}{\alpha^2 - 1}\right)^{\frac{1}{2}} \ln \frac{\alpha + (\alpha^2 + \beta^2)^{\frac{1}{2}}}{1 + (1 + \beta^2)^{\frac{1}{2}}} =$$

$$= \frac{1}{2\pi}\left(\frac{\pi\beta}{\alpha^2 - 1}\right)^{\frac{1}{2}}\left(\operatorname{arcsinh}\frac{\alpha}{\beta} - \operatorname{arcsinh}\frac{1}{\beta}\right).$$

For a coil extending from $-\beta$ to $0$:

$$G_1 = G_1(\alpha, \beta).$$

| $100G_1$ | $\beta=1$ | 2 | 3 | 4 | 5 | 6 | 7 | 8 | 9 | 10 |
|---|---|---|---|---|---|---|---|---|---|---|
| $\alpha=1$ | 0.0000 | 0.0000 | 0.0000 | 0.0000 | 0.0000 | 0.0000 | 0.0000 | 0.0000 | 0.0000 | 0.0000 |
|  | 9.1574 | 9.2169 | 8.3978 | 7.6139 | 6.9685 | 6.4447 | 6.0149 | 5.6564 | 5.3526 | 5.0914 |
|  | 9.3459 | 10.0645 | 9.5689 | 8.8900 | 8.2546 | 7.7030 | 7.2316 | 6.8280 | 6.4798 | 6.1766 |
|  | 8.8375 | 9.9136 | 9.7287 | 9.2343 | 8.6968 | 8.1934 | 7.7429 | 7.3451 | 6.9944 | 6.6842 |
| 5 | 8.2404 | 9.4953 | 9.5382 | 9.2146 | 8.7901 | 8.3582 | 7.9519 | 7.5809 | 7.2460 | 6.9946 |
|  | 7.6789 | 9.0174 | 9.2185 | 9.0339 | 8.7140 | 8.3566 | 8.0020 | 7.6668 | 7.3564 | 7.0717 |
|  | 7.1774 | 8.5482 | 8.8581 | 8.7821 | 8.5518 | 8.2636 | 7.9610 | 7.6641 | 7.3820 | 7.1182 |
|  | 6.7353 | 8.1098 | 8.4948 | 8.5025 | 8.3408 | 8.1198 | 7.8657 | 7.6066 | 7.3537 | 7.1124 |
|  | 6.3459 | 7.7080 | 8.1449 | 8.2172 | 8.1226 | 7.9484 | 7.7381 | 7.5146 | 7.2902 | 7.0716 |
| 10 | 6.0016 | 7.3423 | 7.8150 | 7.9371 | 7.8925 | 7.7634 | 7.5919 | 7.4009 | 7.2034 | 7.0069 |
|  | 5.6956 | 7.0100 | 7.5070 | 7.6679 | 7.6640 | 7.5732 | 7.4357 | 7.2741 | 7.1016 | 6.9260 |
|  | 5.4219 | 6.7075 | 7.2209 | 7.4119 | 7.4415 | 7.3832 | 7.2753 | 7.1399 | 6.9901 | 6.8342 |
|  | 5.1759 | 6.4316 | 6.9553 | 7.1700 | 7.2272 | 7.1963 | 7.1142 | 7.0021 | 6.8731 | 6.7352 |
|  | 4.9536 | 6.1792 | 6.7090 | 6.9422 | 7.0221 | 7.0146 | 6.9549 | 6.8635 | 6.7531 | 6.6319 |
| 15 | 4.7515 | 5.9475 | 6.4802 | 6.7279 | 6.8266 | 6.8391 | 6.7989 | 6.7258 | 6.6322 | 6.5262 |
|  | 4.5671 | 5.7342 | 6.2674 | 6.5265 | 6.6408 | 6.6703 | 6.6471 | 6.5902 | 6.5117 | 6.4195 |
|  | 4.3981 | 5.5372 | 6.0692 | 6.3371 | 6.4644 | 6.5085 | 6.5001 | 6.4576 | 6.3927 | 6.3130 |
|  | 4.2425 | 5.3546 | 5.8841 | 6.1588 | 6.2970 | 6.3536 | 6.3582 | 6.3285 | 6.2757 | 6.2075 |
|  | 4.0989 | 5.1850 | 5.7109 | 5.9909 | 6.1382 | 6.2056 | 6.2215 | 6.2031 | 6.1613 | 6.1034 |
| 20 | 3.9658 | 5.0270 | 5.5487 | 5.8325 | 5.9874 | 6.0641 | 6.0900 | 6.0817 | 6.0498 | 6.0013 |
|  | 3.8420 | 4.8794 | 5.3963 | 5.6829 | 5.8441 | 5.9289 | 5.9636 | 5.9643 | 5.9412 | 5.9013 |
|  | 3.7266 | 4.7412 | 5.2529 | 5.5414 | 5.7080 | 5.7997 | 5.8422 | 5.8509 | 5.8358 | 5.8037 |
|  | 3.6188 | 4.6116 | 5.1178 | 5.4075 | 5.5784 | 5.6762 | 5.7255 | 5.7415 | 5.7336 | 5.7086 |
|  | 3.5178 | 4.4896 | 4.9902 | 5.2805 | 5.4551 | 5.5581 | 5.6135 | 5.6359 | 5.6345 | 5.6160 |
| 25 | 3.4229 | 4.3747 | 4.8695 | 5.1599 | 5.3375 | 5.4451 | 5.5059 | 5.5340 | 5.5386 | 5.5259 |
|  | 3.3336 | 4.2663 | 4.7552 | 5.0453 | 5.2254 | 5.3369 | 5.4024 | 5.4358 | 5.4457 | 5.4384 |
|  | 3.2494 | 4.1637 | 4.6467 | 4.9362 | 5.1183 | 5.2332 | 5.3030 | 5.3410 | 5.3558 | 5.3535 |
|  | 3.1698 | 4.0665 | 4.5437 | 4.8323 | 5.0159 | 5.1338 | 5.2074 | 5.2496 | 5.2688 | 5.2710 |
|  | 3.0945 | 3.9743 | 4.4456 | 4.7331 | 4.9180 | 5.0384 | 5.1153 | 5.1613 | 5.1846 | 5.1909 |
| 30 | 3.0231 | 3.8867 | 4.3522 | 4.6383 | 4.8242 | 4.9468 | 5.0267 | 5.0762 | 5.1031 | 5.1132 |

| $100G_1$ | $\beta=11$ | 12 | 13 | 14 | 15 | 16 | 17 | 18 | 19 | 20 |
|---|---|---|---|---|---|---|---|---|---|---|
| $\alpha=1$ | 0.0000 | 0.0000 | 0.0000 | 0.0000 | 0.0000 | 0.0000 | 0.0000 | 0.0000 | 0.0000 | 0.0000 |
| | 4.8641 | 4.6640 | 4.4863 | 4.3272 | 4.1836 | 4.0533 | 3.9343 | 3.8251 | 3.7244 | 3.6313 |
| | 5.9102 | 5.6740 | 5.4631 | 5.2734 | 5.1016 | 4.9452 | 4.8021 | 4.6705 | 4.5490 | 4.4364 |
| | 6.4084 | 6.1618 | 5.9400 | 5.7393 | 5.5569 | 5.3901 | 5.2370 | 5.0959 | 4.9653 | 4.8440 |
| | 6.6729 | 6.4275 | 6.2049 | 6.0023 | 5.8170 | 5.6469 | 5.4902 | 5.3452 | 5.2108 | 5.0856 |
| 5 | 6.8115 | 6.5737 | 6.3560 | 6.1563 | 5.9727 | 5.8035 | 5.6465 | 5.5010 | 5.3656 | 5.2393 |
| | 6.8733 | 6.6468 | 6.4375 | 6.2439 | 6.0647 | 5.8985 | 5.7440 | 5.6000 | 5.4655 | 5.3397 |
| | 6.8849 | 6.6718 | 6.4728 | 6.2874 | 6.1144 | 5.9531 | 5.8023 | 5.6613 | 5.5291 | 5.4049 |
| | 6.8622 | 6.6636 | 6.4762 | 6.3000 | 6.1345 | 5.9791 | 5.8332 | 5.6961 | 5.5670 | 5.4454 |
| | 6.8156 | 6.6318 | 6.4565 | 6.2903 | 6.1329 | 5.9843 | 5.8439 | 5.7113 | 5.5861 | 5.4677 |
| 10 | 6.7523 | 6.5831 | 6.4201 | 6.2640 | 6.1152 | 5.9737 | 5.8394 | 5.7119 | 5.5909 | 5.4761 |
| | 6.6772 | 6.5222 | 6.3712 | 6.2254 | 6.0853 | 5.9512 | 5.8231 | 5.7009 | 5.5846 | 5.4737 |
| | 6.5939 | 6.4525 | 6.3132 | 6.1774 | 6.0460 | 5.9193 | 5.7976 | 5.6810 | 5.5694 | 5.4627 |
| | 6.5052 | 6.3766 | 6.2486 | 6.1225 | 5.9995 | 5.8802 | 5.7650 | 5.6540 | 5.5473 | 5.4448 |
| | 6.4130 | 6.2965 | 6.1790 | 6.0624 | 5.9476 | 5.8356 | 5.7267 | 5.6213 | 5.5195 | 5.4214 |
| 15 | 6.3189 | 6.2136 | 6.1062 | 5.9984 | 5.8916 | 5.7866 | 5.6840 | 5.5841 | 5.4872 | 5.3934 |
| | 6.2239 | 6.1290 | 6.0310 | 5.9318 | 5.8325 | 5.7343 | 5.6377 | 5.5432 | 5.4512 | 5.3617 |
| | 6.1289 | 6.0437 | 5.9545 | 5.8632 | 5.7712 | 5.6795 | 5.5888 | 5.4996 | 5.4123 | 5.3270 |
| | 6.0345 | 5.9583 | 5.8773 | 5.7936 | 5.7084 | 5.6229 | 5.5378 | 5.4537 | 5.3710 | 5.2899 |
| | 5.9413 | 5.8733 | 5.8000 | 5.7233 | 5.6446 | 5.5650 | 5.4853 | 5.4061 | 5.3278 | 5.2509 |
| 20 | 5.8494 | 5.7891 | 5.7229 | 5.6528 | 5.5802 | 5.5062 | 5.4317 | 5.3572 | 5.2833 | 5.2102 |
| | 5.7593 | 5.7060 | 5.6465 | 5.5825 | 5.5157 | 5.4470 | 5.3774 | 5.3074 | 5.2376 | 5.1684 |
| | 5.6710 | 5.6242 | 5.5708 | 5.5127 | 5.4512 | 5.3876 | 5.3226 | 5.2570 | 5.1912 | 5.1256 |
| | 5.5847 | 5.5439 | 5.4963 | 5.4435 | 5.3871 | 5.3282 | 5.2677 | 5.2062 | 5.1442 | 5.0822 |
| | 5.5004 | 5.4652 | 5.4229 | 5.3752 | 5.3236 | 5.2691 | 5.2128 | 5.1552 | 5.0969 | 5.0383 |
| 25 | 5.4182 | 5.3882 | 5.3508 | 5.3078 | 5.2607 | 5.2105 | 5.1581 | 5.1042 | 5.0494 | 4.9940 |
| | 5.3381 | 5.3128 | 5.2800 | 5.2415 | 5.1985 | 5.1523 | 5.1037 | 5.0534 | 5.0019 | 4.9496 |
| | 5.2601 | 5.2392 | 5.2107 | 5.1763 | 5.1373 | 5.0948 | 5.0498 | 5.0028 | 4.9545 | 4.9052 |
| | 5.1842 | 5.1674 | 5.1429 | 5.1123 | 5.0770 | 5.0380 | 4.9963 | 4.9526 | 4.9073 | 4.8609 |
| 30 | 5.1103 | 5.0973 | 5.0765 | 5.0495 | 5.0177 | 4.9821 | 4.9436 | 4.9028 | 4.8604 | 4.8167 |

| $100G_1$ | $\beta=21$ | 22 | 23 | 24 | 25 | 26 | 27 | 28 | 29 | 30 |
|---|---|---|---|---|---|---|---|---|---|---|
| $\alpha=1$ | 0.0000 | 0.0000 | 0.0000 | 0.0000 | 0.0000 | 0.0000 | 0.0000 | 0.0000 | 0.0000 | 0.0000 |
| | 3.5447 | 3.4640 | 3.3886 | 3.3178 | 3.2513 | 3.1886 | 3.1294 | 3.0733 | 3.0202 | 2.9697 |
| | 4.3316 | 4.2339 | 4.1424 | 4.0565 | 3.9757 | 3.8995 | 3.8275 | 3.7593 | 3.6946 | 3.6331 |
| | 4.7310 | 4.6255 | 4.5265 | 4.4335 | 4.3460 | 4.2634 | 4.1852 | 4.1112 | 4.0409 | 3.9740 |
| 5 | 4.9688 | 4.8594 | 4.7568 | 4.6602 | 4.5692 | 4.4832 | 4.4018 | 4.3245 | 4.2512 | 4.1814 |
| | 5.1210 | 5.0102 | 4.9059 | 4.8077 | 4.7150 | 4.6273 | 4.5441 | 4.4652 | 4.3902 | 4.3188 |
| | 5.2217 | 5.1107 | 5.0062 | 4.9075 | 4.8143 | 4.7259 | 4.6421 | 4.5624 | 4.4866 | 4.4143 |
| | 5.2882 | 5.1781 | 5.0743 | 4.9761 | 4.8830 | 4.7948 | 4.7110 | 4.6312 | 4.5552 | 4.4826 |
| | 5.3307 | 5.2223 | 5.1198 | 5.0226 | 4.9305 | 4.8428 | 4.7595 | 4.6801 | 4.6043 | 4.5319 |
| 10 | 5.3556 | 5.2494 | 5.1487 | 5.0531 | 4.9622 | 4.8756 | 4.7931 | 4.7144 | 4.6393 | 4.5674 |
| | 5.3671 | 5.2635 | 5.1650 | 5.0713 | 4.9820 | 4.8968 | 4.8155 | 4.7378 | 4.6634 | 4.5923 |
| | 5.3681 | 5.2674 | 5.1714 | 5.0798 | 4.9924 | 4.9088 | 4.8289 | 4.7524 | 4.6792 | 4.6089 |
| | 5.3607 | 5.2631 | 5.1699 | 5.0806 | 4.9953 | 4.9135 | 4.8352 | 4.7602 | 4.6881 | 4.6190 |
| | 5.3465 | 5.2523 | 5.1619 | 5.0752 | 4.9921 | 4.9123 | 4.8357 | 4.7622 | 4.6916 | 4.6236 |
| 15 | 5.3269 | 5.2360 | 5.1486 | 5.0646 | 4.9838 | 4.9061 | 4.8314 | 4.7596 | 4.6904 | 4.6238 |
| | 5.3028 | 5.2153 | 5.1310 | 5.0497 | 4.9713 | 4.8958 | 4.8231 | 4.7530 | 4.6854 | 4.6202 |
| | 5.2750 | 5.1910 | 5.1097 | 5.0312 | 4.9553 | 4.8821 | 4.8113 | 4.7430 | 4.6771 | 4.6133 |
| | 5.2441 | 5.1636 | 5.0854 | 5.0097 | 4.9363 | 4.8653 | 4.7967 | 4.7302 | 4.6659 | 4.6038 |
| | 5.2108 | 5.1336 | 5.0586 | 4.9856 | 4.9148 | 4.8461 | 4.7795 | 4.7150 | 4.6524 | 4.5918 |
| 20 | 5.1754 | 5.1016 | 5.0296 | 4.9594 | 4.8911 | 4.8248 | 4.7603 | 4.6976 | 4.6368 | 4.5778 |
| | 5.1384 | 5.0679 | 4.9989 | 4.9314 | 4.8657 | 4.8016 | 4.7392 | 4.6785 | 4.6194 | 4.5620 |
| | 5.1000 | 5.0327 | 4.9667 | 4.9020 | 4.8387 | 4.7769 | 4.7166 | 4.6578 | 4.6005 | 4.5447 |
| | 5.0607 | 4.9965 | 4.9333 | 4.8713 | 4.8104 | 4.7508 | 4.6926 | 4.6357 | 4.5802 | 4.5260 |
| | 5.0205 | 4.9594 | 4.8990 | 4.8395 | 4.7810 | 4.7237 | 4.6675 | 4.6125 | 4.5587 | 4.5062 |
| 25 | 4.9797 | 4.9215 | 4.8639 | 4.8069 | 4.7508 | 4.6956 | 4.6414 | 4.5883 | 4.5363 | 4.4854 |
| | 4.9385 | 4.8832 | 4.8282 | 4.7737 | 4.7198 | 4.6668 | 4.6146 | 4.5633 | 4.5130 | 4.4636 |
| | 4.8971 | 4.8444 | 4.7920 | 4.7399 | 4.6883 | 4.6373 | 4.5870 | 4.5375 | 4.4889 | 4.4411 |
| | 4.8555 | 4.8055 | 4.7555 | 4.7057 | 4.6562 | 4.6073 | 4.5589 | 4.5112 | 4.4642 | 4.4180 |
| | 4.8138 | 4.7664 | 4.7188 | 4.6712 | 4.6239 | 4.5769 | 4.5303 | 4.4844 | 4.4390 | 4.3943 |
| 30 | 4.7723 | 4.7272 | 4.6819 | 4.6365 | 4.5912 | 4.5461 | 4.5014 | 4.4571 | 4.4133 | 4.3701 |

| $100G_1$ $\alpha=1$ | $\beta=31$ | 32 | 33 | 34 | 35 | 36 | 37 | 38 | 39 | 40 |
|---|---|---|---|---|---|---|---|---|---|---|
| 1 | 0.0000 | 0.0000 | 0.0000 | 0.0000 | 0.0000 | 0.0000 | 0.0000 | 0.0000 | 0.0000 | 0.0000 |
|  | 2.9216 | 2.8758 | 2.8321 | 2.7903 | 2.7503 | 2.7120 | 2.6752 | 2.6399 | 2.6060 | 2.5733 |
|  | 3.5746 | 3.5188 | 3.4655 | 3.4145 | 3.3657 | 3.3190 | 3.2741 | 3.2310 | 3.1896 | 3.1497 |
|  | 3.9104 | 3.8496 | 3.7916 | 3.7361 | 3.6830 | 3.6320 | 3.5831 | 3.5361 | 3.4909 | 3.4474 |
| 5 | 4.1149 | 4.0514 | 3.9907 | 3.9326 | 3.8770 | 3.8237 | 3.7724 | 3.7232 | 3.6758 | 3.6302 |
|  | 4.2506 | 4.1856 | 4.1233 | 4.0638 | 4.0067 | 3.9519 | 3.8992 | 3.8486 | 3.7999 | 3.7529 |
|  | 4.3454 | 4.2795 | 4.2164 | 4.1559 | 4.0980 | 4.0423 | 3.9889 | 3.9374 | 3.8879 | 3.8401 |
|  | 4.4134 | 4.3471 | 4.2836 | 4.2228 | 4.1644 | 4.1083 | 4.0544 | 4.0025 | 3.9525 | 3.9042 |
|  | 4.4627 | 4.3965 | 4.3330 | 4.2721 | 4.2136 | 4.1573 | 4.1032 | 4.0511 | 4.0009 | 3.9524 |
| 10 | 4.4986 | 4.4326 | 4.3693 | 4.3086 | 4.2502 | 4.1941 | 4.1400 | 4.0879 | 4.0376 | 3.9891 |
|  | 4.5241 | 4.4586 | 4.3958 | 4.3354 | 4.2774 | 4.2215 | 4.1676 | 4.1156 | 4.0655 | 4.0171 |
|  | 4.5415 | 4.4768 | 4.4146 | 4.3547 | 4.2971 | 4.2416 | 4.1881 | 4.1364 | 4.0866 | 4.0384 |
|  | 4.5525 | 4.4887 | 4.4272 | 4.3680 | 4.3110 | 4.2560 | 4.2029 | 4.1516 | 4.1021 | 4.0543 |
|  | 4.5583 | 4.4954 | 4.4347 | 4.3763 | 4.3200 | 4.2656 | 4.2131 | 4.1623 | 4.1132 | 4.0658 |
| 15 | 4.5596 | 4.4978 | 4.4381 | 4.3806 | 4.3250 | 4.2713 | 4.2194 | 4.1692 | 4.1206 | 4.0736 |
|  | 4.5573 | 4.4966 | 4.4379 | 4.3813 | 4.3266 | 4.2737 | 4.2225 | 4.1729 | 4.1249 | 4.0784 |
|  | 4.5518 | 4.4923 | 4.4348 | 4.3791 | 4.3253 | 4.2732 | 4.2228 | 4.1739 | 4.1266 | 4.0806 |
|  | 4.5436 | 4.4854 | 4.4290 | 4.3744 | 4.3216 | 4.2703 | 4.2207 | 4.1726 | 4.1259 | 4.0806 |
|  | 4.5331 | 4.4761 | 4.4210 | 4.3675 | 4.3156 | 4.2653 | 4.2165 | 4.1692 | 4.1232 | 4.0786 |
| 20 | 4.5205 | 4.4650 | 4.4110 | 4.3587 | 4.3078 | 4.2585 | 4.2106 | 4.1640 | 4.1188 | 4.0748 |
|  | 4.5062 | 4.4520 | 4.3993 | 4.3481 | 4.2984 | 4.2500 | 4.2030 | 4.1573 | 4.1128 | 4.0696 |
|  | 4.4904 | 4.4376 | 4.3862 | 4.3361 | 4.2874 | 4.2401 | 4.1940 | 4.1491 | 4.1055 | 4.0629 |
|  | 4.4732 | 4.4218 | 4.3717 | 4.3228 | 4.2752 | 4.2289 | 4.1837 | 4.1397 | 4.0969 | 4.0551 |
|  | 4.4549 | 4.4048 | 4.3560 | 4.3083 | 4.2619 | 4.2165 | 4.1723 | 4.1293 | 4.0872 | 4.0462 |
| 25 | 4.4355 | 4.3869 | 4.3393 | 4.2928 | 4.2475 | 4.2032 | 4.1600 | 4.1178 | 4.0766 | 4.0364 |
|  | 4.4153 | 4.3680 | 4.3217 | 4.2765 | 4.2322 | 4.1890 | 4.1467 | 4.1054 | 4.0651 | 4.0257 |
|  | 4.3943 | 4.3483 | 4.3033 | 4.2593 | 4.2161 | 4.1739 | 4.1327 | 4.0923 | 4.0528 | 4.0142 |
|  | 4.3726 | 4.3280 | 4.2843 | 4.2414 | 4.1994 | 4.1582 | 4.1179 | 4.0784 | 4.0398 | 4.0020 |
|  | 4.3503 | 4.3071 | 4.2646 | 4.2229 | 4.1820 | 4.1418 | 4.1025 | 4.0639 | 4.0262 | 3.9891 |
| 30 | 4.3276 | 4.2856 | 4.2444 | 4.2038 | 4.1640 | 4.1249 | 4.0865 | 4.0489 | 4.0119 | 3.9757 |

| $100G_1$ / $\alpha$ | 50 | 49 | 48 | 47 | 46 | 45 | 44 | 43 | 42 | $\beta=41$ |
|---|---|---|---|---|---|---|---|---|---|---|
| $\alpha=1$ | 0.0000 | 0.0000 | 0.0000 | 0.0000 | 0.0000 | 0.0000 | 0.0000 | 0.0000 | 0.0000 | 0.0000 |
| | 2.3022 | 2.3255 | 2.3496 | 2.3744 | 2.4000 | 2.4265 | 2.4538 | 2.4821 | 2.5114 | 2.5418 |
| | 2.8185 | 2.8470 | 2.8764 | 2.9067 | 2.9380 | 2.9704 | 3.0038 | 3.0383 | 3.0741 | 3.1112 |
| | 3.0859 | 3.1170 | 3.1491 | 3.1823 | 3.2164 | 3.2517 | 3.2882 | 3.3260 | 3.3650 | 3.4055 |
| 5 | 3.2506 | 3.2834 | 3.3171 | 3.3519 | 3.3878 | 3.4248 | 3.4631 | 3.5027 | 3.5437 | 3.5862 |
| | 3.3621 | 3.3958 | 3.4306 | 3.4664 | 3.5034 | 3.5416 | 3.5810 | 3.6218 | 3.6640 | 3.7077 |
| | 3.4419 | 3.4763 | 3.5118 | 3.5483 | 3.5860 | 3.6249 | 3.6651 | 3.7066 | 3.7496 | 3.7941 |
| | 3.5014 | 3.5363 | 3.5722 | 3.6092 | 3.6473 | 3.6867 | 3.7273 | 3.7693 | 3.8128 | 3.8577 |
| | 3.5469 | 3.5820 | 3.6182 | 3.6555 | 3.6939 | 3.7336 | 3.7745 | 3.8168 | 3.8605 | 3.9057 |
| 10 | 3.5823 | 3.6176 | 3.6540 | 3.6914 | 3.7300 | 3.7698 | 3.8108 | 3.8532 | 3.8970 | 3.9423 |
| | 3.6102 | 3.6456 | 3.6820 | 3.7195 | 3.7581 | 3.7979 | 3.8390 | 3.8813 | 3.9251 | 3.9703 |
| | 3.6323 | 3.6676 | 3.7040 | 3.7415 | 3.7800 | 3.8198 | 3.8608 | 3.9031 | 3.9467 | 3.9918 |
| | 3.6497 | 3.6850 | 3.7213 | 3.7587 | 3.7971 | 3.8367 | 3.8776 | 3.9197 | 3.9631 | 4.0079 |
| | 3.6635 | 3.6986 | 3.7348 | 3.7720 | 3.8103 | 3.8497 | 3.8903 | 3.9321 | 3.9753 | 4.0198 |
| 15 | 3.6741 | 3.7091 | 3.7451 | 3.7821 | 3.8201 | 3.8593 | 3.8996 | 3.9411 | 3.9839 | 4.0281 |
| | 3.6822 | 3.7170 | 3.7527 | 3.7894 | 3.8272 | 3.8661 | 3.9061 | 3.9472 | 3.9896 | 4.0334 |
| | 3.6880 | 3.7226 | 3.7581 | 3.7945 | 3.8320 | 3.8705 | 3.9101 | 3.9509 | 3.9928 | 4.0361 |
| | 3.6920 | 3.7263 | 3.7615 | 3.7976 | 3.8347 | 3.8728 | 3.9121 | 3.9524 | 3.9939 | 4.0366 |
| | 3.6943 | 3.7283 | 3.7632 | 3.7989 | 3.8357 | 3.8734 | 3.9122 | 3.9520 | 3.9930 | 4.0352 |
| 20 | 3.6952 | 3.7289 | 3.7634 | 3.7988 | 3.8351 | 3.8724 | 3.9107 | 3.9501 | 3.9905 | 4.0321 |
| | 3.6948 | 3.7281 | 3.7622 | 3.7973 | 3.8332 | 3.8700 | 3.9078 | 3.9467 | 3.9865 | 4.0275 |
| | 3.6933 | 3.7262 | 3.7600 | 3.7945 | 3.8300 | 3.8664 | 3.9037 | 3.9420 | 3.9812 | 4.0215 |
| | 3.6907 | 3.7233 | 3.7566 | 3.7908 | 3.8258 | 3.8616 | 3.8984 | 3.9361 | 3.9748 | 4.0141 |
| | 3.6872 | 3.7194 | 3.7523 | 3.7860 | 3.8205 | 3.8559 | 3.8921 | 3.9292 | 3.9673 | 4.0063 |
| 25 | 3.6829 | 3.7147 | 3.7471 | 3.7804 | 3.8144 | 3.8493 | 3.8849 | 3.9214 | 3.9588 | 3.9972 |
| | 3.6778 | 3.7092 | 3.7412 | 3.7740 | 3.8075 | 3.8418 | 3.8769 | 3.9128 | 3.9496 | 3.9872 |
| | 3.6721 | 3.7030 | 3.7346 | 3.7669 | 3.7999 | 3.8336 | 3.8681 | 3.9034 | 3.9395 | 3.9764 |
| | 3.6657 | 3.6961 | 3.7273 | 3.7591 | 3.7916 | 3.8248 | 3.8587 | 3.8933 | 3.9288 | 3.9650 |
| | 3.6587 | 3.6887 | 3.7194 | 3.7507 | 3.7826 | 3.8153 | 3.8486 | 3.8827 | 3.9174 | 3.9529 |
| 30 | 3.6512 | 3.6808 | 3.7110 | 3.7418 | 3.7732 | 3.8053 | 3.8380 | 3.8714 | 3.9055 | 3.9403 |

## TABLE FOR $G_2$:

(see also Ch. 3, § 1.3)

$$G_2 = \frac{1}{2\pi}\left(\frac{\pi}{2\beta \ln \alpha}\right)^{\frac{1}{2}} \ln \frac{\alpha\{\beta + (\beta^2 + 1)^{\frac{1}{2}}\}}{\beta + (\beta^2 + \alpha^2)^{\frac{1}{2}}} =$$
$$= (8\pi\beta \ln \alpha)^{-\frac{1}{2}}\left(\operatorname{arcsinh} \beta - \operatorname{arcsinh} \frac{\beta}{\alpha}\right).$$

For a coil extending from $-\beta$ to 0:

$$G_2 = G_2(\alpha, \beta).$$

| $100G_2$ $\alpha$ | $\beta=1$ | 2 | 3 | 4 | 5 | 6 | 7 | 8 | 9 | 10 |
|---|---|---|---|---|---|---|---|---|---|---|
| 1 | 0.0000 | 0.0000 | 0.0000 | 0.0000 | 0.0000 | 0.0000 | 0.0000 | 0.0000 | 0.0000 | 0.0000 |
|  | 9.5874 | 9.5256 | 8.6272 | 7.7996 | 7.1275 | 6.5860 | 6.1433 | 5.7750 | 5.4634 | 5.1958 |
|  | 10.5416 | 11.0143 | 10.2960 | 9.4783 | 8.7546 | 8.1434 | 7.6291 | 7.1931 | 6.8194 | 6.4955 |
|  | 10.7393 | 11.5293 | 11.0068 | 10.2779 | 9.5831 | 8.9706 | 8.4410 | 7.9833 | 7.5858 | 7.2378 |
| 5 | 10.7340 | 11.7140 | 11.3439 | 10.7079 | 10.0628 | 9.4732 | 8.9507 | 8.4913 | 8.0870 | 7.7296 |
|  | 10.6618 | 11.7615 | 11.5050 | 10.9496 | 10.3560 | 9.7972 | 9.2915 | 8.8400 | 8.4378 | 8.0790 |
|  | 10.5672 | 11.7459 | 11.5747 | 11.0859 | 10.5395 | 10.0123 | 9.5271 | 9.0080 | 8.6928 | 8.3372 |
|  | 10.4672 | 11.7000 | 11.5939 | 11.1595 | 10.6544 | 10.1572 | 9.6930 | 9.2682 | 8.8824 | 8.5326 |
|  | 10.3684 | 11.6393 | 11.5840 | 11.1943 | 10.7248 | 10.2548 | 9.8108 | 9.4007 | 9.0254 | 8.6829 |
| 10 | 10.2736 | 11.5720 | 11.5570 | 11.2043 | 10.7654 | 10.3197 | 9.8945 | 9.4988 | 9.1342 | 8.7996 |
|  | 10.1839 | 11.5023 | 11.5200 | 11.1982 | 10.7856 | 10.3614 | 9.9535 | 9.5713 | 9.2173 | 8.8908 |
|  | 10.0996 | 11.4327 | 11.4772 | 11.1814 | 10.7916 | 10.3865 | 9.9942 | 9.6247 | 9.2808 | 8.9624 |
|  | 10.0203 | 11.3644 | 11.4311 | 11.1576 | 10.7876 | 10.3994 | 10.0212 | 9.6634 | 9.3291 | 9.0184 |
|  | 9.9459 | 11.2981 | 11.3836 | 11.1292 | 10.7765 | 10.4033 | 10.0379 | 9.6909 | 9.3655 | 9.0623 |
| 15 | 9.8760 | 11.2341 | 11.3355 | 11.0978 | 10.7603 | 10.4005 | 10.0467 | 9.7095 | 9.3925 | 9.0963 |
|  | 9.8102 | 11.1726 | 11.2877 | 11.0645 | 10.7405 | 10.3928 | 10.0495 | 9.7213 | 9.4120 | 9.1224 |
|  | 9.7481 | 11.1136 | 11.2405 | 11.0302 | 10.7182 | 10.3813 | 10.0475 | 9.7276 | 9.4255 | 9.1420 |
|  | 9.6895 | 11.0570 | 11.1943 | 10.9953 | 10.6942 | 10.3670 | 10.0418 | 9.7295 | 9.4341 | 9.1565 |
|  | 9.6341 | 11.0028 | 11.1491 | 10.9603 | 10.6689 | 10.3505 | 10.0333 | 9.7280 | 9.4388 | 9.1665 |
| 20 | 9.5815 | 10.9509 | 11.1052 | 10.9255 | 10.6428 | 10.3325 | 10.0225 | 9.7237 | 9.4402 | 9.1730 |
|  | 9.5316 | 10.9011 | 11.0625 | 10.8910 | 10.6163 | 10.3134 | 10.0100 | 9.7172 | 9.4390 | 9.1766 |
|  | 9.4842 | 10.8533 | 11.0210 | 10.8571 | 10.5896 | 10.2934 | 9.9962 | 9.7089 | 9.4357 | 9.1777 |
|  | 9.4390 | 10.8075 | 10.9809 | 10.8237 | 10.5629 | 10.2729 | 9.9813 | 9.6992 | 9.4306 | 9.1767 |
|  | 9.3958 | 10.7634 | 10.9419 | 10.7909 | 10.5363 | 10.2520 | 9.9657 | 9.6883 | 9.4240 | 9.1741 |
| 25 | 9.3545 | 10.7211 | 10.9042 | 10.7589 | 10.5098 | 10.2308 | 9.9494 | 9.6765 | 9.4162 | 9.1699 |
|  | 9.3151 | 10.6803 | 10.8676 | 10.7275 | 10.4837 | 10.2096 | 9.9327 | 9.6639 | 9.4075 | 9.1646 |
|  | 9.2772 | 10.6411 | 10.8321 | 10.6968 | 10.4579 | 10.1884 | 9.9157 | 9.6508 | 9.3979 | 9.1583 |
|  | 9.2409 | 10.6032 | 10.7977 | 10.6669 | 10.4325 | 10.1672 | 9.8985 | 9.6373 | 9.3877 | 9.1512 |
|  | 9.2060 | 10.5667 | 10.7644 | 10.6377 | 10.4074 | 10.1462 | 9.8812 | 9.6234 | 9.3770 | 9.1433 |
| 30 | 9.1724 | 10.5315 | 10.7320 | 10.6092 | 10.3829 | 10.1253 | 9.8638 | 9.6092 | 9.3658 | 9.1348 |

| $100G_2$ $\alpha$ | $\beta=11$ | 12 | 13 | 14 | 15 | 16 | 17 | 18 | 19 | 20 |
|---|---|---|---|---|---|---|---|---|---|---|
| 1 | 0.0000 | 0.0000 | 0.0000 | 0.0000 | 0.0000 | 0.0000 | 0.0000 | 0.0000 | 0.0000 | 0.0000 |
| 2 | 4.9631 | 4.7585 | 4.5768 | 4.4142 | 4.2675 | 4.1343 | 4.0128 | 3.9013 | 3.7986 | 3.7035 |
| 3 | 6.2118 | 5.9611 | 5.7376 | 5.5368 | 5.3553 | 5.1902 | 5.0393 | 4.9006 | 4.7726 | 4.6540 |
| 4 | 6.9307 | 6.6578 | 6.4133 | 6.1929 | 5.9931 | 5.8109 | 5.6440 | 5.4904 | 5.3484 | 5.2167 |
| 5 | 7.4119 | 7.1277 | 6.8720 | 6.6406 | 6.4300 | 6.2376 | 6.0609 | 5.8979 | 5.7471 | 5.6070 |
| 6 | 7.7577 | 7.4686 | 7.2071 | 6.9697 | 6.7529 | 6.5542 | 6.3713 | 6.2023 | 6.0457 | 5.8999 |
| 7 | 8.0165 | 7.7264 | 7.4628 | 7.2224 | 7.0022 | 6.7999 | 6.6132 | 6.4404 | 6.2798 | 6.1302 |
| 8 | 8.2152 | 7.9265 | 7.6631 | 7.4219 | 7.2004 | 6.9961 | 6.8073 | 6.6321 | 6.4690 | 6.3169 |
| 9 | 8.3703 | 8.0846 | 7.8229 | 7.5824 | 7.3608 | 7.1561 | 6.9662 | 6.7897 | 6.6252 | 6.4715 |
| 10 | 8.4928 | 8.2111 | 7.9521 | 7.7133 | 7.4927 | 7.2882 | 7.0983 | 6.9213 | 6.7561 | 6.6015 |
| 11 | 8.5901 | 8.3131 | 8.0574 | 7.8210 | 7.6020 | 7.3986 | 7.2091 | 7.0324 | 6.8671 | 6.7121 |
| 12 | 8.6680 | 8.3958 | 8.1439 | 7.9103 | 7.6934 | 7.4914 | 7.3030 | 7.1269 | 6.9619 | 6.8070 |
| 13 | 8.7303 | 8.4631 | 8.2152 | 7.9847 | 7.7702 | 7.5701 | 7.3830 | 7.2079 | 7.0435 | 6.8890 |
| 14 | 8.7802 | 8.5180 | 8.2741 | 8.0469 | 7.8350 | 7.6369 | 7.4515 | 7.2775 | 7.1141 | 6.9602 |
| 15 | 8.8201 | 8.5628 | 8.3229 | 8.0991 | 7.8898 | 7.6940 | 7.5103 | 7.3378 | 7.1754 | 7.0224 |
| 16 | 8.8518 | 8.5992 | 8.3633 | 8.1428 | 7.9363 | 7.7427 | 7.5610 | 7.3900 | 7.2289 | 7.0769 |
| 17 | 8.8768 | 8.6287 | 8.3967 | 8.1794 | 7.9758 | 7.7845 | 7.6047 | 7.4353 | 7.2756 | 7.1247 |
| 18 | 8.8962 | 8.6525 | 8.4242 | 8.2102 | 8.0092 | 7.8203 | 7.6425 | 7.4748 | 7.3165 | 7.1667 |
| 19 | 8.9110 | 8.6715 | 8.4468 | 8.2358 | 8.0376 | 7.8510 | 7.6751 | 7.5092 | 7.3523 | 7.2038 |
| 20 | 8.9220 | 8.6864 | 8.4651 | 8.2572 | 8.0615 | 7.8772 | 7.7034 | 7.5391 | 7.3837 | 7.2365 |
| 21 | 8.9298 | 8.6978 | 8.4799 | 8.2748 | 8.0817 | 7.8997 | 7.7278 | 7.5652 | 7.4113 | 7.2654 |
| 22 | 8.9348 | 8.7064 | 8.4916 | 8.2893 | 8.0987 | 7.9188 | 7.7488 | 7.5880 | 7.4356 | 7.2909 |
| 23 | 8.9376 | 8.7125 | 8.5007 | 8.3010 | 8.1128 | 7.9350 | 7.7669 | 7.6077 | 7.4568 | 7.3135 |
| 24 | 8.9384 | 8.7165 | 8.5075 | 8.3104 | 8.1245 | 7.9487 | 7.7824 | 7.6249 | 7.4754 | 7.3334 |
| 25 | 8.9376 | 8.7187 | 8.5124 | 8.3178 | 8.1340 | 7.9602 | 7.7957 | 7.6397 | 7.4916 | 7.3509 |
| 26 | 8.9354 | 8.7194 | 8.5156 | 8.3233 | 8.1416 | 7.9697 | 7.8069 | 7.6525 | 7.5058 | 7.3663 |
| 27 | 8.9321 | 8.7187 | 8.5174 | 8.3273 | 8.1476 | 7.9776 | 7.8164 | 7.6635 | 7.5182 | 7.3799 |
| 28 | 8.9277 | 8.7169 | 8.5179 | 8.3299 | 8.1522 | 7.9839 | 7.8243 | 7.6729 | 7.5289 | 7.3918 |
| 29 | 8.9225 | 8.7141 | 8.5173 | 8.3313 | 8.1555 | 7.9889 | 7.8309 | 7.6808 | 7.5381 | 7.4022 |
| 30 | 8.9165 | 8.7104 | 8.5157 | 8.3317 | 8.1576 | 7.9927 | 7.8362 | 7.6874 | 7.5460 | 7.4112 |

| $100G_2$ | $\beta=21$ | 22 | 23 | 24 | 25 | 26 | 27 | 28 | 29 | 30 |
|---|---|---|---|---|---|---|---|---|---|---|
| $\alpha=1$ | 0.0000 | 0.0000 | 0.0000 | 0.0000 | 0.0000 | 0.0000 | 0.0000 | 0.0000 | 0.0000 | 0.0000 |
|  | 3.6151 | 3.5328 | 3.4558 | 3.3836 | 3.3157 | 3.2517 | 3.1913 | 3.1341 | 3.0799 | 3.0284 |
|  | 4.5437 | 4.4409 | 4.3446 | 4.2543 | 4.1694 | 4.0893 | 4.0137 | 3.9420 | 3.8741 | 3.8095 |
|  | 5.0941 | 4.9796 | 4.8724 | 4.7718 | 4.6774 | 4.5877 | 4.5032 | 4.4232 | 4.3473 | 4.2751 |
| 5 | 5.4765 | 5.3544 | 5.2401 | 5.1326 | 5.0314 | 4.9359 | 4.8455 | 4.7599 | 4.6785 | 4.6012 |
|  | 5.7640 | 5.6367 | 5.5173 | 5.4051 | 5.2993 | 5.1993 | 5.1047 | 5.0150 | 4.9298 | 4.8488 |
|  | 5.9905 | 5.8596 | 5.7366 | 5.6209 | 5.5117 | 5.4086 | 5.3108 | 5.2181 | 5.1300 | 5.0461 |
|  | 6.1746 | 6.0411 | 5.9156 | 5.7974 | 5.6857 | 5.5801 | 5.4800 | 5.3850 | 5.2946 | 5.2086 |
|  | 6.3275 | 6.1922 | 6.0649 | 5.9448 | 5.8314 | 5.7240 | 5.6221 | 5.5253 | 5.4332 | 5.3455 |
| 10 | 6.4564 | 6.3200 | 6.1915 | 6.0701 | 5.9553 | 5.8466 | 5.7434 | 5.6453 | 5.5519 | 5.4628 |
|  | 6.5664 | 6.4294 | 6.3001 | 6.1779 | 6.0622 | 5.9525 | 5.8483 | 5.7492 | 5.6548 | 5.5647 |
|  | 6.6612 | 6.5239 | 6.3941 | 6.2714 | 6.1552 | 6.0449 | 5.9400 | 5.8401 | 5.7450 | 5.6542 |
|  | 6.7434 | 6.6061 | 6.4762 | 6.3533 | 6.2367 | 6.1260 | 6.0207 | 5.9203 | 5.8247 | 5.7333 |
|  | 6.8151 | 6.6780 | 6.5483 | 6.4254 | 6.3087 | 6.1978 | 6.0922 | 5.9915 | 5.8955 | 5.8037 |
| 15 | 6.8779 | 6.7413 | 6.6119 | 6.4891 | 6.3725 | 6.2616 | 6.1559 | 6.0551 | 5.9588 | 5.8668 |
|  | 6.9332 | 6.7971 | 6.6682 | 6.5457 | 6.4293 | 6.3185 | 6.2129 | 6.1120 | 6.0157 | 5.9235 |
|  | 6.9819 | 6.8466 | 6.7182 | 6.5962 | 6.4801 | 6.3695 | 6.2640 | 6.1633 | 6.0669 | 5.9747 |
|  | 7.0249 | 6.8905 | 6.7627 | 6.6413 | 6.5256 | 6.4153 | 6.3101 | 6.2095 | 6.1133 | 6.0211 |
|  | 7.0631 | 6.9295 | 6.8025 | 6.6816 | 6.5665 | 6.4566 | 6.3517 | 6.2513 | 6.1553 | 6.0633 |
| 20 | 7.0969 | 6.9642 | 6.8380 | 6.7178 | 6.6032 | 6.4938 | 6.3893 | 6.2893 | 6.1935 | 6.1016 |
|  | 7.1269 | 6.9952 | 6.8698 | 6.7504 | 6.6364 | 6.5275 | 6.4234 | 6.3237 | 6.2282 | 6.1366 |
|  | 7.1535 | 7.0228 | 6.8984 | 6.7796 | 6.6663 | 6.5580 | 6.4543 | 6.3551 | 6.2599 | 6.1686 |
|  | 7.1772 | 7.0475 | 6.9239 | 6.8060 | 6.6933 | 6.5856 | 6.4825 | 6.3836 | 6.2888 | 6.1978 |
|  | 7.1983 | 7.0696 | 6.9469 | 6.8297 | 6.7178 | 6.6106 | 6.5080 | 6.4097 | 6.3153 | 6.2247 |
| 25 | 7.2169 | 7.0893 | 6.9675 | 6.8511 | 6.7399 | 6.6334 | 6.5313 | 6.4335 | 6.3395 | 6.2492 |
|  | 7.2335 | 7.1068 | 6.9859 | 6.8704 | 6.7599 | 6.6540 | 6.5525 | 6.4552 | 6.3617 | 6.2718 |
|  | 7.2482 | 7.1225 | 7.0025 | 6.8878 | 6.7780 | 6.6728 | 6.5719 | 6.4750 | 6.3820 | 6.2925 |
|  | 7.2611 | 7.1365 | 7.0173 | 6.9034 | 6.7943 | 6.6898 | 6.5895 | 6.4932 | 6.4006 | 6.3116 |
|  | 7.2726 | 7.1489 | 7.0306 | 6.9175 | 6.8092 | 6.7053 | 6.6056 | 6.5098 | 6.4177 | 6.3291 |
| 30 | 7.2827 | 7.1599 | 7.0425 | 6.9302 | 6.8226 | 6.7193 | 6.6202 | 6.5250 | 6.4334 | 6.3452 |

$100 G_2$

| $\alpha$ | $\beta=31$ | 32 | 33 | 34 | 35 | 36 | 37 | 38 | 39 | 40 |
|---|---|---|---|---|---|---|---|---|---|---|
| 1 | 0.0000 | 0.0000 | 0.0000 | 0.0000 | 0.0000 | 0.0000 | 0.0000 | 0.0000 | 0.0000 | 0.0000 |
| 2 | 2.9794 | 2.9326 | 2.8881 | 2.8454 | 2.8046 | 2.7655 | 2.7280 | 2.6920 | 2.6574 | 2.6240 |
| 3 | 3.7480 | 3.6894 | 3.6335 | 3.5800 | 3.5288 | 3.4797 | 3.4326 | 3.3874 | 3.3439 | 3.3020 |
| 4 | 4.2064 | 4.1409 | 4.0783 | 4.0184 | 3.9611 | 3.9062 | 3.8535 | 3.8028 | 3.7541 | 3.7072 |
| 5 | 4.5276 | 4.4573 | 4.3902 | 4.3260 | 4.2645 | 4.2056 | 4.1490 | 4.0946 | 4.0423 | 3.9919 |
| 6 | 4.7715 | 4.6978 | 4.6274 | 4.5600 | 4.4954 | 4.4335 | 4.3740 | 4.3169 | 4.2619 | 4.2089 |
| 7 | 4.9661 | 4.8898 | 4.8168 | 4.7470 | 4.6800 | 4.6158 | 4.5541 | 4.4948 | 4.4378 | 4.3828 |
| 8 | 5.1265 | 5.0481 | 4.9731 | 4.9011 | 4.8326 | 4.7665 | 4.7031 | 4.6421 | 4.5834 | 4.5268 |
| 9 | 5.2618 | 5.1818 | 5.1052 | 5.0319 | 4.9616 | 4.8941 | 4.8293 | 4.7669 | 4.7068 | 4.6490 |
| 10 | 5.3778 | 5.2965 | 5.2187 | 5.1442 | 5.0727 | 5.0040 | 4.9380 | 4.8745 | 4.8134 | 4.7544 |
| 11 | 5.4787 | 5.3964 | 5.3176 | 5.2421 | 5.1697 | 5.1000 | 5.0331 | 4.9687 | 4.9066 | 4.8467 |
| 12 | 5.5673 | 5.4843 | 5.4047 | 5.3284 | 5.2552 | 5.1848 | 5.1170 | 5.0519 | 4.9890 | 4.9284 |
| 13 | 5.6459 | 5.5622 | 5.4820 | 5.4051 | 5.3312 | 5.2602 | 5.1918 | 5.1260 | 5.0626 | 5.0014 |
| 14 | 5.7159 | 5.6318 | 5.5511 | 5.4737 | 5.3993 | 5.3278 | 5.2590 | 5.1926 | 5.1287 | 5.0670 |
| 15 | 5.7787 | 5.6942 | 5.6132 | 5.5355 | 5.4607 | 5.3888 | 5.3196 | 5.2528 | 5.1885 | 5.1264 |
| 16 | 5.8352 | 5.7506 | 5.6693 | 5.5913 | 5.5163 | 5.4441 | 5.3745 | 5.3075 | 5.2428 | 5.1803 |
| 17 | 5.8864 | 5.8016 | 5.7202 | 5.6420 | 5.5668 | 5.4944 | 5.4246 | 5.3573 | 5.2923 | 5.2296 |
| 18 | 5.9328 | 5.8480 | 5.7665 | 5.6882 | 5.6129 | 5.5403 | 5.4703 | 5.4029 | 5.3377 | 5.2748 |
| 19 | 5.9750 | 5.8902 | 5.8088 | 5.7304 | 5.6550 | 5.5824 | 5.5123 | 5.4447 | 5.3794 | 5.3163 |
| 20 | 6.0135 | 5.9288 | 5.8474 | 5.7691 | 5.6937 | 5.6210 | 5.5509 | 5.4832 | 5.4178 | 5.3547 |
| 21 | 6.0487 | 5.9641 | 5.8829 | 5.8046 | 5.7292 | 5.6566 | 5.5864 | 5.5187 | 5.4533 | 5.3901 |
| 22 | 6.0809 | 5.9965 | 5.9154 | 5.8373 | 5.7620 | 5.6894 | 5.6193 | 5.5516 | 5.4861 | 5.4229 |
| 23 | 6.1104 | 6.0263 | 5.9454 | 5.8674 | 5.7922 | 5.7197 | 5.6496 | 5.5820 | 5.5166 | 5.4533 |
| 24 | 6.1375 | 6.0537 | 5.9729 | 5.8951 | 5.8201 | 5.7477 | 5.6778 | 5.6102 | 5.5448 | 5.4816 |
| 25 | 6.1624 | 6.0789 | 5.9984 | 5.9208 | 5.8459 | 5.7737 | 5.7039 | 5.6364 | 5.5711 | 5.5079 |
| 26 | 6.1853 | 6.1021 | 6.0219 | 5.9445 | 5.8699 | 5.7978 | 5.7281 | 5.6607 | 5.5955 | 5.5324 |
| 27 | 6.2064 | 6.1235 | 6.0436 | 5.9665 | 5.8920 | 5.8201 | 5.7506 | 5.6834 | 5.6183 | 5.5553 |
| 28 | 6.2259 | 6.1433 | 6.0637 | 5.9868 | 5.9126 | 5.8409 | 5.7716 | 5.7045 | 5.6396 | 5.5767 |
| 29 | 6.2438 | 6.1616 | 6.0822 | 6.0057 | 5.9317 | 5.8603 | 5.7911 | 5.7242 | 5.6595 | 5.5967 |
| 30 | 6.2603 | 6.1784 | 6.0994 | 6.0232 | 5.9495 | 5.8783 | 5.8093 | 5.7426 | 5.6780 | 5.6154 |

| $100G_2$ / $\alpha$ | 50 | 49 | 48 | 47 | 46 | 45 | 44 | 43 | 42 | $\beta=41$ |
|---|---|---|---|---|---|---|---|---|---|---|
| 1 | 0.0000 | 0.0000 | 0.0000 | 0.0000 | 0.0000 | 0.0000 | 0.0000 | 0.0000 | 0.0000 | 0.0000 |
|  | 2.3476 | 2.3714 | 2.3959 | 2.4212 | 2.4473 | 2.4743 | 2.5022 | 2.5311 | 2.5610 | 2.5919 |
|  | 2.9546 | 2.9845 | 3.0154 | 3.0472 | 3.0800 | 3.1139 | 3.1490 | 3.1852 | 3.2228 | 3.2617 |
|  | 3.3178 | 3.3514 | 3.3859 | 3.4216 | 3.4584 | 3.4964 | 3.5357 | 3.5763 | 3.6184 | 3.6620 |
|  | 3.5734 | 3.6095 | 3.6467 | 3.6850 | 3.7246 | 3.7654 | 3.8077 | 3.8513 | 3.8965 | 3.9434 |
| 5 | 3.7687 | 3.8066 | 3.8458 | 3.8861 | 3.9278 | 3.9707 | 4.0152 | 4.0611 | 4.1087 | 4.1579 |
|  | 3.9255 | 3.9649 | 4.0056 | 4.0475 | 4.0908 | 4.1354 | 4.1816 | 4.2293 | 4.2787 | 4.3298 |
|  | 4.0557 | 4.0963 | 4.1383 | 4.1815 | 4.2261 | 4.2721 | 4.3196 | 4.3688 | 4.4196 | 4.4723 |
|  | 4.1665 | 4.2081 | 4.2511 | 4.2954 | 4.3410 | 4.3882 | 4.4369 | 4.4872 | 4.5393 | 4.5931 |
|  | 4.2625 | 4.3050 | 4.3488 | 4.3940 | 4.4405 | 4.4886 | 4.5383 | 4.5896 | 4.6426 | 4.6975 |
| 10 | 4.3468 | 4.3901 | 4.4346 | 4.4805 | 4.5279 | 4.5767 | 4.6272 | 4.6793 | 4.7332 | 4.7890 |
|  | 4.4218 | 4.4656 | 4.5108 | 4.5574 | 4.6054 | 4.6549 | 4.7061 | 4.7589 | 4.8135 | 4.8700 |
|  | 4.4890 | 4.5334 | 4.5791 | 4.6262 | 4.6748 | 4.7249 | 4.7766 | 4.8300 | 4.8852 | 4.9423 |
|  | 4.5498 | 4.5946 | 4.6408 | 4.6884 | 4.7374 | 4.7880 | 4.8402 | 4.8941 | 4.9498 | 5.0074 |
|  | 4.6050 | 4.6503 | 4.6969 | 4.7449 | 4.7943 | 4.8453 | 4.8979 | 4.9522 | 5.0083 | 5.0663 |
| 15 | 4.6556 | 4.7012 | 4.7481 | 4.7964 | 4.8462 | 4.8976 | 4.9505 | 5.0052 | 5.0616 | 5.1200 |
|  | 4.7020 | 4.7479 | 4.7951 | 4.8437 | 4.8938 | 4.9454 | 4.9987 | 5.0536 | 5.1104 | 5.1690 |
|  | 4.7448 | 4.7909 | 4.8384 | 4.8872 | 4.9376 | 4.9895 | 5.0429 | 5.0981 | 5.1551 | 5.2140 |
|  | 4.7844 | 4.8307 | 4.8784 | 4.9275 | 4.9780 | 5.0301 | 5.0838 | 5.1392 | 5.1963 | 5.2553 |
|  | 4.8211 | 4.8676 | 4.9155 | 4.9648 | 5.0155 | 5.0677 | 5.1215 | 5.1771 | 5.2344 | 5.2935 |
| 20 | 4.8553 | 4.9020 | 4.9500 | 4.9994 | 5.0502 | 5.1026 | 5.1566 | 5.2122 | 5.2696 | 5.3289 |
|  | 4.8872 | 4.9340 | 4.9821 | 5.0316 | 5.0826 | 5.1351 | 5.1891 | 5.2448 | 5.3023 | 5.3616 |
|  | 4.9170 | 4.9639 | 5.0121 | 5.0617 | 5.1128 | 5.1653 | 5.2194 | 5.2752 | 5.3327 | 5.3920 |
|  | 4.9449 | 4.9919 | 5.0402 | 5.0899 | 5.1409 | 5.1935 | 5.2477 | 5.3035 | 5.3610 | 5.4203 |
|  | 4.9711 | 5.0182 | 5.0665 | 5.1162 | 5.1673 | 5.2199 | 5.2741 | 5.3299 | 5.3874 | 5.4467 |
| 25 | 4.9957 | 5.0428 | 5.0911 | 5.1409 | 5.1920 | 5.2446 | 5.2988 | 5.3545 | 5.4120 | 5.4713 |
|  | 5.0188 | 5.0659 | 5.1143 | 5.1640 | 5.2152 | 5.2678 | 5.3219 | 5.3776 | 5.4351 | 5.4943 |
|  | 5.0406 | 5.0877 | 5.1361 | 5.1858 | 5.2369 | 5.2895 | 5.3436 | 5.3993 | 5.4566 | 5.5157 |
|  | 5.0612 | 5.1083 | 5.1566 | 5.2063 | 5.2574 | 5.3099 | 5.3639 | 5.4195 | 5.4768 | 5.5358 |
| 30 | 5.0805 | 5.1276 | 5.1759 | 5.2256 | 5.2766 | 5.3291 | 5.3830 | 5.4386 | 5.4958 | 5.5547 |

# REFERENCES

Ahern, S. A., 1961, Rev. Sci. Instr. **32** 814.

Bacon, G. E., 1955, Neutron Diffraction (Clarendon Press, Oxford).

Behrendt, D. R., S. Legvold and F. H. Spedding, 1958, Phys. Rev. **109** 1544.

Bergles, A. E., 1963 (unpublished, quoted by BITTER [1963]).

Berlincourt, T. G., 1963, Brit. J. Appl. Phys. **14** 749.

Bitter, F., 1936a, Rev. Sci. Instr. **7** 479.

Bitter, F., 1936b, Rev. Sci. Instr. **7** 482.

Bitter, F., 1937, Rev. Sci. Instr. **8** 318.

Bitter, F., 1939, Rev. Sci. Instr. **10** 373.

Bitter, F., 1962, Rev. Sci. Instr. **33** 342.

Bitter, F., 1963, Brit. J. Appl. Phys. **14** 759.

Blamey, J. W., and W.I.B. Smith, 1962, High Magnetic Fields (M.I.T. Press/ Wiley, New York) p. 217.

Boom, R. W., L. D. Roberts and R. S. Livingston, 1963, Nuclear Instr. and Methods **20** 495.

Brechna, H., and D. B. Montgomery, 1962, N.M.L. Report 62-1 (National Magnet Laboratory, M.I.T., Cambridge, Mass.).

Carey, R., and E. D. Isaac, 1966, Magnetic Domains and Techniques for their Observation (The English University Press, London).

Carruthers, R., 1962, High Magnetic Fields (M.I.T. Press/Wiley, New York) p. 307.

Champion, K. S. W., 1950, Proc. Phys. Soc. **B63** 795.

Chandrasekhar, S., 1956, Proc. Nat. Acad. Sci. **42** 1.

Cioffi, P. P., 1962, High Magnetic Fields (M.I.T. Press/Wiley, New York) p. 202.

Cockcroft, J. D., 1928, Phil. Trans. Roy. Soc. **A227** 314.

Cornelius, P., 1961, Electrical Theory on the Giorgi System (Cleaver-Hume Press, London; Dover, New York).

Cotti, P., 1960, Z. Angew. Math. u. Phys. **11** 17.

Craik, D. J., and R. S. Tebble, 1965, Ferromagnetism and Ferromagnetic Domains (North-Holland Publ. Co., Amsterdam).

Daniels, J. M., 1953, Brit. J. Appl. Phys. **4** 50.

DeBlois, R. W., 1961, Rev. Sci. Instr. **32** 816.

DeBlois, R. W., 1962, High Magnetic Fields (M.I.T. Press/Wiley, New York) p. 568.

Debye, P., 1912, Ann. Phys. (4) **39** 789.

De Klerk, D., 1962, High Magnetic Fields (M.I.T. Press/Wiley, New York) p. 412.

De Klerk, D., and C. J. Gorter, 1962, High Magnetic Fields (M.I.T. Press/ Wiley, New York) p. 194.

Donadieu, L. J., 1963, M.I.T. Quart. Progr. Rep. No. 68, p. 86.

Dreyfus, L., 1931, Arch. f. Elektrotechn. **25** 392.

Elliott, J. F., S. Legvold and F. H. Spedding, 1953, Phys. Rev. **91** 28.

Fabry, C., 1898, Eclairage Electrique **17** 133.

Felici, N. J., 1940, Ann. Phys. (Paris) **13** 266.

Foner, S., and H. H. Kolm, 1957, Rev. Sci. Instr. **28** 799.

Fowler, C. M., W. B. Garn and R. S. Caird, 1960, J. Appl. Phys. **31** 588.

Furth, H. P., M. A. Levine and R. W. Waniek, 1957, Rev. Sci. Instr. **28** 949.

Furth, H. P., 1962, High Magnetic Fields (M.I.T. Press/Wiley, New York) p. 235.

Garrett, M. W., 1951, J. Appl. Phys. **22** 1091.

Gaume, F., 1958, J. Rech. C.N.R.S. **9** 93, **9** 247, **9** 287.

Gaume, F., 1962, High Magnetic Fields (M.I.T. Press/Wiley, New York) p. 27.

Gauster, W. F., and C. E. Parker, 1962, High Magnetic Fields (M.I.T. Press/ Wiley, New York) p. 3.

Grüneisen, E., 1933, Ann. Phys. (5) **16** 530.

Hart, H. R., I. S. Jacobs, C. L. Kolbe and P. E. Lawrence, 1962, High Magnetic Fields (M.I.T. Press/Wiley, New York) p. 584.

Howland, B., and S. Foner, 1962, High Magnetic Fields (M.I.T. Press/Wiley, New York) p. 249.

Hulm, J. K., B. S. Chandrasekhar and H. Riemersma, 1963, Int. Science and Technology (May 1963) p. 50.

Huth, F., 1962, Cryogenics **2** 368.

Ishikawa, Y., and S. Chikazumi, 1962, Jap. J. Appl. Phys. **1** 155.

Jeans, J. H., 1923, The Mathematical Theory of Electricity and Magnetism (University Press, Cambridge).

Kamerlingh Onnes, H., 1911, Comm. Phys. Lab. Univ. Leiden **133d** 65.

Kapitza, P., 1924, Proc. Roy. Soc. **A105** 691.

Kapitza, P., 1927, Proc. Roy. Soc. **A115** 658.

Kim, Y. B., and E. D. Platner, 1959, Rev. Sci. Instr. **30** 524.

Kohler, M., 1949, Ann. Phys. (6) **6** 18.

Kolm, H. H., B. Lax, F. Bitter and R. G. Mills (editors), 1962, High Magnetic Fields (M.I.T. Press/Wiley, New York).

Kronauer, R. E., 1962, High Magnetic Fields (M.I.T. Press/Wiley, New York) p. 116.

Kropschot, R. H., and V. Arp, 1961, Cryogenics **2** 1.

Kunzler, J. E., 1961, Rev. Mod. Phys. **33** 501.

Kunzler, J. E., E. Buehler, F. S. Hsu and J. H. Wernick, 1961, Phys. Rev. Letters **6** 89.

Kuznetsov, A. A., 1960, Soviet Physics – Tech. Phys. **5** 555.

Laquer, H. L., and E. F. Hammel, 1957, Rev. Sci. Instr. **28** 875.

Laquer, H. L., 1963, Cryogenics **3** 27.

Laurence, J. C., G. V. Brown, J. Geist and K. Zeitz, 1962, High Magnetic Fields (M.I.T. Press/Wiley, New York) p. 170.

Lenders, W. L. L., 1961/62; Philips Tech. Rev. **23** 365.

Levine, M. A., 1962, High Magnetic Fields (M.I.T. Press/Wiley, New York) p. 277.

Love, A. E. H., 1927, Mathematical Theory of Elasticity, 4th ed. (University Press, Cambridge. Reprinted by Dover, New York, 1944).

Lüst, R., and A. Schlüter, 1954, Z. Astrophys. **34** 263.

Luteijn, A. I., and K. J. De Vos, 1956, Philips Res. Rep. **11** 489.

Lüthi, B., 1960, Helv. Phys. Acta **33** 161.

Mammel, W. L., and S. P. Morgan, 1962, J. Appl. Phys. **33** 2244.

Margenau, H., and G. M. Murphy, 1956, The Mathematics of Physics and Chemistry, 2nd ed. (Van Nostrand, Princeton).

Matthias, B. T., 1953, Phys. Rev. **92** 874.

Matthias, B. T., T. H. Geballe, S. Geller and E. Corenzwit, 1954, Phys. Rev. **95** 1435.

Maxwell, J. C., 1873, A Treatise on Electricity and Magnetism (First published in 1873. Reprinted by Dover, New York, 1954).

McAdams, W. H., 1954, Heat Transmission, 3rd ed. (McGraw-Hill, New York).

Meijering, J. L., 1952/53, Philips Tech. Rev. **14** 203.

Montgomery, D. B., 1963, Rep. Progr. Phys. **26** 69.

Post, R. F., and C. E. Taylor, 1960, Adv. Cryog. Eng. **5** 13.

Rhodes, B. L., S. Legvold and F. H. Spedding, 1958, Phys. Rev. **109** 1547.

Roeland, L. W., and F. A. Muller, High Magnetic Fields (M.I.T. Press/Wiley, New York) p. 287.

Rohsenow, W. M., 1954, Trans. A.S.M.E. **76** 553.

Ruhmkorff, H. D., 1846, C. R. Acad. Sci. (Paris) **23** 417.

Salter Jr., L. C., S. H. Autler, H. H. Kolm, D. J. Rose and K. Gooen, 1962, High Magnetic Fields (M.I.T. Press/Wiley, New York) p. 344.

Scott, R. B., 1959, Cryogenic Engineering (Van Nostrand, Princeton).

Skellett, S., 1962, High Magnetic Fields (M.I.T. Press/Wiley, New York) p. 296.

Stuijts, A. L., G. W. Rathenau and G. H. Weber, 1954/55, Philips Tech. Rev. **16** 141.

Thoburn, W. C., S. Legvold and F. H. Spedding, 1958, Phys. Rev. **112** 56.

Van Suchtelen, J., J. Volger and D. Van Houwelingen, 1965, Cryogenics **5** 256.

Volger, J., and P. S. Admiraal, 1962, Phys. Letters **2** 257. See also Philips Tech. Rev. **25** (1963/64) 16.

Wakefield, K. E., 1962, High Magnetic Fields (M.I.T. Press/Wiley, New York) p. 39.

Weil, L., 1951, Proc. 8th Int. Congress of Refrigeration, London, 1951, p. 181.

Wells, D. R., and R. G. Mills, 1962, High Magnetic Fields (M.I.T. Press/Wiley, New York) p. 44.

Wernick, J. H., F. J. Morin, F. S. L. Hsu, D. Dorsi, J. P. Maita and J. E. Kunzler, 1962, High Magnetic Fields (M.I.T. Press/Wiley, New York) p. 609.

Zijlstra, H., 1962, High Magnetic Fields (M.I.T. Press/Wiley, New York) p. 281.

# SUBJECT INDEX

Upright numbers refer to Part 1, Generation and Computation of Magnetic Fields; page numbers in italics refer to Part 2, Measurement of Magnetic Quantities